INSTITUTION OF METALLURGISTS

Modern Metallurgical Texts

edited by

Professor C. R. Tottle, M.Met., F.I.M., F.Inst.P.
University of Manchester
and

Professor J. C. Wright, B.Sc., Ph.D., A.C.T. (Birm.), F.I.M.
University of Aston in Birmingham

No. 2
PHYSICAL CHEMISTRY
FOR METALLURGISTS

J. MACKOWIAK
B.Sc., Ph.D., A.I.M.
University of Surrey

Physical Chemistry for Metallurgists

ILLUSTRATED

London
GEORGE ALLEN AND UNWIN LTD

PRINTED IN GREAT BRITAIN

in 10–11 *Times Roman type*

AT THE PITMAN PRESS
BATH

PREFACE

When commissioned by the Institution to write this introductory text, I was well aware of the difficulty of writing a book that is compact enough to keep its price within the reach of the majority of students and is at the same time able to cover the intended syllabus.

The aim of this book is to explain the basic physico-chemical principles of interest to metallurgists. No chapters on structure of matter are included, as this has been described so well for students of metallurgy in books published by the Institute of Metals.

A historical and practical approach has been adopted throughout, since, from teaching experience, I am well aware that students confronted for the first time with a new subject are likely to become more interested when given a historical outline of events leading to the development of the subject and when shown the advantages of the given theory and its application to the treatment of practical problems.

In the development of each chapter a great deal of care has been taken to state all the assumptions and all the steps in the deduction of thermodynamic, kinetic, and electrochemical equations. In this way it is hoped that students should be able to follow these deductions more easily and should also be aware of their limitations. Numerous worked examples have been included to illustrate the application of various theories.

In certain cases I decided to use more old-fashioned methods of approach, as, for example, in the deduction of the van't Hoff Isotherm, which is derived via the "reaction box". In this particular case I felt that this method had the definite advantage of conveying pictorially the physical meaning of the "correction term". This should help students to visualise the significance of the initial conditions of reactants and final conditions of products, and their influence on the overall value of the free energy change for a given process. This method also has the additional advantage of clarifying the meaning of the standard free energy concept.

I would like to express my thanks to all who have contributed in any way to the completion of this book and in particular to Dr. P. Howard of the Chemistry Department, Battersea College of Technology, for reading the manuscript and offering suggestions on many points of presentation.

I would also like to express my gratitude to Dr. O. Kubaschewski for his invaluable advice regarding certain aspects of thermodynamics and permission to use some diagrams, to Professor C. B. Alcock and Professor F. C. Thompson for very helpful discussions, to Dr. L. L. Shreir and Professor C. W. Davies for discussions on electrochemistry, to Professor L. W. Derry for certain facilities and Professor C. R. Tottle for advice and patience. I am indebted to the following for permission to reproduce diagrams and tables:

U.S. Government Printing Office,
American Institute of Mining Metallurgical and Petroleum Engineers Inc.,
British Ceramic Society,
British Iron & Steel Research Association,
Faraday Society,
Society of Chemical Industry,
D. Van Nostrand Co. Inc.

Finally I wish to thank Mr. R. F. Eatwell, librarian of the Battersea College of Technology and Mr. Blagden, librarian of the ZDA/LDA joint library, for the help and facilities provided by them.

J.M.

FOREWORD

THE SERIES IN GENERAL

'Students are very sensitive to certain qualities in their books. They like them to be reasonably weighty and good value for money, but they must not be so long and formidable as to be overpowering. They must be direct and forthright in their approach, and have a note of authority. Much arguing of the point, back and forth, is to be avoided, except in treatments which are admittedly "advanced". Padding is anathema. Personally I never liked treatments that were so sub-divided that there was nothing in each section: I liked to feel that if I had read a section I had something to get hold of, and I liked the logical thread to be clear and continuous . . .'

This passage from the Presidential Address delivered to the Institution of Metallurgists in 1961 by Dr N. P. Allen, M.MET., D.Sc., F.I.M., F.R.S., expresses very clearly the ideal and the approach of the Institution and its Editors in preparing this series of texts.

In metallurgy particularly, because of the nature of the technology and its underlying sciences, students have found difficulty in obtaining, at a reasonable total cost over the whole of their courses, a consistent range of texts giving balanced up-to-date treatment of the various aspects of their subject. The Institution of Metallurgists has sought to reduce this difficulty by arranging this planned series of texts. In it, the content of the present day graduate and diploma courses in metallurgy and those for the Institution's Associateship examination has been divided so far into about twenty different books; each, it is hoped, will prove reasonably complete in itself, while bearing an integral relationship to its companions in the series. Further volumes will follow as the need arises or specialised fields are introduced into syllabuses.

Duplication of introductory or background material is avoided; where it is necessary to set a particular volume in a wider context, the background needed will be found elsewhere in the series. The aim has been to provide a comprehensive coverage and yet to eliminate the overlapping of material—expensive to the student— that is so frequent among books not written to a common plan. The volumes include no more specialised treatments (also expensive to publish) than students really need, but they do aim to encourage reading reasonably beyond the minimum requirement of any particular syllabuses and examinations. The series emphatically does *not* represent, for students approaching the Institution of Metallurgists' own examinations, a 'maximum reading course', so to speak, within which examiners may be counted on to restrict their questions.

Each volume has been planned with an eye to a fair balance of logical treatment and published price. The total material could have been arranged in a greater number of smaller and therefore cheaper units, or a smaller number of more expensive ones. The effect of this inevitably, however, would have been that the student, to cover the same essential ground, would in the long run find he spent more money.

The quality of each book, it is hoped, will justify its retention in a personal library. Each develops its theme from a relatively simple introductory level to the standard of knowledge expected of a modern qualified metallurgist. Thus, a student should find no need to buy increasingly advanced books at increasing cost as his course progresses; yet at the end of his reading of each book he should find himself influenced to look ahead and read more widely. Suggestions to guide further reading are given in each book, but large numbers of precise references have been considered more appropriate to research monographs.

THIS BOOK IN PARTICULAR

The study of metallurgy can be divided generally into two main divisions of chemical and physical metallurgy, since the subject is largely concerned with the physics and chemistry of metals. The chemical aspects are concerned with reactions between solids, liquids, and gases and the metals and their principal compounds. At once, this includes the separation of metals from their ores, the purification of metals or their compounds, the formation of alloys, and all aspects of corrosion whether in liquids or gases.

The fundamental principles of chemical metallurgy are therefore those of physical chemistry, whether concerned with thermodynamics or reaction kinetics. The majority of text-books of physical chemistry deal mainly with materials readily appreciated by a student of chemistry but not necessarily of interest to a metallurgist. In this book therefore, the basis of physical chemistry is presented in those aspects which are of concern to chemical metallurgy, and with examples, so far as possible, drawn from metallurgical science. Such a book forms the background to several volumes published later in the series, and is intended as a preparation for more advanced studies.

C. R. TOTTLE

Manchester
June 1964

CONTENTS

Contents

Contents

LIST OF SYMBOLS

A Arrhenius proportionality constant

A area

A Helmholtz free energy

C number of components

$\bar{C}$ mean heat capacity

C_A concentration of component A

C_p, C_v heat capacity at constant pressure, volume;

E energy

E_{rev}° standard reversible electromotive force

F force

F Faraday (unit of electricity)

F degrees of freedom

G Gibbs free energy

ΔG° standard free energy change

$\bar{G}_A$ partial free energy of A

ΔG^{*} free energy change of activated complex

H enthalpy, heat content

I electric current

K equilibrium constant

K_a dissociation constant

K_c, K_p, K_N equilibrium constants in terms of concentrations, pressures and mole fractions

K_s solubility product

K_w ionic product of water

L latent heat

L_e, L_f, L_s, L_t latent heats of evaporation, fusion, sublimation and transformation

M molecular weight

N Avogadro's number

N_A mole fraction of component A

P, p total and partial pressures

Q Arrhenius energy of activation

Q heat of reaction (process)

Q quotient

R gas constant

R electrical resistance

S entropy

S_t, S_r, S_v, S_e translational, rotational, vibrational and electronic entropies

S_{AgCl} solubility of silver chloride

T absolute temperature

T_e, T_f, T_s, T_t absolute temperatures of evaporation, fusion, sublimation and transformation

V, v volume

V rate of diffusion

V_c, v_c critical volume

$\bar{V}_A$ partial molal volume of component A

U internal energy

a, b constants: heat capacity equations; number of molecules; van der Waals' constants; Tafel line constants

a_A Raoultian activity of component A

a_A^H Henrian activity of component A

d density

d distance

d differential operator

f_A fugacity of component A

f_A Henrian activity coefficient

g gravitational constant

h height

h Plancks' constant

i Van't Hoff factor

k specific reaction rate or velocity constant

k Boltzmann's constant

l length

m mass

n_A number of g atoms or g mole of A

q heat or energy supplied

r radius

t temperature $^{\circ}C$

t_- transport number of anion

v_1 velocity of forward reaction

v_A volume of component A

w work

w weight

α degree of dissociation

α_v coefficient of expansion of a gas

γ ratio of heat contents

γ_A Raoultian activity coefficient of A

∂ partial differential operator

δ small increment

η polarisation

κ specific conductance

λ_+, λ_- equivalent ionic conductances

μ molar conductance

μ_A chemical potential of component A

μ_j Joule–Thomson coefficient

ν frequency of radiation

ν number of ions

ρ_A density of component A

ρ specific resistance

Δ change in

Λ equivalent conductance

NOTE ON TERMINOLOGY

g atom gramme atom; that amount of an element having a mass in grammes numerically equal to the atomic weight.

g mole gramme molecule; that amount of a *pure substance* having a mass in grammes numerically equal to the molecular weight.

For *alloys* and *mixtures*—that amount of an alloy or a mixture having a mass in grammes numerically equal to the sum of the products of each mole fraction multiplied by the molecular (or atomic) weight of that component.

Normality and *molarity* units of concentration have the disadvantage that they vary with temperature owing to the thermal expansion of the solution; the normality and molarity of a solution decrease as the temperature increases. For this reason the *molality* unit of concentration is preferred for accurate work as it is independent of the temperature. The molality unit has the additional advantage of being directly convertible to mole fraction using the following formula:

$$N_A = \frac{m_A}{m_A + 1000/M_B}$$

where N_A = the mole fraction of component A (solute)

m_A = molal concentration of A

M_B = molecular weight of component B (solvent).

CHAPTER 1

The Properties of Gases

1.1 SUMMARY OF IDEAL GAS LAWS

Matter in a gaseous state is characterised by the non-existence of a boundary surface and therefore normally it fills up completely any available space. Its volume is also extremely sensitive to pressure and temperature. For many thousands of years attempts had been made to show that gases possess weight, but it was Galileo (1617) who probably first proved it by weighing. The main properties of ideal gases are described quantitatively by the various gas laws and will be quoted and then explained briefly, since more accurate description of these can be found in elementary books on physics. However, it is intended to deal more fully with the simple kinetic theory of gases, since some of the results will be referred to later in chapters dealing with Thermodynamics and Kinetics.

There are seven main gas laws which are now widely accepted and these are as follows:

(i) Boyle's Law.   (v) Dalton's Law.

(ii) Gay-Lussac's Law.   (vi) Graham's Law.

(iii) Avogadro's Hypothesis.   (vii) The General Law.

(iv) Henry's Law.

Let us revise each of these laws in turn and underline the main contributions they make.

(i) **Boyle's Law** can be stated as follows: **At constant temperature and mass the volume of a gas is inversely proportional to the pressure:**

or
$$v \propto \left(\frac{1}{p}\right)_{T,m} \qquad \ldots(1.1)$$

where v = volume of the gas

    p = pressure

    T, m = at constant absolute temperature T, and constant mass m.

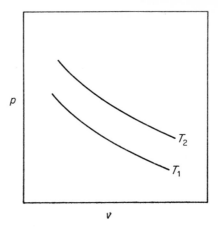

p

v

1.1 *Boyle's isotherms T_1 and T_2 of an ideal gas.*

Equation (1.1) becomes $v = \dfrac{C}{p}$ or $vp = C$ where C is the pro-portionality constant. A plot of pressure against volume (Fig. 1.1) shows typical curves. The magnitude of the constant C depends on the nature of the gas, its mass, and temperature. From this equation it follows that at a constant temperature for the same gas

$$p_1 v_1 = c \quad \text{and} \quad p_2 v_2 = c$$

Thus

$$p_1 v_1 = p_2 v_2 \qquad \qquad \ldots (1.2)$$

(ii) **Gay-Lussac's Law** (1802) (Charles' Law of 1787 was not published until later) can be stated *either* as

At constant pressure and mass the same rise in temperature produces in all gases the same increase in volume,

or as

Equal volumes of all gases at constant pressure and mass have the same increase in volume for the same rise in temperature.

$$v \propto (T)_{p,m} \qquad \qquad \ldots (1.3)$$

In Table (1.1) coefficients of expansion of some gases are given. α_v of a gas is the increase in the volume of a gas when the temperature changes from $0°C$ to $1°C$. From these coefficients it can be seen that their values are approximately equal to $\dfrac{1}{273}$.

TABLE 1.1

Gas	α_v — Coefficient of expansion cc deg^{-1}
Air	0·003665
Hydrogen	0·003667
Carbon monoxide	0·003667
Carbon dioxide	0·003688
Sulphur dioxide	0·003845

If v_0 is the volume of a mass of gas at 0°C, then the volume v_t of the same mass of the gas at the temperature t is given by

$$v_t = v_0 + \alpha_v v_0 t = v_0(1 + \alpha_v t) \qquad \ldots(1.4)$$

and since

$$\alpha_v \simeq \frac{1}{273}$$

then

$$v_t = v_0 \left(1 + \frac{t}{273}\right) = v_0 \frac{(273 + t)}{273} \qquad \ldots(1.5)$$

Let v_0 and v_{273} be the volumes of the same mass of a gas at 0°C and 273°C; assuming that the coefficient of expansion of the given gas is constant over the whole range of temperatures, then, using the Celsius scale, −273°C is the temperature at which the volume of the gas would become zero (Fig. 1.2).

This temperature is then the lowest within our conception. For convenience the temperature −273°C* has been adopted as zero and the new temperature scale is known as the Absolute Scate and the symbol T is used for temperatures in this scale.

$$T = 273 + t$$

where $t =$ temperature in °C.

From (1.5) it follows that the volume v_{T_1} at the temperature T_1 is given by

$$v_{T_1} = \frac{v_0 T_1}{273} \quad \text{and} \quad v_{T_2} = \frac{v_0 T_2}{273}$$

$$\therefore \qquad \frac{v_{T_1}}{v_{T_2}} = \frac{T_1}{T_2} \qquad \ldots(1.6)$$

or

$$\left(\frac{v}{T}\right)_{p,m} = \text{constant} \qquad \ldots(1.7)$$

* The present accepted value of the melting point of ice at 1 atm of pressure $T_m = 273\cdot15°K$.

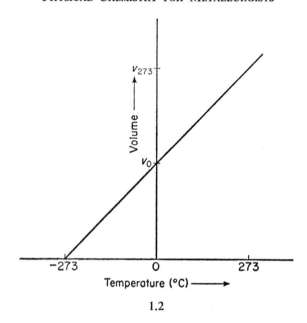

1.2

The Combination of Boyle's and Gay-Lussac's Laws. Let us combine these two laws to obtain a single equation:

From Boyle's Law

$$v \propto \left(\frac{1}{p}\right)_{T,m}$$

and from Gay-Lussac's Law

$$v \propto (T)_{p,m}$$

Combining these two equations we have

$$v \propto \left(\frac{T}{p}\right) \quad \text{at a constant mass}$$

Multiplying both sides by pressure p one obtains

$$pv \propto T \quad \text{at a constant mass}$$

or

$$pv = kT \qquad \qquad \ldots(1.8)$$

where k is the proportionality constant.

The equation (1.8) for a gas which obeys Boyle's and Gay-Lussac's Laws is known as the **equation of state**, and it allows us to express the relation between T, p, and v of a gaseous system at a constant mass. It is clear that the constant k depends on the mass and nature of the given gas.

(iii) **Avogadro's Hypothesis.** This states that **equal volumes of all gases under the same conditions of temperature and pressure contain the same number of molecules.**

That is,

$$n_1 = n_2 \quad \text{when} \quad p_1 = p_2, v_1 = v_2$$

From this hypothesis it also follows that

$$\frac{pv}{T} = \text{constant} = R$$

or

$$pv = RT \qquad \qquad \dots(1.9)$$

where R is the gas constant for any gas, if v the gas volume is one g mole ($R = 1.987$ cal deg^{-1} g mole^{-1}).

In general we can write this equation as

$$pv = nRT$$

where $n =$ number of gramme molecules of a gaseous system.

(iv) **Henry's Law (1803).** The mass of a gas dissolved by a given mass of liquid at a given temperature is directly proportional to the pressure of the gas in contact with the liquid.

Most gases obey Henry's Law providing the pressures are not too high or temperatures too low. This law, however, does not apply to gases which enter into a chemical reaction with the solvent.

For example, ammonia gas in contact with an acid solution such as hydrochloric acid will not obey Henry's Law.

(v) **Dalton's Law of Partial Pressures.** When two or more gases which exert no physical or chemical action on one another are mixed together at constant temperature, each gas exerts the same pressure as if it alone occupied the whole of the containing vessel, and the total pressure exerted by the mixture is equal to the sum of the pressures exerted by all the gases.

This law can be expressed mathematically by the equation

$$P = p_1 + p_2 + p_3 + \dots p_n \qquad \dots(1.10)$$

where $P =$ total pressure of all the gases (the mixture); p_1, p_2, p_3, etc., the partial pressure of the gases one, two and three respectively in the mixture.

Thus the pressure p_1 of n_1 g moles of the first component in the mixture can be calculated from the equation

$$p_1 v = n_1 RT$$

where v = volume of the mixture
and T = the absolute temperature of the gas.
   Similarly

$$p_n v = n_n RT$$

   (vi) **Graham's Law of Diffusion. The relative rates of diffusion of different gases are inversely proportional to the square roots of their densities.**

Thus
$$V \propto \sqrt{\frac{1}{d}} \propto \sqrt{\frac{1}{M}}$$

where V = rate of diffusion
   d = density of the gas
   M = molecular weight.

1.2 THE KINETIC THEORY OF GASES

All the laws discussed in the previous section and all the quantitative equations given there were obtained empirically from experimental results. It was a challenge to the nineteenth century scientists to explain these equations from theoretical considerations. **The kinetic theory of gases,** which has this as an object, had developed gradually but Maxwell (1850), Clausius (1857), and Boltzmann (1868) gave finally the precise mathematical form of this theory. In order to make the mathematics more simple, and to account for the constant pressure of a mass of a gas under given conditions of temperature and volume, the following assumptions were made:

   (i) The gas consists of a large number of molecules that are perfectly elastic.
   (ii) The size of molecules and the space they actually occupy is very small as compared with the total volume occupied by the gas (e.g. 1 cc of water = 1,700 cc of steam).
   (iii) The molecules are separated by relatively large distances.
   (iv) The molecules are in constant random motion and since they are very small they can be regarded as mathematical points that store their energy in translatory motion.
   (v) Pressure on the walls of the container is due to the incessant bombardment by the moving molecules of the gas.
   (vi) The kinetic energy of the gas molecules is proportional to the absolute temperature of the gas.

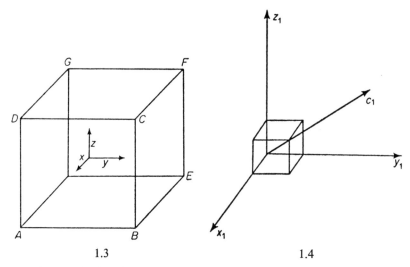

1.3   1.4

On the basis of these assumptions and by applying the laws of mechanics the relation between the pressure p, volume v of the gas and the total number of molecules n enclosed in the volume of a cube whose sides are of length l can be calculated. Consider a particular molecule enclosed in the box (Fig. 1.3) having a velocity c_1, and its component velocities being x_1, y_1, and z_1.

From solid geometry it follows that

$$c_1^2 = x_1^2 + y_1^2 + z_1^2$$

(extended Pythagoras theorem).

Imagine the molecule with a component velocity x_1 approaching and striking the face ABCD (Fig. 1.3).

The original momentum of the molecule $= mx_1$.

Momentum after collision $= -mx_1$ for a perfectly elastic molecule.

The change of momentum

$$= \text{initial momentum} - \text{final momentum}$$
$$= mx_1 - (-mx_1) = 2mx_1,$$

i.e. $2mx_1$ g cm sec^{-1} for each impact of the molecule with a wall. Similarly for the other component velocities the momenta are $2my_1$ and $2mz_1$. Since each side of the cube is l cm long the number of collisions per second $= \dfrac{x_1}{l}$.

The force exerted by the molecule is measured by the rate of change of momentum and in the x_1 direction it equals

$$2mx_1 \cdot \frac{x_1}{l} = \frac{2mx_1^2}{l} \text{ g cm sec}^{-2}$$

Considering the component velocities in all directions the force exerted by the molecule will be

$$\frac{2m}{l}(x_1^2 + y_1^2 + z_1^2) = \frac{2mc_1^2}{l}$$

The force (F) for n molecules that are confined in the cube is then

$$F = \frac{2mnc^2}{l} \qquad \qquad \ldots(1.11)$$

However, by definition pressure = force per unit area

$$\therefore \qquad \qquad p = \frac{F}{6l^2} \qquad \qquad \ldots(1.12)$$

Substituting (1.12) into (1.11) we obtain

$$p = \frac{mnc^2}{3l^3}$$

and since l^3 = volume of the cube

$$p = \frac{1}{3} \cdot \frac{mnc^2}{v} \quad \text{or} \quad pv = \frac{1}{3}mnc^2 \qquad \ldots(1.13)$$

This mathematical expression is very convenient since it correlates the volume and pressure with the number of molecules and their velocities.

1.3 KINETIC THEORY OF GASES AND THE GAS LAWS

In this section it is intended to show that the mathematical expression (1.13) derived from the kinetic theory of gases allows us to account for some of the gas laws.

Boyle's Law. Let us consider first Boyle's Law which states that pv = constant at a constant temperature. From the terms in the equation (1.13) it can be seen that for a given mass of gas the right-hand side contains constants only and therefore the left-hand side must be constant.

Thus pv = constant and Boyle's Law is accounted for.

Graham's Law. Let us consider now how Graham's Law of diffusion which states that

$$v \propto \sqrt{\frac{1}{d}} = \sqrt{\frac{1}{M}}$$

can be derived from equation (1.13), $pv = \frac{1}{3}mnc^2$.

Rearranging the terms of this equation we obtain

$$c^2 = \frac{3pv}{mn}$$

Since mn = mass of the gas, $\dfrac{mn}{v}$ = density,

$$\therefore \qquad c^2 = \frac{3p}{d} \quad \text{or} \quad c = \sqrt{\frac{3p}{d}} \qquad \qquad \dots(1.14)$$

For molecules A of velocity c_A equation (1.14) becomes

$$c_A = \sqrt{\frac{3p}{d_A}}$$

Similarly for molecules of gas B

$$c_B = \sqrt{\frac{3p}{d_B}}$$

dividing

$$\frac{c_A}{c_B} = \sqrt{\frac{d_B}{d_A}}$$

or in general

$$c \propto \sqrt{\frac{1}{d}}$$

thus showing that the Graham's Law can be deduced from the kinetic theory of gases.

Dalton's Law. Dalton's Law of partial pressures can be accounted for from this theory by considering n molecules of one gas in a volume v and each having mass m, and mean square velocity $\bar{c}_1^2$.

It is evident from equation (1.13) that $p_1 = \dfrac{n_1 m_1 \bar{c}_1^2}{3v}$. Similarly, if n_2 molecules of gas two occupies the volume v, then

$$p_2 = \frac{n_2 m_2^2 \bar{c}_2^2}{3v}$$

Therefore the total pressure P of a mixture of gases

$$m_1 + m_2 + \dots m_n$$

occupying the same volume v will be given by the equation

$$P = \frac{n_1 m_1 \bar{c}_1^2}{3v} + \frac{n_2 m_2 \bar{c}_2^2}{3v} + \ldots + \frac{n_n m_m \bar{c}_m^2}{3v}$$

or

$$P = p_1 + p_2 + \ldots + p_n$$

This equation is identical with that which is obtained from Dalton's Law showing that the simple kinetic theory of gases enables us to predict this relation.

1.4 THE KINETIC THEORY AND TEMPERATURE

The equation (1.13) allows us conveniently to establish the relation between the temperature of a gas and its energy.

Combining the equations (1.13) and (1.9) one obtains

$$p \cdot v = \tfrac{1}{3} m n c^2 = \tfrac{1}{3} m N c^2 = RT \qquad \ldots (1.15)$$

since $n = N$ for 1 g mole of a gas
where $N = 6 \cdot 023 \times 10^{23}$ molecules.

The energy of the gas is the kinetic energy of its molecules since the theory assumes that they have translatory energy only.

Thus

$$E = \tfrac{1}{2} m N c^2 \qquad \ldots (1.16)$$

where E = energy of 1 g mole of gas.

Combining (1.15) and (1.16) we have

$$RT = \tfrac{2}{3} E \qquad \ldots (1.17)$$

But $R = 1 \cdot 987$ cal deg^{-1} g mole^{-1}, so

$$T \simeq \tfrac{1}{3} E$$

The total energy of the molecules in one g mole of an ideal gas is approximately equal to $3T$.

The Kinetic Theory and Heat Capacities of a Gas. The heat capacity of a gas is the quantity of heat required to raise its temperature by one degree. For gases the heat capacity for the same gas will depend on whether the rise in temperature takes place under conditions of constant volume or constant pressure.

Molar Heat Capacity at Constant Volume (C_v). Let us consider first the value of heat capacity of a g mole of a gas at constant volume of an ideal gas. Rewriting equation (1.17) we obtain the energy value

$$E = \tfrac{3}{2} RT \qquad \ldots (1.18)$$

Let us now supply heat to the gas just sufficient to raise its temperature by 1°C. The temperature of the gas then becomes $(T + 1)$, and the energy of the system will become $E + \Delta E$.

Using the previous relation (1.18) we have

$$(E + \Delta E) = \tfrac{3}{2}R(T + 1) \qquad \ldots(1.19)$$

Subtracting (1.18) from (1.19) gives

$$\Delta E = \tfrac{3}{2}R \simeq 3 \text{ cal}$$

Thus $C_v \simeq 3$ cal deg^{-1} g mole^{-1} since $R \simeq 2$ cal deg^{-1} g mole^{-1}. This result shows that, if the only physical effect upon the molecules of a gas were the increase of their translational energy, the value of the heat capacity of 1 g mole of a gas would be 3 cal.

Molecular heat capacity at constant pressure (C_p). Consider again 1 g mole of an ideal gas confined in a cylinder fitted with a piston exerting a constant pressure p (Fig. 1.5). Let the volume of the gas at the temperature T be v. Using the equation of state $pv = RT$ one can calculate its volume at the temperature $(T + 1)$. Initially

$$pv = RT$$

When T is raised, the volume has to increase to keep the pressure constant.

$$p(v + \Delta v) \simeq R(T + 1) \qquad \ldots(1.20)$$

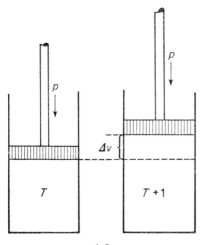

1.5

The energy required for doing this work can be calculated by subtracting (1.9) from (1.20).

$$\therefore \qquad p\Delta v = R \simeq 2 \text{ cal deg}^{-1} \text{ g mole}^{-1}$$

Since the total heat required at constant pressure will be the sum of heats required to raise the temperature at constant volume and to expand the gas we have

$$C_p = C_v + R = \tfrac{3}{2}R + R = \tfrac{5}{2}R$$

or $C_p \simeq 5$ cal g mole^{-1} deg^{-1}.

From these calculations it can be seen that the difference between the molar heat capacities of an ideal gas at constant pressure and constant volume should be equal to R.

Thus

$$C_p - C_v = 1\cdot987 \text{ cal g mole}^{-1} \text{ deg}^{-1}$$

In practice it is found that these figures agree well with the determined values for monatomic gases such as krypton, mercury, argon, sodium, but for polyatomic molecules we have to apply corrections. In general the specific heats of these molecules at constant volume and pressure can be evaluated from

$$C_v = 3 + x \qquad\qquad \text{...(1.21)}$$

$$C_p = 5 + x \qquad\qquad \text{...(1.22)}$$

where $x =$ the number of atoms in the molecule, e.g. $x = 2$ for diatomic molecules.

Deviations from the ideal behaviour can be best observed from the values of the ratio of C_p to C_v.

The theoretical ratio for an ideal gas should be

$$\frac{C_p}{C_v} = \gamma = \frac{\tfrac{3}{2}R + R}{\tfrac{3}{2}R} = \frac{5}{3} = 1\cdot67$$

A few values of γ for various elements and compounds given below (Table 1.2) show how it varies with the number of atoms in a molecule in a gaseous state.

TABLE 1.2

Monatomic	Diatomic	Complex
He = 1·67	H$_2$ = 1·41	CO$_2$ = 1·30
A = 1·67	O$_2$ = 1·40	C$_3$H$_8$ = 1·13
Hg = 1·67	N$_2$ = 1·41	C$_6$H$_6$ = 1·13
K = 1·68	CO = 1·40	

It is interesting to note that the above values conform very closely to those predicted by equations (1.21) and (1.22). From the values for mercury and potassium it is evident that these metals are monatomic in their vapour state. This is the case with the majority of metallic vapours under normal temperatures and pressures.

1.5 REAL GASES

Deviations of Real Gases from Ideal Behaviour. In the previous section it was shown that the simple kinetic theory of gases allows us to account for some of the ideal gas laws. However, the more complex the gaseous molecule under consideration, the more it deviates from this ideal behaviour. At low pressures and room temperature the majority of gases obey the ideal gas equation $pv = RT$, but as the pressure is increased and the temperature decreased the deviations become large. This is shown in Table 1.3 and Fig. 1.6. (Both of these are taken from Glasstone's *Textbook of Physical Chemistry*, copyright 1946, D. Van Nostrand Company Inc., Princeton, N.J.)

TABLE 1.3

Pressure	Hydrogen	Nitrogen	Carbon dioxide
atm			
1	1·000	1·000	1·000
50	1·033	0·985	0·741
100	1·064	0·985	0·270
200	1·134	1·037	0·409
400	1·277	1·256	0·718
800	1·566	1·796	1·299

In Fig. 1.6 it can be seen that the permanent gas H_2 shows a positive deviation from the ideal gas line, whereas the other gases (N_2 and CO_2) show first a negative deviation, and then the slopes of their lines become positive.

Andrews studied in great detail the effect of pressure and temperature on carbon dioxide. Fig. 1.7 shows the outline of isothermal plots of pressure against volume. Let us follow some of the isothermal curves. The lowest isothermal shown is at 13·1°C and it can be considered to consist of three separate curves. The AB section approximately conforms to Boyle's Law and represents the gaseous part of the isothermal. At the point B any further decrease in volume

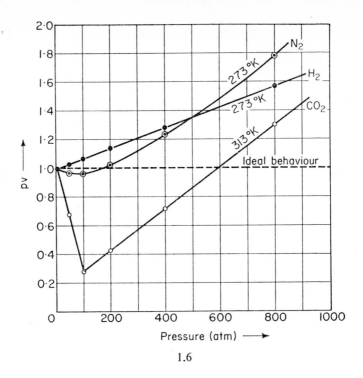

1.6

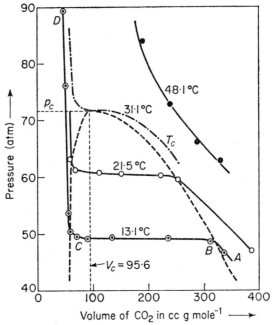

1.7

of a given mass of carbon dioxide has no effect on the overall pressure of the system. The line BC represents the gas at equilibrium with liquid, and, as the volume of the gas is decreased, more gas liquefies until at C the whole gas is converted into liquid. The curve CD is very steep, since it represents the compression of the liquid carbon dioxide. The dotted boundary curve limits the two-phase system of liquid and gas. The isothermal 31·1°C is marked as T_c (i.e. the critical temperature) since it is highest temperature at which the gas can be just liquefied. Above this temperature there is no two-phase region, i.e. the gas will not have any bounding surface with liquid at very high pressures even at 400 atmospheres.

Critical temperature T_c can be therefore defined as the maximum temperature at which the gas can be still liquefied.

Critical pressure P_c, p_c, is the pressure required to liquefy a gas at its critical temperature.

Critical volume V_c, v_c is the volume occupied by one g mole of the gas at the critical temperature and pressure.

1.5.1 Van der Waals' Equation

Andrews' work on various gases and the deviations of gases from the ideal gas behaviour exposed the shortcomings of the ideal gas equation. The equation $pv = RT$ could neither predict the critical phenomena of gases nor the positive and negative deviations of pv/p plots. It is, therefore, not surprising that van der Waals and other research workers tried to formulate new equations to overcome these short-comings. We shall only be concerned with van der Waals' equation since many of the subsequent equations use his constants. Van der Waals argued that at high pressures the volume of molecules, as compared with the total space they occupy, cannot be neglected. He therefore corrected the volume v in the ideal gas equation by subtracting from it a constant b, and thus the new effective volume became $(v - b)$. It is worth noting that the value of b is a few times greater than the absolute volume of the gas molecules.

Van der Waals also considered that at higher pressures the attraction between molecules cannot be neglected. According to him molecules in the bulk of the gas exert a force (p') on molecules just about to strike the wall of the container, and this force has the net effect of pulling them away from the wall. As a result of this force, the measured pressure p is smaller than that inside the container which is given by the sum $p + p'$. The pressure p' is proportional to the product of the force exerted on a single molecule just about to strike the wall and the number of molecules striking the wall at any given moment. The force acting on a single molecule must be proportional to the number of molecules in the bulk of the gas which in turn is

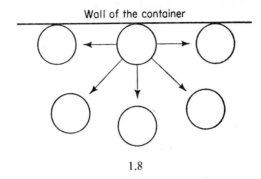

1.8

proportional to the density (ρ) of the gas. The number of molecules striking the wall at any instant is again proportional to the density of the gas. Thus the attractive force is given by $p' \propto$ Number of molecules inside the bulk $\times$ Number striking the wall. Using the relationship between the density of the gas and the R.H.S. terms we have $p' \propto \rho \times \rho$. Since the density ρ of one g mole of a gas is proportional to the reciprocal of its volume, then the inter-attractive force p' is given by

$$p' \propto \rho^2 \propto \frac{1}{v^2}$$

Therefore we can write $p' = \frac{a}{v^2}$ where a is the proportionality constant. Thus the "corrected pressure" becomes $\left(p + \frac{a}{v^2}\right).$

Combining these two new values and inserting them into the ideal gas equation, van der Waals' equation becomes

$$\left(p + \frac{a}{v^2}\right)(v - b) = RT \qquad \ldots(1.23)$$

for 1 g mole of a gas.

This equation contains two constants a and b, whose values can be determined experimentally. These constants for various gases can be found in critical tables.

This equation was found to be a great improvement on the ideal gas equation, since it explained the positive and negative deviations of the pv/p graphs and it also allows us to predict the values of T_c, P_c and V_c for many gases.

1.5.2 *Van der Waals' Equation and Positive and Negative Deviations from Ideal Gas Behaviour*

Let us expand the equation

$$\left(p + \frac{a}{v^2}\right)(v - b) = RT$$

By multiplying out the brackets and rearranging terms in such a way that pv remains on the left-hand side

$$pv = RT + pb - \frac{a}{v} + \frac{ab}{v^2} \qquad \ldots(1.24)$$

Consider this equation first at low pressures. Since at low pressures the value of v^2 becomes very large, the term ab/v^2 may be neglected.

Thus
$$pv = RT + pb - \frac{a}{v}$$

$$pv = RT + p\left(b - \frac{a}{pv}\right)$$

and since at low pressure $pv = RT$

$$pv = RT + p\left(b - \frac{a}{RT}\right) \qquad \ldots(1.25)$$

The equation (1.25) is now in a linear form and at constant temperature T we can write

$$y = mx + c$$

where $y = pv$

$$m = \left(b - \frac{a}{RT}\right)$$

$$c = RT$$

$$x = p$$

This equation therefore should give a straight line of slope $\left(b - \frac{a}{RT}\right)$. The value of the slope will obviously depend on the relative values of b and a.

Thus if

$$b > \frac{a}{RT} \text{ the slope will be positive}$$

$$b = \frac{a}{RT} \text{ we have ideal behaviour}$$

$$b < \frac{a}{RT} \text{ the slope will be negative}$$

Hydrogen is an example of a gas which shows a **positive deviation** (Fig. 1.6), and carbon dioxide one which, at room temperature exhibits **negative deviation** from ideality at low pressures and positive deviation at high pressures.

This reversion from negative to positive deviation as the pressure increases can be explained by considering equation (1.24) at higher pressures.

At higher pressures the positive term $\dfrac{ab}{v^2}$ has to be taken into account and thus the slope becomes

$$b + \frac{ab}{pv^2} - \frac{a}{RT}$$

For the slope to be positive

$$b + \frac{ab}{RTv} \text{ must be greater than } \frac{a}{RT}$$

The slope becomes zero when

$$b + \frac{ab}{RTv} = \frac{a}{RT}$$

and becomes negative when

$$b + \frac{ab}{RTv} < \frac{a}{RT}$$

From these simple calculations it can be seen that, providing the van der Waals' constants a and b are known for a given gas at the given experimental conditions, it is possible to calculate the slope at lower pressures and the point at which reversion from, say, negative to positive values occurs.

The Boyle Temperature. The Boyle temperature may be expressed mathematically by $(\partial pv/\partial p)_{T_B} = 0$; it is the temperature at which the gas obeys Boyle's Law.

The knowledge of this temperature for a real gas can be of great practical importance in engineering where gases are subjected to some extremely drastic conditions. Van der Waals' equation can be used to calculate these temperatures.

Let us multiply out the equation and then rearrange the terms:

$$\left(p + \frac{a}{v^2}\right)(v - b) = RT$$

$$\therefore \qquad p = \frac{RT}{(v-b)} - \frac{a}{v^2}$$

$$\therefore \qquad pv = \frac{RTv}{(v-b)} - \frac{a}{v}$$

$$\therefore \qquad \left(\frac{\partial pv}{\partial p}\right)_T = \left[\frac{RT(v-b) - v}{(v-b)^2} + \frac{a}{v^2}\right]\left(\frac{\partial v}{\partial p}\right)_T$$

If

$$\left(\frac{\partial v}{\partial p}\right) \neq 0 \quad \text{then} \quad \left(\frac{\partial pv}{\partial p}\right)_{T_B} = 0 \quad \text{when} \quad \frac{RTb}{(v-b)^2} = \frac{a}{v^2}$$

This temperature T will be now the Boyle temperature T_B. Thus for conditions of $p \to 0$, $v \to \infty$:

$$\therefore \qquad (v-b)^2 = v^2$$

so

$$T_B = \frac{a}{Rb} \qquad \qquad ...(1.26)$$

Expression (1.26) allows us to calculate the Boyle temperature T_B, providing the van der Waals' constants a and b for a given gas are known.

Table 1.4 shows the calculated and experimental values of T_B for hydrogen and oxygen.

TABLE 1.4

	T_B calculated	T_B determined	Difference
Hydrogen	112°K	108°K	4°K
Oxygen	529°K	423°K	116°K

The difference between the calculated and the experimental value for hydrogen is small, but for oxygen it is rather large. In general the results calculated for easily liquefiable gases differ from the experimental values.

1.5.3 *Van der Waals' Equation and the Critical Phenomena of Gases*

From the Andrews isothermal plots of pressures against volume for carbon dioxide it is evident that the ideal gas equation can only be applied within certain ranges of volumes and pressures.

Let us therefore consider whether the van der Waals' equation is an improvement and will give us an explanation for the existence

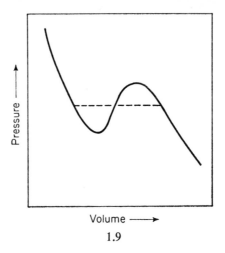

Volume ⟶

1.9

of the various regions (gas, gas-liquid, liquid), and allow us to predict from fundamental data the critical pressure, volume and temperature.

The van der Waals' equation on rearrangement is an equation of the third order, i.e. it contains a term in the third power. In general mathematical expressions of that order give curves of the shape shown in Fig. 1.9. According to the value of T we can obtain either three solutions or one. Let us rearrange this equation into a form comprising volume to the third power:

$$\left(\frac{pv^2 + a}{v^2}\right)(v - b) = RT$$

multiplying out

$$pv^3 + av - bpv^2 - ab = RTv^2$$

or

$$v^3 - v^2\left(\frac{RT}{p} + b\right) + \frac{av}{p} - \frac{a}{p}b = 0$$

or

$$v^3 - \left(\frac{RT}{p} + b\right)v^2 + \frac{a}{p}v - \frac{ab}{p} = 0 \qquad \ldots(1.27)$$

At higher values of T there is one root, and at lower values of T there are three roots.

The three roots can be calculated from a general equation of the form

$$(v - v_1)(v - v_2)(v - v_3) = 0 \qquad \ldots(1.28)$$

by comparing the appropriate coefficients of the equations (1.28) and (1.27). For the critical volume v_c there will be only one root and thus (1.28) becomes $(v - v_c)^3 = 0$.

Expanding

$$v^3 - 3v_c v^2 + 3v_c^2 v - v_c^3 = 0$$

and comparing with (1.27)

$$v^3 - \left(b + \frac{RT_c}{p_c} \right) v^2 + \frac{a}{p_c} v - \frac{ab}{p_c} = 0$$

The coefficients can be written as

$$3v_c = b + \frac{RT_c}{p_c} \qquad \text{...(1.29)}$$

$$3v_c^2 = \frac{a}{p_c} \qquad \text{...(1.30)}$$

$$v_c^3 = \frac{ab}{p_c} \qquad \text{...(1.31)}$$

There are three independent equations comprising three unknowns. Their critical values can then be calculated, providing a and b, the van der Waals' constants, are known.

From (1.31) and (1.30)

$$v_c = 3b \qquad \text{...(1.32)}$$

substituting (1.31) into (1.29)

$$p_c = \frac{a}{27b^2} \qquad \text{...(1.34)}$$

and (1.32) into (1.29)

$$T_c = \frac{8a}{27bR} \qquad \text{...(1.33)}$$

The values of v_c, p_c and T_c in the equations (1.32), (1.33) and (1.34) are expressed by means of constants, and therefore can be easily calculated.

At the critical volume, pressure and temperature the value of

$$\frac{RT_c}{p_c v_c} = \frac{R \cdot 8a}{27bR} \cdot \frac{27b^2}{a} \cdot \frac{1}{3b} = \frac{8}{3} \simeq 2 \cdot 67$$

Let us compare the predicted value with some experimental values shown in Table 1.5.

TABLE 1.5

Gas	Experimental values	Predicted
H_2	3·05	2·67
He	3·08	2·67
N_2	3·42	2·67
CO_2	3·68	2·67
Ethyl ether	3·83	2·67

It is clear that the predicted values do not agree very well with the experimental ones. However, the very fact that it is possible to predict the value to that extent shows the usefulness of this equation.

1.5.4 Summary

(i) The simple kinetic theory of gases allows us to explain some of the ideal gas laws.

(ii) Real gases usually depart from the ideal gas behaviour, and van der Waals has shown that the original assumptions made in the kinetic theory were not always correct.

(iii) Van der Waals' equation $\left(p + \dfrac{a}{v^2}\right)(v - b) = RT$ can be used conveniently for:

(a) the approximate calculation of P_c, V_c and T_c,
(b) accounting for the liquefaction of gases,
(c) calculation of the Boyle Temperature (T_B),
(d) inversion of slopes from negative to positive,
(e) explaining the existence of positive and negative slopes for the same gas at different temperatures.

(iv) Several other gas equations have been proposed but these are usually valuable only for specific gases.

CHAPTER II

The First Law of Thermodynamics

The origin of thermodynamics can be found in the discovery of the quantitative aspects of the interconvertibility of heat and energy. Thermodynamics as an exact study has grown stepwise. It is therefore very convenient to expand the basic ideas according to the different laws.

2.1 HISTORICAL OUTLINES

Until the beginning of the nineteenth century heat was regarded by the majority of scientists as a fluid called caloric, which existed between the ultimate particles of matter, and which could pass from one body to another without actually being lost. The first recorded quantitative data that seemed to disprove this officially considered nature of heat were recorded by Thompson. He noticed that during the boring of metal cannon a tremendous amount of heat was generated, which he attributed (1798) to the expended mechanical energy of boring. Subsequently he determined the amount of heat produced by a certain amount of work to be 940 ft lb to heat 1 lb of water by 1°F (the correct value is about 780 ft lb),[1] and thus he initiated the study of the quantitative aspects of the interconvertibility of heat and energy. The next half century witnessed many disputes regarding the nature of heat and correct value of the mechanical equivalent of heat, i.e. the amount of work that is equivalent to one calorie.[2] Thompson's hypothesis that heat is energy was finally proved in the classical work by J. Joule, who in his father's laboratory in a Manchester brewery carried out numerous experiments on the mechanical equivalent of heat. He found that 10^7 ergs of work expended by paddles[3] in water contained in a calorimeter produced 0·241 calorie (the present accepted value is 0·239). In 1843 he published[4] his results on the heating effect on water of an electric current, and he compared this with the previous result.

Joule then systematically converted electrical and mechanical energy into heat in a variety of ways such as electric heating, mechanical stirring, compression of gases, and friction. In every case he found nearly the same value for the conversion factor, thus showing that a given amount of work always produced the same amount of heat, within the experimental errors of his techniques.

2.2 THE NATURE OF THE FIRST LAW

This law can be regarded as an extension of the principle of the conservation of mechanical energy and it is frequently called the **Law of Conservation of Energy.** Joule (1842) summarised this law as follows: **Energy can neither be created nor destroyed in a system* of constant mass, although it may be converted from one form to another.†**

In Fig. 2.1 an attempt is made to represent this law in a pictorial way. The outer boundary of Fig. 2.1 represents a system of constant mass and constant energy. The arrows pointing to and from the

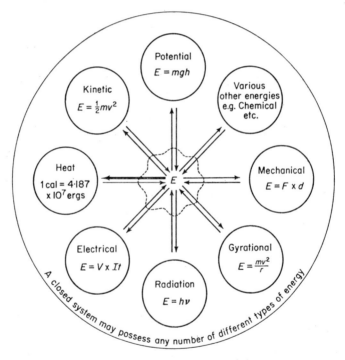

2.1. *A system of constant mass and energy*

---

* The term 'system' denotes a specified portion of matter under consideration.

† This statement of the First Law is valid even in the nuclear age, since Einstein (1905) has shown the equivalence of mass and energy; thus mass may be regarded as a form of energy.

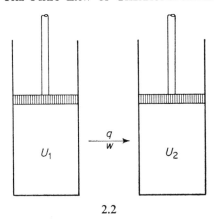

2.2

'pool of energy' E represent the interconvertibility of energies, i.e. when one form of energy is spent it will be converted into one or more different forms of energy. In this drawing the arrow pointing from the energy pool to heat energy is thicker than the other way round. This will be shown later on to have an extremely important significance and forms the basis of the **Second Law of Thermodynamics.**

Consider mechanical and heat energy only; then according to the First Law heat is energy and may be converted to other energies. Thus

Heat energy $\rightleftharpoons$ Mechanical energy

Let us formulate a mathematical expression based on this law by considering a system in its simplest state, i.e. in the gaseous state. Consider a mass of gas contained in a cylinder fitted with a frictionless piston (Fig. 2.2), and let the internal energy of this gaseous system be denoted by U. Suppose that external energy in the form of heat or other energy is supplied to the system, and the system, while absorbing this energy, performs the amount of work w.

There will naturally be a relationship between the supplied energy, the work done by the system, and the increase in energy of the system (see Fig. 2.3).

$$U_2 - U_1 = \Delta U = q - w \qquad \ldots(2.1)$$

where ΔU = the increase in the internal energy

q = the heat (or energy) supplied to the system

w = the work (in calories) done by the system.

Any work done by the system can be expressed in calories, since 1 calorie = $4 \cdot 184 \times 10^7$ ergs, and this value is known as the mechanical equivalent of heat.

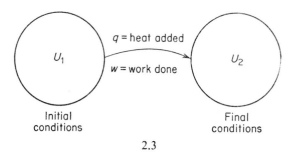

Initial   Final
conditions   conditions

2.3

2.2.1 Change in Internal Energy (ΔU) of an Ideal Gas at Constant Volume

The change in internal energy of a gas depends on whether the heat is added to the gaseous system at constant volume or constant pressure.

Let us first consider the system when heat is added to a mass of gas at constant volume and no work is done. Thus

$$w = 0 \quad \text{and} \quad \Delta U = q_v \qquad \ldots (2.2)$$

where $q_v = $ heat absorbed at constant volume.

It is worth noting that the increase in the internal energy of this system will be due to changes in the translational, rotational and vibrational energies of the gaseous molecules.

2.2.2 Change in Internal Energy (ΔU) of an Ideal Gas at Constant Pressure

Consider again a mass of an ideal gas confined in a cylinder that is fitted with a piston compressing the gas with a constant pressure p. Let the initial internal energy of this mass of gas be U_1 and its volume v_1. Introduce q calories of heat into the system. The net effect of this addition will be an increase in temperature and volume to keep the internal pressure of the gas constant. Let the final volume of the gas be v_2 and its energy U_2 (see Fig. 2.4).

Substituting these values into the equation (2.1) we obtain

$$\Delta U = U_2 - U_1 = q_p - w$$

The value of the work done by the system during the expansion can be calculated since by definition work equals a force multiplied by distance, i.e.

$$w = F \times d \qquad \ldots (2.3)$$

where $w = $ work done in ergs
$F = $ force in dynes
$d = $ distance in cm.

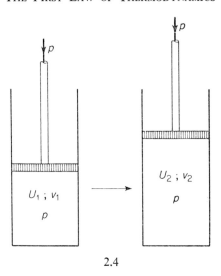

2.4

In this case the gas has done work by pushing the piston during expansion to keep the pressure constant. The force F in the equation can be calculated from the pressure p since by definition

$$\text{pressure} = \frac{\text{force}}{\text{area}} = \frac{F}{A}$$

(A = area of the piston, p = pressure)

$$\therefore \qquad\qquad F = A \times p \qquad\qquad\qquad ...(2.4)$$

Substitution of (2.4) into (2.3) gives

$$w = p \times A \times d$$
$$w = p \times \Delta v \qquad\qquad\qquad ...(2.5)$$

since $A \times d$ = the increase in volume of the gas Δv. Substituting the value of w from (2.5) into the equation (2.1)

$$\Delta U = U_2 - U_1 = q_p - p(v_2 - v_1)$$

or

$$(U_2 + pv_2) - (U_1 + pv_1) = q_p$$
$$\Delta(U + pv) = q_p \qquad\qquad\qquad ...(2.6)$$

The term $(U + pv)$ on the left-hand side of this equation occurs in thermodynamics so often that, in order to simplify our calculations concerning constant pressure processes, it is given the symbol H and is called **enthalpy**.

Thus by definition

$$H = U + pv \qquad \ldots(2.7)$$

Heat content, enthalpy	=	Internal energy	+	Energy term dependent on the state of the system

From (2.6) and (2.7)

$$\Delta H = q_p \qquad \ldots(2.8)$$

An increase in enthalpy therefore denotes the heat absorbed during a process at a constant pressure.

Example
Calculate the increase in (i) internal energy ΔU, and (ii) enthalpy ΔH of a gaseous system at a constant pressure of one atmosphere when 10 calories of heat (or energy) are added and the volume of the system increases by 100 cc.

(i) Let the initial and final internal energies of the system be U_1 and U_2 respectively (see Fig. 2.5). From the first law of thermodynamics it follows that the increase in the internal energy of the system will be

$$U_2 - U_1 = q_p - w$$

or

$$\Delta U = \text{(heat added)} - \text{(work done by the system)}$$

From equation (2.5) it follows that $w = p(v_2 - v_1)$. Since the heat added was given in calories, both the pressure and the volume have to be expressed in cgs units.

Thus

$$1 \text{ atm} = h\rho g = 76 \times 13 \cdot 8 \times 981 \text{ dynes cm}^{-2}$$

where $h =$ height of a mercury column supported by the pressure of one atmosphere, i.e. 76 cm

$\rho = 13 \cdot 8 =$ specific gravity of mercury

$g =$ gravitational constant in cm sec^{-2}.

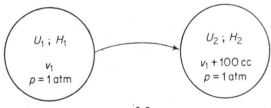

'2.5

This value is good enough for the majority of calculations, but, using more accurate data for the values of ρ and g,

$$1 \text{ atm} = 1.013 \times 10^6 \text{ dynes cm}^{-2}$$

Therefore

$$\text{Work done} = w = p(v_2 - v_1) = 1.013 \times 10^6 \times 100$$
$$= 1.013 \times 10^8 \text{ dynes cm, i.e. ergs}$$

The work done in ergs can then be converted into calories:

$$w = \frac{1.013 \times 10^8}{4.184 \times 10^7} = 2.42 \text{ cal} \qquad \qquad \ldots(2.9)$$

Substituting (2.9) into the equation (2.1)

$$\Delta U = q_p - w = 10 - 2.42 = 7.58 \text{ cal}$$

Answer to (i)*:* The increase in the internal energy of this gaseous system was 7.58 cal.

(ii) The increase in enthalpy of this system can be calculated from equation (2.8); thus $\Delta H = q_p = 10$ cal.

Answer to (ii)*:* The enthalpy change of this gaseous system is 10 cal. This example shows clearly that the value of enthalpy change and internal energy change are different, and that the value of enthalpy change gives the true value of the total energy involved in a process at constant pressure.

2.3 REVERSIBLE AND IRREVERSIBLE PROCESSES: MAXIMUM WORK

When the system is changed from one state to another the energy change during the process depends on the way it is carried out. To illustrate this fact consider a process during which 1 g mole of a perfect gas is expanded from 4 atmospheres to 1 atmosphere pressure at 300°K (i) isothermally, and (ii) under adiabatic conditions. Assume that the expansion is carried out under ideal conditions, i.e. there is no other work done during this process apart from the expansion (frictionless piston, etc.).

2.3.1 *Isothermal Expansion of an Ideal Gas*

This change can be carried out in an infinite number of ways, but, to be brief, let us consider just three ways—firstly, when the opposing pressure to the expansion, p_{ext}, is zero, secondly, when the opposing pressure is always equal to one atmosphere, and finally, when the

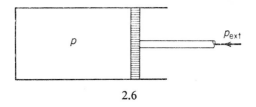

2.6

opposing pressure p_{ext} is virtually always equal to the pressure of the gas in the container (see Fig. 2.6).

Cases (i) $p_{ext} = 0$
     (ii) $p_{ext} = 1$ atm
     (iii) $p_{ext} = p$

The work done by a gas during its expansion is given by

$$w = p_{ext} \cdot \Delta v$$

and for small changes in volume

$$w = p_{ext} \, dv$$

Case (i). Since $p_{ext} = 0$ the value $w_{(i)} = p_{ext} \cdot \Delta v = 0$ and the heat absorbed during the process $q = w = 0$.

Case (ii). $p_{ext} = 1$ atm. The gas during the process of expansion has to push the piston at constant pressure

$$p_{ext} = 1 \text{ atm} = \text{constant}$$

Since

$$w = p_{ext} \cdot \Delta v$$

$$w = \int_{v_1}^{v_2} p_{ext} \, dv = p_{ext} \int_{v_1}^{v_2} dv = p_{ext}(v_2 - v_1)$$

but since

$$v_1 p_1 = RT \qquad \therefore \; v_1 = \frac{RT}{p_1} \qquad \text{given } p_1 = 4 \text{ atm}$$

$$v_2 p_2 = RT \qquad \therefore \; v_2 = \frac{RT}{p_2} \qquad \qquad p_2 = 1 \text{ atm}$$

Substitute the value of v_1 and v_2 into the above equation:

$$w_{(ii)} = p_{ext} \, RT \left(\frac{1}{p_2} - \frac{1}{p_1} \right) = 1 \times 1 \cdot 987 \times 300 \left(\frac{1}{1} - \frac{1}{4} \right)$$

$$= 450 \text{ cal g mole}^{-1}$$

Case (iii). Thus the total work done by the gas when expanding from volume $v_1 \rightarrow v_2$ will be the integral of this expression:

$$w = \int_{v_1}^{v_2} p\, dv$$

In this equation there are two variables p and v and therefore p has to be expressed in terms of v, the integration variable. This can be conveniently done for a perfect gas since $p = RT/v$.
Thus equation (2.9) becomes

$$w = \int_{v_1}^{v_2} \frac{RT}{v} \cdot dv$$

Integrating

$$w = RT \log_e \frac{v_2}{v_1} \qquad \ldots(2.10)$$

Substituting the given data into the equation

$$w_{(iii)} = RT \log_e \tfrac{4}{1} = 1 \cdot 978 \times 2 \cdot 303 \times 300 \log_{10} 4$$

$$w_{(iii)} = 826 \cdot 3 \text{ cal g mole}^{-1}$$

These calculations show without any doubt that the energy involved in the expansion of 1 g mole of ideal gas from 4 to 1 atmosphere at 300°K can vary from zero to 826·3 cal and **it depends on the way the gas is expanded.** It is also clear that one can obtain any number of answers, even though the initial and final conditions of this 1 g mole of gas are always the same. Therefore in classical thermodynamics one is concerned with processes that give maximum energy changes, i.e. they are considered to be carried out infinitesimally slowly, so that the system is always at temperature and pressure equilibrium with its surroundings. Processes carried out under these conditions are called **reversible processes** or are said to be **thermodynamically reversible.** In general a reversible process may be defined as a process in which the driving force is equal to the resisting force. An ideal process or reversible process is a process in which all friction, electrical resistance, or other sources of dissipation of energy have been eliminated.

2.3.2 *Adiabatic Expansion of Ideal Gases*

An adiabatic process can be defined as a process during which there is no loss or gain of heat by the system, that is, the system is thermally insulated from its surroundings. Consider an adiabatic expansion of 1 g mole of an ideal gas. The gas on expanding will perform external

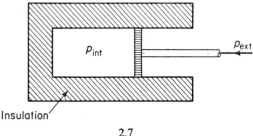

2.7

work by pushing the piston. Since heat cannot enter or leave this system, the heat energy required to maintain the work done during expansion must come from within the gas itself.

Using the First Law of Thermodynamics

$$\Delta U = q - w$$

but, since $q = 0$ for an adiabatic process, there is no heat absorbed from outside.

Therefore

$$\Delta U = -w$$

and the work done in an infinitesimal expansion is

$$dU = -dw = -p \, dv \qquad \ldots(2.11)$$

where p is the external pressure opposing the expansion.

From a practical point of view it is of utmost interest to calculate the change in temperature resulting from the expansion of the gas. Let us derive from the First Law of Thermodynamics the gas equation that would allow us to correlate the p, v and T of an adiabatic process.

U, the internal energy of the gas for constant mass, is a function of its temperature, pressure, and volume. These functions are interrelated, and therefore any two of these functions can be used to determine the change in the internal energy of the gaseous system.

Since $U = f(T, p, v)$, we can use temperature and volume to determine dU from its total differential.*

Thus

$$dU = \left(\frac{\partial U}{\partial v}\right)_T dv + \left(\frac{\partial U}{\partial T}\right)_v dT \qquad \ldots(2.12)$$

* E.g. see S. J. Smith, *Advanced Chemical Calculations*, (London 1950), Appendix p. 428, Macmillan.

where the first term gives the value of the change in internal energy with change in volume at constant temperature, and the second term the change with temperature at constant volume.

Consider the adiabatic expansion of an ideal gas. Because there is no intermolecular attraction, $\left(\dfrac{\partial U}{\partial v}\right)_T = 0$. The value $\left(\dfrac{\partial U}{\partial T}\right)_v = C_v$, i.e. the change in internal energy with temperature at constant volume. Thus from (2.11) and (2.12) we get

$$dU = C_v dT = -pdv \qquad \ldots(2.13)$$

The force opposing the expansion, that is the external pressure p_{ext}, may vary again from zero to equal to the internal pressure of the expanding gas (Fig. 2.7). When the process is carried out under reversible conditions, i.e. $p_{ext} = p_{int}$, the maximum cooling of the gas will occur.

The expression (2.13) cannot be evaluated by integration, as in a reversible process the pressure p will vary with the changing volume. However, for an ideal gas we have $p = RT/v$.

Substituting into (2.13) the expression becomes

$$C_v dT = -\frac{RTdv}{v} = dU = -dw \qquad \ldots(2.14)$$

The work done on reversible adiabatic expansion is obtained by integrating this equation from v_1, the original volume, to v_2, the final volume, and between T_1 and T_2, its initial and final temperatures respectively (see Fig. 2.8).

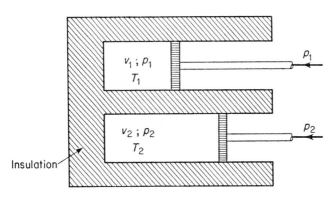

2.8

Thus

$$C_v \int_{T_1}^{T_2} \frac{dT}{T} = -R \int_{v_1}^{v_2} \frac{dv}{v}$$

Solving

$$C_v \log_e \frac{T_2}{T_1} = -R \log_e \frac{v_2}{v_1} = R \log_e \frac{v_1}{v_2}$$

or

$$\log_e \frac{T_2}{T_1} = \frac{R}{C_v} \log_e \frac{v_1}{v_2}$$

Since

$$C_p - C_v = R \qquad \therefore \frac{C_p}{C_v} - 1 = \frac{R}{C_v} \qquad \therefore \gamma - 1 = \frac{R}{C_v}$$

Thus

$$\log_e \frac{T_2}{T_1} = (\gamma - 1) \log_e \frac{v_1}{v_2} = \log_e \left(\frac{v_1}{v_2}\right)^{(\gamma-1)}$$

or

$$\frac{T_2}{T_1} = \left(\frac{v_1}{v_2}\right)^{\gamma-1}$$

or

$$T_2 v_2^{(\gamma-1)} = T_1 v_1^{(\gamma-1)} \qquad \qquad \ldots(2.15)$$

Since during an expansion process $v_2 > v_1$, then it follows that $T_2 < T_1$.

Conversely, during compression of a perfect gas, a rise in temperature will occur.

Equation (2.15) can be written in general terms as $Tv^{(\gamma-1)} =$ constant for an adiabatic expansion of a perfect gas. Using the perfect gas equation of state and substituting into (2.15) one obtains

$$p_1 v_1^{\gamma} = p_2 v_2^{\gamma} \qquad \qquad \ldots(2.16)$$

or in general $pv^{\gamma} =$ constant.

This equation is true for any adiabatic change of a perfect gas, and can be compared with $p_1 v_1 = p_2 v_2$ for isothermal changes. Fig. (2.9) shows the differences in the p versus v plots of adiabatic and isothermal changes.

2.3.3 The Joule Experiment

J. L. Gay-Lussac (1807), J. P. Joule (1843), and others have attempted to determine experimentally the effect of expansion of gases into vacuum when there is no loss or gain of heat by the gaseous system.

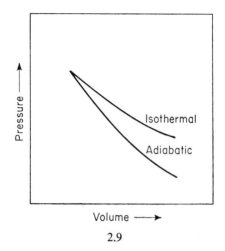

2.9

They attempted to measure the term $\left(\dfrac{\partial U}{\partial v}\right)_T$ which is known as the internal pressure. Joule devised an apparatus to measure the thermal effect of expansion of air under adiabatic conditions. Fig. 2.10 represents Joule's apparatus, which consisted of two similar copper vessels (R and E) connected by a tube fitted with a stopcock (D); E was evacuated, and R contained compressed dry air (at 22 atm). The whole was placed in a tin can filled with water. The temperature of the well stirred water was taken. The stopcock (D) was then opened. The gas was allowed to pass to E until equilibrium was established between the two vessels. The water was then stirred and its temperature taken. Experimentally it was found that there

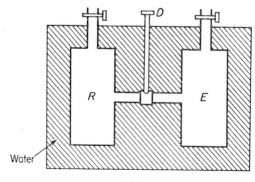

2.10

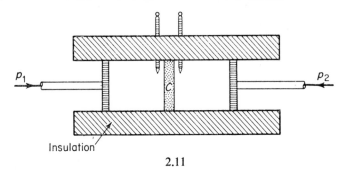

p_1 p_2

Insulation

2.11

was no change in the temperature of the water in the can, therefore Joule concluded that an increase in volume of the air under adiabatic conditions did not produce any net heat change.

2.3.4 The Joule-Thomson Experiment

Joule's experiment was not capable of detecting small effects of heat, since the heat capacity of his water calorimeter was very large compared with the heat capacity of the mass of gas used in his experiment. To overcome this difficulty Joule and Thomson devised an experiment in which the changes in temperatures were measured directly. The apparatus (Fig. 2.11) consisted of an insulated tube divided by a porous plug (C), and with both ends fitted with pistons p_1 and p_2. Consider 1 g mole of the gas being transferred across the porous plug by moving pistons so that the original pressures p_1 and p_2 are maintained throughout the whole experiment.

We can apply the First Law of Thermodynamics to calculate the energy changes during the process.

Equation (2.1) states

$$\Delta U = U_2 - U_1 = q - w$$

Since the process proceeds under adiabatic conditions $q = 0$. The work done by the system during the transfer of 1 g mole of the gas across C can be expressed as

$$w = p_2 v_2 - p_1 v_1$$

i.e. the work done by expansion $p_2 v_2$ less the work done on compression $p_1 v_1$.

Substitute (2.16) into equation (2.1):

$$U_2 - U_1 = -(p_2 v_2 - p_1 v_1)$$

Rearranging terms

$$U_2 + p_2 v_2 = U_1 + p_1 v_1 \quad \text{or } H_2 = H_1 \quad \ldots (2.17)$$

From (2.17) it follows that during the Joule-Thomson experiment the initial enthalpy was equal to the final enthalpy, and that an adiabatic process is **isenthalpic**.

The Joule-Thomson experiment did show experimentally that there was a net change in temperature of the gaseous system caused by the expansion of the gas.

2.3.5   The Joule-Thomson Coefficient (μ_j)

The Joule-Thomson coefficient may be defined as the change of temperature of a given gas with pressure at constant enthalpy:

$$\mu_j = \left(\frac{\partial T}{\partial p}\right)_{H.m}$$

The knowledge of the value and the sign of this coefficient is important in practice, for example in refrigeration and low temperature work, since a positive value corresponds to cooling and a negative value to heating of a gas. It is therefore intended to show how this coefficient can be calculated for a given gas from the First Law of Thermodynamics and the van der Waals' constants.

Enthalpy or heat content (H) is a function of temperature, pressure and volume. Since these variables are mutually dependent, the heat content can be determined by any two variables. Let us therefore consider the enthalpy to be a function of temperature and pressure, $H = f(T, p)$; similarly to equation (2.12) we can write the variation of enthalpy for a small change of T and p as

$$dH = \left(\frac{\partial H}{\partial T}\right)_p dT + \left(\frac{\partial H}{\partial p}\right)_T dp \qquad \ldots(2.18)$$

For the isenthalpic Joule-Thomson effect at constant H, $dH = 0$. Thus equation (2.18) becomes

$$\left(\frac{\partial H}{\partial T}\right)_p . dT + \left(\frac{\partial H}{\partial p}\right)_T . dp = 0$$

or

$$\left(\frac{dT}{dp}\right)_H = \frac{-\left(\frac{\partial H}{\partial p}\right)_T}{\left(\frac{\partial H}{\partial T}\right)_p} = -\frac{\left(\frac{\partial U}{\partial p}\right)_T + \left(\frac{\partial pv}{\partial p}\right)_T}{C_p} \qquad \ldots(2.19)$$

The first term of the numerator represents the work done in expansion against the attractive forces between molecules, and the second term has already been shown in Chapter I, equation (1.25), to be equal to $\left(b - \dfrac{a}{RT}\right)$ at low pressure.

Let us therefore calculate the value of the term $\left(\dfrac{\partial U}{\partial p}\right)_T$ in equation (2.19): van der Waals' assumption can be used to calculate the variation of the internal energy U of a gas when its pressure changes.

Let U_∞ be the internal energy of the gas at an infinite volume, and $\dfrac{a}{v^2}$ the van der Waals' attractive force between the molecules; then U, the internal energy at a volume v, is given by

$$U = U_\infty + \int_\infty^v \frac{a}{v^2} \cdot dv$$

or

$$U = U_\infty - \frac{a}{v}$$

then

$$U = U_\infty - \frac{ap}{RT}$$

and

$$\left(\frac{\partial U}{\partial p}\right)_T = -\frac{a}{RT} \qquad \ldots(2.20)$$

Substituting (2.20) and the value obtained from (1.25) into (2.19) gives

$$\left(\frac{dT}{dp}\right)_H = -\frac{-\dfrac{a}{RT} + b - \dfrac{a}{RT}}{C_p}$$

Thus

$$\left(\frac{dT}{dp}\right)_H = \frac{1}{C_p}\left(\frac{2a}{RT} - b\right) \qquad \ldots(2.21)$$

From this equation it can be seen that in isenthalpic processes the pressure coefficient of temperature of a gas obeying the van der Waals' equation depends on the specific heat of the gas, van der Waals' constants a and b, and the initial temperature T at which it is expanded. It is therefore evident that the coefficient will vary with temperature, and thus this equation allows us to calculate the temperature ranges for positive and negative coefficients.

Assuming that a and b are temperature independent then the condition for $\left(\dfrac{dT}{dp}\right)_H$ to be positive is that $\dfrac{2a}{RT} > b$.

The Joule-Thomson effect for hydrogen changes from a slight warming at ordinary temperature to cooling below $-80 \cdot 5°C$ at 113 atm initial pressure. This result shows that hydrogen can be liquefied by expansion, providing it is initially cooled to below a certain temperature.[5] The $-80 \cdot 5°C$ is called the Joule-Thomson inversion temperature for hydrogen. For helium this inversion temperature is $-240°C$.

2.4 THERMOCHEMISTRY

Thermochemistry is the study of heat effects accompanying chemical reactions, the formation of solutions, and changes in the state of matter such as melting or vaporization, and other physicochemical processes.

Physicochemical processes can be classified as exothermic, accompanied by the evolution of heat, and endothermic, accompanied by the absorption of heat.

In this section we shall be dealing only with heats of formation and heats of reactions.

2.4.1 *Heat of Formation and Enthalpy*

The heat of formation of a compound is the heat evolved or absorbed when one g mole of that compound is formed from its elements. Consider for example the formation of carbon dioxide from graphite and oxygen. Thus the chemical equation is

$$C_{(s)} + O_{2(g)} = CO_{2(g)}$$
$$+ 94,050 \text{ cal at } 25°C \text{ and normal pressure (1 atm)}$$

The conditions under which this reaction is carried out must be stated, since the value of the heat of formation will depend on the temperature and on whether it is carried out at constant volume or constant pressure.

The value of $+94,050$ cal g mole^{-1} represents the heat that appears during the reaction, i.e. the heat evolved. It follows then that a **positive sign for the heat of formation Q denotes that the reaction is exothermic.** Conversely **a negative sign denotes an endothermic reaction.** Briefly, when heat is generated during a reaction, the reaction is exothermic.

This sign convention in thermochemistry is the reverse of that used in thermodynamics, where any heat added to a system is considered to be positive, and vice versa. Thus the enthalpy change accompanying the formation of carbon dioxide is numerically equal to the heat of formation, but will have an opposite sign:

$$\therefore \qquad \Delta H_{CO_2} = -94,050 \text{ cal g mole}^{-1}$$
$$Q_{CO_2} = +94,050 \text{ cal g mole}^{-1}$$
$$\Delta H = -Q$$

An example of an endothermic reaction is

$$2Mg_{(s)} + 3C_{(s)} = Mg_2C_{3(s)}$$

$$-19,000 \text{ cal at } 25°C \text{ and } 1 \text{ atm pressure}$$

In this case the heat of formation of magnesium carbide is negative, and the enthalpy change of formation will have a positive sign. Thus

$$Q_{Mg_2C_3} = -19,000 \text{ cal g mole}^{-1} \text{ at } 25°C, 1 \text{ atm}$$

$$\Delta H_{Mg_2C_3} = +19,000 \text{ cal g mole}^{-1} \text{ at } 25°C, 1 \text{ atm}$$

For convenience the enthalpies of all elements in their pure states are arbitrarily taken to be zero at all temperatures. The standard enthalpy of formation ΔH_{298} is then the enthalpy change (or heat of reaction with an opposite sign) which accompanies the formation of this compound at 25°C and 1 atm.

This may be appreciated from the following calculation of the heat of formation of aluminium oxide:

$$2Al + \tfrac{3}{2}O_2 = Al_2O_3$$
$$(\Delta H \text{ values are} \quad 0 \qquad 0 \quad -400,000)$$
$$\therefore \qquad \Delta H_{298} = -400,000 \text{ cal g mole}^{-1} \text{ at } 25°C$$

This chemical equation refers to two gram atoms of aluminium combining with $\tfrac{3}{2}$ g mole of oxygen to give 1 g mole of aluminium oxide, all being in their standard states, i.e. pure and in their stable forms at 25°C and at 1 atm pressure. The value of $-400,000$ cal shows that the difference in enthalpy between the products and reactants amounts to $-400,000$ cal g mole^{-1} of Al_2O_3. By choosing arbitrarily the value for pure elements as $\Delta H_{298} = 0$ the calculations become more simple.

It is worth noting that the ΔH_{298} values are greatly influenced by the purity of the elements. This can be easily appreciated from the list of the $-\Delta H_{298}$ of Al_2O_3 (see Table 2.1).

It is, however, probable that the differences in these values were not only due to the purity of the starting aluminium, but also to inaccurate calorimetric measurement, fluxing with the crucible material, and the possible existence of more than one form of Al_2O_3.

The change in enthalpies of chemical compounds are usually recorded in the thermodynamic tables at the standard temperature of 25°C and 1 atm and are denoted by ΔH_{298}. Table 2.2 shows some of these enthalpy changes. Since $\Delta H = -Q$, therefore standard enthalpy changes with an opposite sign are actually standard heats of formation.

TABLE 2.1

Observers	Year	$-\Delta H_{298}$ (kcal g mole^{-1})	Purity of Al in %
Berthelot	1881	380·2	99·5
Von Wartenberg and Witzel	1919	396·0 ± 0·4	95·0
Moose and Parr	1924	375·8 ± 0·2	98·4
Roth and Muller	1929	380·8 ± 0·4	99·83
Meichsner and Roth	1934	393·3 ± 0·3	99·9
Roth, Wolf and Fritz	1940	402·9 ± 0·3	99·9
Synder and Seltz	1945	399·0 ± 0·24	99·98
Holley and Huber	1951	400·29 ± 0·31	99·96
Schneider	1954	400·3 ± 1·6	99·99

From Kubaschewski & Evans, *Metallurgical Thermochemistry*, 2nd edition, Pergamon Press Ltd., London, 1958.

TABLE 2.2

Standard Heats of Formation at 25°C, 1 atm pressure[6]

Compound	State	$-\Delta H_{298}$ (kcal g mole^{-1})	Compound	State	$-\Delta H_{298}$ (kcal g mole^{-1})
Al_2O_3	s	400·0 ± 1·5	Fe	s	0
Graphite	s	0	Fe_2O_3	s	196·3 ± 0·8
Diamond	s	0·454	H_2O	l	68·38 ± 0·01
B_2O_3	s	306·1 + 4·5	H_2O	g	57·8 ± 0·1
CO	g	26·40 ± 0·03	H_2S	g	4·8 ± 0·1
CO_2	g	94·05 ± 0·01	ZnS	s	48·2 ± 2·0

From Kubaschewski & Evans, *Metallurgical Thermochemistry*, 2nd edition, Pergamon Press Ltd., London, 1958.

From Table 2.2 it can be seen that graphite is taken as the standard state of carbon, and that a process at 1 atm that would allow us to convert graphite into diamond would be accompanied by the evolution of 454 cal g atom^{-1} of carbon. It may also be worth pointing out that the difference in the enthalpies of formation between liquid water and water vapour is equal to the latent heat of liquefaction.

2.4.2 Hess's Law and Heats of Reaction

Hess's Law states that the heat content change in a chemical reaction is the same whether it takes place in one or several stages, providing that in each case the initial conditions of reactants and final conditions of products in the various processes are the same. This law is illustrated in Fig. 2.12. The reaction $A \rightarrow Y$ can be achieved in a direct way or via many stages.

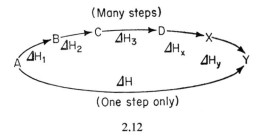

2.12

According to Hess's Law

$$\Delta H = \Delta H_1 + \Delta H_2 + \Delta H_3 + \Delta H_x + \Delta H_y$$

This additive property of heats of reactions can be illustrated by the following example.

Calculate the enthalpy change for the reduction reaction of ferric oxide with carbon monoxide using suitable data from Table 2.2.

The balanced equation for this reduction reaction is

$$Fe_2O_{3(s)} + 3CO_{(g)} = 2Fe_{(s)} + 3CO_2$$

From Table 2·2 $-196·3$ $-3 \times 26·4$ 0 $-3 \times 94·05$

$$\Delta H_{298} = (2\Delta H_{Fe} + 3\Delta H_{CO_2}) - (\Delta H_{Fe_2O_3} + 3\Delta H_{CO})$$

$$\Delta H_{298} = -(2 \times 0 + 3 \times 94·05) + (196·3 + 3 \times 26·4)$$

$$= -6·65 \text{ kcal g mole}^{-1}$$

The enthalpy change of this reaction comes to $-6·65$ kcal g mole^{-1} of Fe_2O_3 at 25°C. Since the enthalpy change sign is negative, the reaction is exothermic. However, in cases similar to this reaction where the ΔH value is comparatively small and its evaluation involved a few multiplications, it is always useful to check the experimental errors of quantities used. These are as follows:

Compound	Error	Error after multiplication
	kcal	
CO	0·03	0·09
CO$_2$	0·01	0·03
Fe$_2$O$_3$	0·8	0·8

The maximum error in ΔH_{298} for this reaction will be the sum of errors = $0·09 + 0·03 + 0·8 = 0·92$.

Thus

$$\Delta H_{298} = -6.65 \pm 0.92 \text{ kcal g mole}^{-1}$$

In this case the percentage possible error will be quite considerable, being $\dfrac{0.92}{6.65} \times 100 \simeq 13.7\%$.

It is interesting to note that the percentage possible error of the calculated ΔH_{298} may be considerable, even though the original experimental errors in the enthalpies of the various compounds are small.

2.5 THE VARIATION OF ENTHALPY CHANGE WITH TEMPERATURE; KIRCHHOFF'S EQUATION

The heat content change accompanying a chemical process usually varies with temperature. It is difficult in many cases to determine these values experimentally. For example the heat of formation of oxides is difficult to measure at high temperatures, although it may be of great industrial interest. Kirchhoff's equation is very useful in this respect, since it allows us to calculate the enthalpy changes at various temperatures, providing the heat of the process is known at some other temperature (T), and the heat capacities of reactants and products are known in the range of temperatures under consideration.

2.5.1   *Heat Capacities of a System*

The heat capacity can be defined as the average quantity of heat necessary to raise a system from the lower temperature to the higher. Mathematically it can be represented as follows:

$$\text{Mean heat capacity } \bar{C}_{T_1 \to T_2} = \frac{q}{T_2 - T_1}$$

where $\bar{C}$ = mean heat capacity

q = the heat required to raise the temperature of the system from $T_1 \to T_2$.

Since the heat capacity varies with temperature (see Table 2.3), it is more convenient to express it as a differential:

$$C_{T \to T + \delta T} = \frac{\delta q}{\delta T}; \quad \text{as } \delta T \to 0 \quad C = \frac{dq}{dT} \quad \dots(2.22)$$

Equation (2.22) is true for heat capacities at either constant pressure or constant volume.

As shown previously in the case of gases, the heat capacity of a substance will be different for experiments carried out under constant pressure or constant volume conditions. Let us therefore consider their relationship to other thermodynamic functions.

Heat Capacity at Constant Volume. Using the same argument as in subsection 2.5.1 we have

$$C_v = \left(\frac{\delta q}{\delta T}\right)_v$$

From the First Law of Thermodynamics it follows that $\Delta U = q - w$. Differentiating this equation with respect to temperature we obtain

$$\frac{\delta U}{\delta T} = \frac{\delta q}{\delta T} - \frac{\delta w}{\delta T} \qquad \ldots(2.23)$$

As $\delta T \to 0$ equation (2.23) becomes

$$\frac{dU}{dT} = \frac{dq}{dT} - \frac{dw}{dT}$$

and, since the experiment is carried out at constant volume, none of the heat is used up for any external work. Thus

$$\frac{dU}{dT} = \left(\frac{dq}{dT}\right)_v = C_v \qquad \ldots(2.24)$$

This equation is a general one, and therefore it will apply to any system, homogeneous or heterogeneous.[7]

Heat Capacity at Constant Pressure. In this case the heat absorbed q is used up in raising the temperature of the system, and for the external work done by the system.

$$\Delta U = q - w \quad \text{(First Law of Thermodynamics)}$$

For gases $w = p\Delta v$: for very small heat changes

$$dU = dq - dw = dq - p(dv)$$

thus

$$\frac{dq}{dT} = \frac{dU}{dT} + \frac{pdv}{dT}$$

However, at constant pressure

$$pdv = d(pv)$$

so

$$\left(\frac{dq}{dT}\right)_p = \left(\frac{dU}{dT}\right)_p + \left(\frac{d(pv)}{dT}\right)_p = \left\{\frac{d(U + pv)}{dT}\right\}_p$$

Thus

$$\left(\frac{dq}{dT}\right)_p = C_p = \left(\frac{dH}{dT}\right)_p \qquad \ldots(2.25)$$

The heat capacities of some elements are tabulated to show the order of magnitude of values and their variation with temperature.

TABLE 2.3[8]

Aluminium		Lead		Nickel	
Temp °C	$C_{p_{Al}}$ cal g mole^{-1} deg^{-1}	Temp °C	$C_{p_{Pb}}$ cal g mole^{-1} deg^{-1}	Temp °C	$C_{p_{Ni}}$ cal g mole^{-1} deg^{-1}
−250	0·0039	−270	0·00001	−258	0·0008
−240	0·0092	−267	0·00086	−247·9	0·0024
−233	0·0165	−259	0·0073	−201·2	0·0363
−200	0·076	−150	0·0279	−150	0·066
−150	0·1367	−100	0·0283	−100	0·0817
−100	0·208	0	0·0297	−50	0·094
0	0·214	20	0·0306	0	0·1032
20	0·225	100	0·0320	20	0·105
100	0·277	300	0·0356	100	0·1146
600	0·277	360	0·0375	500	0·127

From Table 2.3 it is evident that the heat capacities C_p of aluminium, lead and nickel are extremely small at temperatures in the vicinity of absolute zero, but at room temperatures and above they vary little with temperature. It is also clear from this table that tabulation of heat capacities in this way is rather tedious and space consuming, and for this reason the heat capacities of the majority of substances are expressed by empirical equations, either[9] $C_p = a + bT + cT^{-2}$, or[10] $C_p = a + 2bT - cT^{-2}$ cal g mole^{-1} deg^{-1}. Let us compare these two equations from Kubaschewski et al. and Kelley to get acquainted with these forms of presentation of heat capacities. It is intended to compare equations for the same three metals as are found in Table 2.3; the first of each pair is from Kubaschewski's and the second from Kelley's calculations.

For Lead

$$C_{p_{Pb}} = 5·63 + 2·33 \times 10^{-3}T; \qquad (300 \text{ to } 630°K)$$

$$C_{p_{Pb}} = 5·29 + 2·80 \times 10^{-3}T + 0·23 \times 10^5 \times T^{-2};$$

$$(300 \text{ to } 630°K)$$

For Nickel

$$C_{p_{\text{Ni}_{(\alpha)}}} = 6.03 + 2.49 \times 10^{-3}T; \quad (300 \text{ to } 630°\text{K})$$

$$C_{p_{\text{Ni}_{(\alpha)}}} = 4.06 + 7.04 \times 10^{-3}T$$

$$C_{p_{\text{Ni}_{(\beta)}}} = 5.83 + 2.05 \times 10^{-3}T; \quad (630 \text{ to } 1725°\text{K})$$

$$C_{p_{\text{Ni}_{(\beta)}}} = 6.00 + 1.80 \times 10^{-3}T$$

$$C_{p_{\text{Ni}_{(\text{Liq})}}} = 9.20$$

For Aluminium. Both Kubaschewski and Kelley give the same coefficients:

$$C_{p_{\text{Al}}} = 4.94 + 2.96 \times 10^{-3}T$$

The C_p values for various temperatures, when calculated from these two different equations above for lead and nickel, will in all cases be virtually the same. The difference in the constants arises from the mathematical interpretation of the experimental data. There is generally a tendency to use in this type of equation as few terms as possible, providing the accuracy of the equation is not impaired too much.

2.5.2   *Derivation of the Kirchhoff's Equation*

Consider a chemical reaction at temperature T_1 whose enthalpy change is ΔH_1. Calculate the enthalpy change ΔH_2 at temperature T_2.

The products of this reaction at T_2 can be obtained in many different ways. Let us, however, consider the reaction to be carried out, first by reacting the reactants $(x + y)$ at T_1 (see Fig. 2.13), and then

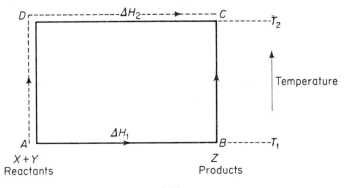

2.13

raising the temperature of the products from $T_1 \rightarrow T_2$, i.e. along ABC in Fig. 2.13. The heat absorbed by this process will be

$$\Delta H_1 + \int_{T_1}^{T_2} \bar{C}_{p_z} dT \qquad \ldots(2.26)$$

The second way of obtaining the same result is to raise the temperature of the reactants from $T_1 \rightarrow T_2$, and then react them together at T_2, i.e. along ADC (Fig. 2.13):

$$\Delta H_2 + \int_{T_1}^{T_2} (\bar{C}_{p_x} + \bar{C}_{p_y}) dT \qquad \ldots(2.27)$$

According to Hess's Law the heats absorbed during the two ways of producing z must be the same, since the initial conditions of the reactants and the final conditions of the products are in each case the same.

Thus from (2.26) and (2.27)

$$\Delta H_2 + \int_{T_1}^{T_2} (\bar{C}_{p_x} + \bar{C}_{p_y}) dT = \Delta H_1 + \int_{T_1}^{T_2} (\bar{C}_{p_z}) dT$$

or

$$\Delta H_2 - \Delta H_1 = \int_{T_1}^{T_2} [(\overline{C_{p_z}}) - (\overline{C_{p_x}} + \overline{C_{p_y}})] dT$$

or

$$\Delta H_2 - \Delta H_1 = \int_{T_1}^{T_2} \Delta C_p \, dT$$

or

$$\Delta H_2 = \Delta H_1 + \int_{T_1}^{T_2} \Delta C_p \, dT \qquad \ldots(2.28)$$

Since all the terms are known on the right-hand side of the equation, ΔH_2 can be calculated. From equation (2.28)

$$\left(\frac{\partial \Delta H}{\partial T}\right)_p = \Delta C_p \qquad \ldots(2.29)$$

where ΔC_p is the difference between the heat capacity of the products and reactants, and ΔH is the heat content change for a temperature change. Equation (2.29) is a differential equation first derived by Kirchhoff (1858) and it gives the rate of change of the enthalpy of a reaction with the temperature in terms of the heat capacities of the substances taking part in the reaction.

General Solution of Kirchhoff's Equation. For the limits ΔH_1, ΔH_2 and T_1, T_2, equation (2.29) becomes

$$\int_{\Delta H_1}^{\Delta H_2} d(\Delta H) = \int_{T_1}^{T_2} \Delta C_p \, dT \qquad \ldots (2.29 \, (a))$$

where ΔH_1 and ΔH_2 are the appropriate enthalpy changes at T_1 and T_2. Assuming that C_p is constant with temperature, which is true over a limited range of temperatures, then (2.29 (a)) on integration becomes

$$\Delta H_2 - \Delta H_1 = \Delta C_p (T_2 - T_1)$$

In the majority of cases ΔC_p is a function of temperature; then the functions of $\overline{C_p}$ for the appropriate substances taking part in the reaction have to be substituted in place of ΔC_p.

For example: let

$$\overline{C_{p_x}} = a_x + b_x T + c_x T^{-2}$$

$$\overline{C_{p_y}} = a_y + b_y T + c_y T^{-2}$$

and

$$\overline{C_{p_z}} = a_z + b_z T + c_z T^{-2}$$

Then

$$\Delta C_p = \Sigma \bar{C}_p \text{ products} - \Sigma \bar{C}_p \text{ reactants} = [a_z - (a_x + a_y)] +$$
$$+ [b_z - (b_x + b_y)]T + [c_z - (c_x + c_y)]T^{-2} = a + bT + cT^{-2}$$
$$\ldots (2.30)$$

On substitution of the value of (2.30) into (2.29 (a)) we have

$$\int_{\Delta H_1}^{\Delta H_2} d(\Delta H) = \int_{T_1}^{T_2} (a + bT + cT^{-2}) dT$$

where a, b, and c are now new constants derived from the appropriate constants of the products and reactants.
On integration

$$\Delta H_2 - \Delta H_1 = \left[aT + \frac{bT^2}{2} - cT^{-1} \right]_{T_1}^{T_2}$$

or

$$\Delta H_2 - \Delta H_1 = a(T_2 - T_1) + \tfrac{1}{2}b(T_2^2 - T_1^2) - c\left(\frac{1}{T_2} - \frac{1}{T_1} \right)$$

and

$$\Delta H_2 = \Delta H_1 + a(T_2 - T_1) + \tfrac{1}{2}b(T_2^2 - T_1^2) - c\left(\frac{1}{T_2} - \frac{1}{T_1} \right)$$
$$\ldots (2.31)$$

Example

Assume that the alumino-thermic reaction of aluminium with iron oxide can be represented by the equation

$$2Al + 3FeO = Al_2O_3 + 3Fe$$

Assume also that all substances in the reaction are always in their pure states. The standard enthalpy changes and the heat capacities of the reactants and products are as follows:

$$\Delta H_{Al_2O_3} = -400 \text{ kcal g mole}^{-1}$$

$$\Delta H_{FeO} = -63\cdot3 \text{ kcal g mole}^{-1}$$

$$C_{p_{Al_2O_3}} = 27\cdot38 + 3\cdot08 \times 10^{-3}T - 8\cdot20 \times 10^5 T^{-2}$$

$$C_{p_{Fe}} = 4\cdot18 + 5\cdot92 \times 10^{-3}T$$

$$C_{p_{Al}} = 4\cdot94 + 2\cdot96 \times 10^{-3}T$$
$$\text{(for the temperature range 298}^\circ \text{ to 932}^\circ\text{K)}$$

$$L_{f_{Al}} = 2{,}500 \text{ cal g atom}^{-1}$$

$$C_{p_{Al(l)}} = 7\cdot00$$

$$C_{p_{FeO}} = 11\cdot66 + 2\cdot00 \times 10^{-3}T - 0\cdot67 \times 10^5 \times T^{-2}$$

Calculate the enthalpy change of this reaction at 298°K, 850°K and 1,000°K.

At 298°K the appropriate enthalpy change terms are

$$2Al + 3FeO \rightarrow Al_2O_3 + 3Fe,$$
$$0 \quad 3(-63\cdot2) \quad -400 \quad 0$$

∴

$$\Delta H_{298} = \Delta H_{Al_2O_3} - 3\Delta H_{FeO}$$

$$= -400\cdot0 - (-189\cdot6)$$

$$= -210\cdot4$$

$$\Delta H_{298} = -210\cdot4 \text{ kcal g mole}^{-1} Al_2O_3$$

The enthalpy change at 850°K can now be calculated from Kirchhoff's Equation. Thus

$$\Delta H_{850} = \Delta H_{298} + \int_{298}^{850} \Delta C_p \, dT \qquad \ldots(2.32)$$

To calculate ΔC_p the heat capacity equations of all the products and reactants have to be known, since

$$\Delta C_p = C_p \text{ products} - C_p \text{ reactants}$$

Thus the heat capacities of the products are found to be

$$C_{p_{Al_2O_3}} = 27 \cdot 38 + 3 \cdot 08 \times 10^{-3}T - 8 \cdot 20 \times 10^5 \times T^{-2}$$

$$3C_{p_{Fe}} = 3(4 \cdot 18 + 5 \cdot 92 \times 10^{-3}T)$$

$$C_{p_{products}} = 39 \cdot 92 + 20 \cdot 84 \times 10^3T - 8 \cdot 20 \times 10^5T^{-2}$$

The heat capacities of reactants are found to be

$$2C_{p_{Al}} = 2(4 \cdot 94 + 2 \cdot 96 \times 10^{-3}T)$$

$$3C_{p_{FeO}} = 3(11 \cdot 66 + 2 \cdot 00 \times 10^{-3}T - 0 \cdot 67 \times 10^5T^{-2})$$

$$C_{p_{reactants}} = 44 \cdot 86 + 11 \cdot 92 \times 10^{-3}T - 2 \cdot 01 \times 10^5T^{-2}$$

Thus

$$C_{p_{products}} = 39 \cdot 92 + 20 \cdot 84 \times 10^{-3}T - 8 \cdot 20 \times 10^5T^{-2}$$

Subtract

$$C_{p_{reactants}} = 44 \cdot 86 + 11 \cdot 92 \times 10^{-3}T - 2 \cdot 01 \times 10^5 \times T^{-2}$$

gives

$$\Delta C_p = -4 \cdot 94 + 8 \cdot 92 \times 10^{-3}T - 6 \cdot 19 \times 10^5 \times T^{-2}$$
$$\ldots(2.33)$$

Substitute (2.33) into (2.32). Thus

$$\Delta H_{850} = \Delta H_{298} +$$

$$+ \int_{298}^{850} (-4 \cdot 94 + 8 \cdot 92 \times 10^{-3}T - 6 \cdot 19 \times 10^5 \times T^{-2})dT$$

or

$$\Delta H_{850} = -210,400 +$$

$$+ \left[-4 \cdot 94T + 4 \cdot 46 \times 10^{-3}T^2 + 6 \cdot 19 \times 10^5T^{-1} \right]_{298}^{850}$$

$$H_{850} = -210,400 + \left[-4 \cdot 94(850 - 298) + \right.$$

$$\left. + 4 \cdot 46 \times 10^{-3}(850^2 - 298^2) + 6 \cdot 19 \times 10^5 \left(\frac{1}{850} - \frac{1}{298} \right) \right]$$

$$\Delta H_{850} = -210,400 + [-2,726 \cdot 88 + 2,826 \cdot 28 - 1,348 \cdot 9]$$

$$= -211,249 \cdot 4 \text{ cal g mole}^{-1} \text{ Al}_2O_3$$

The conditions of this example were so chosen that there was no phase transformation or change in the state of reactants and products. However, above 932°K aluminium will melt and this fact complicates any calculations, since (i) latent heat of fusion of aluminium has to be added to the heat balance of reactants, and (ii) above the melting point the value of the $C_{p_{Al}}$ changes. These effects make calculations both tedious and long. To illustrate this fact the $\Delta H_{1,000}$ for the previous example will be calculated.

In this case it is more convenient to calculate separately each way of obtaining the product at 1,000°K (see Fig. 2.13). ΔH_1 will be the same as calculated previously.

$$C_{p_{Al(l)}} = 7\cdot00; \; L_{f_{Al}} = 2{,}500 \text{ cal g atom}^{-1}$$

The heat absorbed to raise the temperature of reactants from 298°K → 1,000°K is given by

$$\int_{298}^{1,000} 3(C_{p_{FeO}}) \, dT + \int_{298}^{932} 2 \, (C_{p_{Al}}) \, dT. +$$

$$+ 2L_{f_{Al}} + 2C_{p_{Al(l)}}(1{,}000 - 932)$$

Heat absorbed to raise the temperature of products from 298°K to 1,000°K can be calculated from

$$\int_{298}^{1,000} (C_{p_{Al_2O_3}} + 3C_{p_{Fe}}) \, dT$$

$$\Delta H_{1,000} - \Delta H_{298} = \int_{298}^{1,000} (C_{p_{Al_2O_3}} + 3C_{p_{Fe}}) \, dT - 2\int_{298}^{932} (C_{p_{Al}}) \, dT -$$

$$- 2L_{f_{Al}} - 2C_{p_{Al(l)}}(1{,}000 - 932) - \int_{298}^{1,000} 3(C_{p_{FeO}}) \, dT$$

$$= -5{,}080 \text{ cal g mole}^{-1}$$

This example shows that the calculation of the enthalpy change at higher temperatures becomes a very tedious process. To simplify our calculations there are tables which give the value of $H_T - H_{298\cdot15}$ for elements and compounds, where H_T is the heat content at the temperature T. To illustrate these tables, Table 2.4 is given. This table will be used in the calculation of the above example.

The values $H_T - H_{298\cdot15}$ give the amount of heat that is necessary to raise the temperature of the given element or compound from the standard state at 298·15°K to the temperature $T°K$. These tables

TABLE 2.4

Heat Content $(H_T - H_{298 \cdot 15})$ cal g mole^{-1}

$T°K$	Al	Al_2O_3	Fe	FeO
400	600	2,150	640	1,210
500	1,230	4,850	1,320	2,440
600	1,890	7,200	2,045	3,700
700	2,580	9,960	2,830	4,980
800	3,310	12,810	3,705	6,280
900	4,060	15,720	4,695	7,590
932	4,280			
932	6,850			
1,000	7,330	18,670	5,900	8,920

From K. K. Kelley, *Contributions to the Data on Theoretical Metallurgy*, U.S. Bureau of Mines, Bulletin No. 584, 1960.

therefore allow us a rapid calculation of the heat required to raise the temperature of reactants and products from the standard states to the required temperature at which the ΔH_T has to be calculated.

In our example the change in heat content for the reaction can be calculated as follows:

From Table 2.4 $2Al \quad + \quad 3FeO \quad = \quad Al_2O_3 + \quad 3Fe$

$H_{1,000} - H_{298 \cdot 15}$ $2 \times 7,330$ $3 \times 8,920$ $18,670$ $3 \times 5,900$

$\Delta H_{1,000} = -210,400 + (18,670 + 17,700) - (14,660 + 26,760)$

$\Delta H_{1,000} = -210,400 - 5,050 = -215,450$ cal g mole^{-1} Al_2O_3

The reaction will be exothermic and the heat evolved when 2 g atoms of aluminium react with 3 g moles of ferrous oxide will be 215,450 cal at 1,000°K.

REFERENCES

1 THOMPSON, B., "On the Calorific Effects of Magnets—Electricity and on the Mechanical Value of Heat," *Phil. Mag.*, 1843, **23**, 263, 347 and 435.
2 PARTINGTON, J. R., *An Advanced Treatise on Physical Chemistry*, Vol. I, p. 133, Longmans, Green & Co. Ltd., London, 1949.
3 For reference to the more important works on the subject see reference 2 above.
4 JOULE, J., *Phil. Mag.*, 1843, **23**, 263.
5 See reference 2 above, p. 261.
6 KUBASCHEWSKI, O. and E. L. EVANS, (after Roth *et al.*), *Metallurgical Thermochemistry*, second edition, p. 85, Pergamon Press Ltd., London, 1958.

7 LEWIS, G. N. and M. RANDALL, revised by K. S. PITZER and L. BREWER, *Thermodynamics*, second edition, p. 36, McGraw-Hill Publishing Co. Ltd., London, 1961.

8 HODGMAN, C. D. (Ed.), *Handbook of Chemistry and Physics*, 27th edition, pp. 1685–1686, Chemical Rubber Publishing Co., Cleveland.

9 See reference 6 above, p. 310.

10 KELLEY, K. K., *Contributions to the Data on Theoretical Metallurgy*, U.S. Bureau of Mines, Bulletin No. 584, p. 6, U.S. Govt. Printing Office, Washington, 1960.

CHAPTER III

The Second Law of Thermodynamics

The First Law of Thermodynamics is concerned with the quantitative aspects of the interconversion of energies. However, this law does not allow us to predict in what direction the conversion will take place or whether it will take place at all. Furthermore, it is impossible to calculate from this law how efficient the conversion would be, when heat energy is converted into mechanical energy.

It is not surprising that the second half of the nineteenth century witnessed a concentrated effort by many scientists to apply the First Law of Thermodynamics to:

(i) the calculation of the maximum work that can be obtained from a perfect engine working under a given set of temperature conditions,

(ii) the prediction from thermochemical data of the possibility of obtaining a reaction in a presupposed direction.

These considerations led to the discovery of the **Second Law of Thermodynamics** which has had a far-reaching influence on the subsequent development of science and technology.

3.1 THE EFFICIENCY OF A CYCLIC PROCESS— THE CARNOT CYCLE

The problem of how much useful work can be obtained from a given quantity of heat has been of great practical interest to engineers, ever since James Watt improved the steam engine (1769). Here a quantity of heat is obtained from the chemical reaction between coal or wood and oxygen from the air, and this heat is used to expand steam (the working substance) through an appropriate valve into the cylinder fitted with a piston, which in turn drives the engine by means of suitable mechanical devices. During the expansion the steam is cooled and then returned to the boiler.

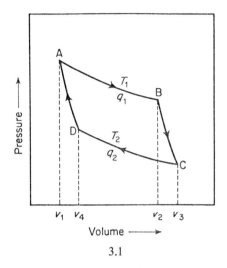

3.1

This process can be considered as one in which heat energy is given to the working substance at temperature T_1, followed by its expansion producing useful work (loss of energy), then cooling to temperature T_2, and finally returning to its original state at temperature T_1. This process is thus a cyclic process, providing the mass of the steam returned and the temperature and pressure of the returned steam are eventually identical with those at the beginning of the process. The working substance, in so far as microscopic properties are concerned, returns after each cycle to its original condition.

Sadi Carnot (1824) calculated theoretically the efficiency of such an ideal heat engine. For convenience he used in his cyclic process 1 g mole of a perfect gas as a working substance, since its behaviour with changes of temperature and pressure is described by the ideal gas equations. In order to obtain the maximum work in a cycle of operations, every stage was calculated as proceeding under reversible conditions. Let the initial pressure and volume of the 1 g mole of the perfect gas to be represented by the point A in Fig. 3.1 at temperature T_1. It is possible then to complete a full cycle of operations so as to bring the working substance back to its original condition at A in the following four stages.

Stage 1. The gas is allowed to expand isothermally under reversible conditions to the volume v_2 and pressure p_2. Since the temperature remains constant and the internal energy of a given mass of a gas is constant at constant temperature (p. 72), then the gas must have gained heat from the surroundings. Let the heat gained be q_1, then this must be equal to the work done by the gas w_1.

$$q_1 \quad = \quad w_1 \quad = RT_1 \log_e \frac{v_2}{v_1}$$

heat	work
absorbed	done

Stage 2. The gas is allowed to expand under adiabatic conditions until its temperature becomes T_2. Since heat cannot enter or leave the system, no heat is gained during the process, $q = 0$, and the work performed at the expense of the internal energy of the system may be expressed thus:

$$w_2 = C_v(T_1 - T_2)$$

Stage 3. The gas is then compressed isothermally at temperature T_2, until its volume becomes v_4 and its pressure p_4. Work is done in this process on the gas, and this work is converted into heat energy q_2, which is lost to the surroundings.

Since this is an isothermal process

$$q_2 = w_3 = RT \log_e \frac{v_4}{v_3}$$

$w_3 =$ work done on the gas, and its value will be negative, since $v_3 > v_4$.

Stage 4. Finally the gas is compressed under adiabatic conditions, until it reaches its original temperature and volume, i.e. the point A on Fig. 3.1.

$$q = 0 \text{ (as no heat is gained or lost by the gas)}$$

$$\text{work done by the gas} = w_4 = C_v(T_2 - T_1)$$

Total net work done by this cyclic process

$$= w_1 + w_2 + w_3 + w_4 = w$$

Substituting the appropriate values

$$w = RT_1 \log_e \frac{v_2}{v_1} + C_v(T_1 - T_2) + RT_2 \log_e \frac{v_4}{v_3} + C_v(T_2 - T_1)$$

$$w = RT_1 \log_e \frac{v_2}{v_1} + RT_2 \log_e \frac{v_4}{v_3} \qquad \ldots(3.1)$$

From equation (3.1) for an adiabatic expansion we have

$$T_1 v_2^{\gamma-1} = T_2 v_3^{\gamma-1}$$

$$T_1 v_1^{\gamma-1} = T_2 v_4^{\gamma-1}$$

and on dividing

$$\frac{v_2}{v_1} = \frac{v_3}{v_4} \qquad \ldots (3.2)$$

Substitute (3.2) into (3.1)

$$w = RT_1 \log_e \frac{v_2}{v_1} - RT_2 \log_e \frac{v_2}{v_1}$$

or

$$w = R(T_1 - T_2) \log_e \frac{v_2}{v_1}$$

where w is the work done by the gas in a cycle.

In practice, however, we are interested to know how much heat can be converted into useful work, i.e. in the efficiency of the process.

$$\text{Efficiency} = \frac{\text{work done}}{\text{heat supplied at the higher temperature}}$$

$$= \frac{w}{q_1} = \frac{R(T_1 - T_2) \log_e \frac{v_2}{v_1}}{RT_1 \log_e \frac{v_2}{v_1}}$$

Thus

$$\text{Efficiency} = \frac{T_1 - T_2}{T_1} = \frac{w}{q_1} \qquad \ldots (3.3)$$

From this equation it follows that the efficiency of a perfect engine depends on the temperature difference between the two isothermal stages of the cyclic process. There is an ideal upper limit to the quantity of work that can be produced by a given input of heat energy for the perfect engine. This equation gave one of the answers practical engineers were waiting for. It made it possible to assess the efficiency of engines, and it also showed that under normal conditions not all the heat supplied to the engine can be converted into work even by perfect engines. A perfect engine would convert all the heat supplied into work, if the lower temperature of the process could be made equal to zero on the absolute temperature scale.

This proof of the practical impossibility of complete conversion of heat energy into mechanical energy (even by a perfect engine) was the starting point of the Second Law of Thermodynamics. Sadi Carnot himself did not realise the implication of his discovery, and it was more than twenty years later before the implications were considered.

The Second Law of Thermodynamics can be stated as follows:

Energy is transferred of its own accord from a higher to a lower energy level; but, although the mechanical energy in any process can be completely changed into heat energy, the heat energy can never be completely transformed into mechanical energy, unless the process is reversible and the part of the process which is at the lowest temperature is at absolute zero (a condition never fulfilled in practice).

From equation (3.3) it is evident that the efficiency of a process expressed in percentages will become 100% when $T_2 = 0$ since then

$$\% \text{ Efficiency} = \left(\frac{T_1 - T_2}{T_1} \right) \times 100 = \left(\frac{T_1 - 0}{T_1} \right) \times 100 = 100\%$$

Let us now analyse equation (3.3) and see whether the heat absorbed at the higher temperature q_1 is equal to the heat evolved at the lower temperature q_2.

It is clear that the quantity of heat converted into work w may be expressed as

$$w = q_1 + q_2 \qquad \qquad \ldots (3.4)$$

Substituting (3.4) into (3.3) we obtain

$$\frac{q_1 + q_2}{q_1} = \frac{T_1 - T_2}{T_1}$$

Thus

$$1 + \frac{q_2}{q_1} = 1 - \frac{T_2}{T_1}$$

or

$$\frac{q_2}{T_2} = - \frac{q_1}{T_1}$$

Rearranging the terms we have

$$\frac{q_1}{T_1} + \frac{q_2}{T_2} = 0 \qquad \qquad \ldots (3.5)$$

Equation (3.5) shows that the heats absorbed at the various temperatures are not numerically equal, since $T_1 > T_2$, but the sum of the ratios of heats absorbed reversibly to temperature at the different temperatures come to zero. Thus

$$\sum \frac{q_{rev}}{T} = 0$$

where the sign Σ denotes the sum of all the $\frac{q}{T}$ terms.

It can be shown that equation (3.3) *is true for any working substance whether solid, liquid or gas.*

Carnot proposed the theorem which states "Every perfect engine working reversibly between the same temperature limits has the same efficiency, whatever the working substance".[1]

3.2 ENTROPY

In Carnot's cycle the calculated heats absorbed or evolved during the isothermal steps were found to depend on the temperatures at which the steps occurred. However, the numerical values of the ratios $\frac{q_{rev}}{T}$ were the same, so that, for example, $\frac{q_1}{T_1} = -\frac{q_2}{T_2}$, etc., and the sums of these terms for a complete cycle, irrespective of the number of stages, come to zero.

Clausius[2] in 1850 recognised the fact that $\frac{dq_{rev}}{T}$ was a characteristic (state property) of the system and not the value dq_{rev}, since this varies from temperature to temperature.

W. Thomson[3] gave the standard notation of $\sum \left(\frac{q}{T}\right) = 0$ for a number of steps forming a cyclic process. The name entropy change was finally given to the ratio $\frac{\delta q}{T}$ by Clausius[4] who denoted the entropy change by the symbol ΔS and who considered it to be a state function. Subsequently it was shown that the entropy depends on the state of a substance or system and not on its previous history, irrespective of whether the path from initial to final states is thermodynamically reversible or not, and it is also independent of the substance involved. However, to calculate the actual magnitude of ΔS of a process one must use the actual values of the heats absorbed in the reversible changes along the path from initial to final states since these can be calculated.[5]

Let us now prove that an entropy change is a state property of a system. Consider a reversible process in which the system absorbs reversibly an infinitesimal quantity of heat.

Then from Clausius' definition the entropy change will be given as $dS = \dfrac{dq_{rev}}{T}$. It has been shown previously that dq is not a state property, therefore we have to express it in terms of other functions. From the First Law of Thermodynamics $dU = dq - pdv$ at constant pressure, so

$$dq = dU + pdv$$

But $dU = C_v dT$ and, for a perfect gas, $p = RT/v$. Thus

$$dq = C_v \, dT + \frac{RT \, dv}{v}$$

Dividing through this equation by T one obtains

$$\frac{dq}{T} = \frac{C_v \, dT}{T} + \frac{R \, dv}{v} \qquad \ldots(3.6)$$

where C_v and R are constants.

The right-hand side of the equation (3.6) is an exact differential, since it can be integrated, and therefore the quantity $\dfrac{dq}{T}$ on the left-hand side must also be an exact differential, and will depend only on the state of the system and not on the path by which it was obtained.

3.2.1 Entropy Changes in Gases

In an adiabatic process by definition $dq = 0$, i.e. $\Delta S = 0$.

The entropy change for an ideal gas can be calculated from the equation (3.6)

$$\frac{dq}{T} = C_v \frac{dT}{T} + R \frac{dv}{v} = dS$$

Let a system comprising an ideal gas, have an initial entropy S_1, pressure p_1, volume v_1, and temperature T_1 (see Fig. 3.2), and let the final values be S_2, v_2, p_2 and T_2.

$$\Delta S = S_2 - S_1 = C_v \int_{T_1}^{T_2} \frac{dT}{T} + R \int_{v_1}^{v_2} \frac{dv}{v}$$

Integrating we obtain

$$\Delta S = C_v \log_e \frac{T_2}{T_1} + R \log_e \frac{v_2}{v_1} \qquad \ldots(3.7)$$

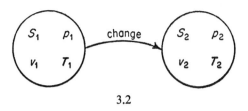

3.2

This equation allows us to calculate the entropy change of an ideal gas when it changes its volume and temperature on heating, providing the heat capacity C_v at constant volume is known.

The equation (3.7) is very useful as a general equation for calculating entropy changes of gases. However, the majority of our processes are carried out under conditions of either constant pressure or constant volume. Let us therefore apply the equation (3.7) in such a way that ΔS_p or ΔS_v can be calculated.

$$p_1 v_1 = RT \quad \text{and} \quad p_2 v_2 = RT$$

for one g mole of a perfect gas.

$$\therefore \quad \frac{v_2}{v_1} = \frac{\dfrac{RT_2}{p_2}}{\dfrac{RT_1}{p_1}} = \frac{T_2 p_1}{T_1 p_2} \qquad \ldots(3.8)$$

Combining (3.8) with (3.7) we have

$$\Delta S = C_v \log_e \frac{T_2}{T_1} + R \log_e \frac{T_2 p_1}{T_1 p_2}$$

$$\therefore \quad \Delta S = C_v \log_e \frac{T_2}{T_1} + R \log_e \frac{T_2}{T_1} + R \log_e \frac{p_1}{p_2}$$

or

$$\Delta S = (C_v + R) \log_e \frac{T_2}{T_1} + R \log_e \frac{p_1}{p_2} \qquad \ldots(3.9)$$

Since $C_v + R = C_p$ equation 3.9 may be written as

$$\Delta S = C_p \log_e \frac{T_2}{T_1} - R \log_e \frac{p_2}{p_1} \qquad \ldots(3.10)$$

In an Isothermal Process, i.e. at constant temperature, $T_1 = T_2$; thus the first term in the equation (3.10) becomes zero, and

$$\Delta S = -R \log_e \frac{p_2}{p_1} = R \log_e \frac{v_2}{v_1} \qquad \ldots(3.11)$$

For an Isobaric System $p_2 = p_1$, and equation (3.10) becomes

$$\Delta S_p = C_p \log_e \frac{T_2}{T_1} \qquad \ldots(3.12)$$

since the second term becomes zero.

Let us illustrate the application of equation (3.11) to the following example.

Example

Calculate the entropy change of a perfect gas which is allowed to expand isothermally so that its volume increases twofold.

Since the change in volume takes place isothermally, equation (3.11) has to be used.

Thus

$$\Delta S_T = R \log_e \frac{2v_1}{v_1} = 1 \cdot 984 \times 2 \cdot 303 \log 2 \text{ cal g mole}^{-1} \text{ deg}^{-1}$$

$$\therefore \quad \Delta S_T = 1 \cdot 38 \text{ cal g mole}^{-1} \text{ deg}^{-1}$$

3.2.2 *The Significance of the Sign of Entropy Change of a Process in a Closed or Isolated System*

A closed system is a system of constant energy and mass.

The significance of the entropy change of a closed system can be conveniently shown by considering a system consisting of two large identical copper vessels, touching each other (Fig. 3.3), full of water, and each at a different temperature. Let us assume that these vessels are completely insulated, so that heat can neither enter nor leave this system. Let the temperature $T_1 > T_2$ (see Fig. 3.3). From the properties of heat it follows that heat will flow of its own accord from the higher temperature to the lower, providing there are no external forces to prevent it. Let the amount of heat which flows be q cal. It is obvious that in a closed system the amount of heat vessel I loses, vessel II must gain.

The difference between temperatures $[T_1 - T_2]$ is a measure of the irreversibility of this process. This difference will also denote how much heat can be transferred from vessel I to vessel II,

$$\therefore \qquad\qquad [T_1 - T_2] \propto q$$

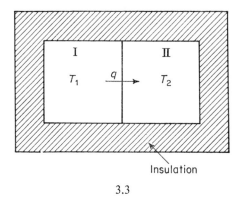

Insulation

3.3

Entropy is a very useful function since it allows us to correlate the amount of heat lost or gained at a given temperature. Using Clausius' definition we have

$$\Delta S = \frac{q_{\text{rev}}}{T}$$

Thus

Entropy change of the vessel I $= \dfrac{-q}{T_1}$

since q is a negative value, and

Entropy change of vessel II $= \dfrac{q}{T_2}$

The total entropy change will be the sum of the entropy changes of the two vessels. Thus

$$\Delta S_{\text{process}} = \Delta S_1 + \Delta S_2 = \left(\frac{q}{T_2} - \frac{q}{T_1} \right) \qquad \ldots (3.13)$$

$$\Delta S_{\text{process}} = \frac{q(T_1 - T_2)}{T_1 T_2} \qquad \ldots (3.14)$$

Let us examine the significance of equation (3.14). The value of the total entropy change of this process depends on the two quantities, the value of q and the ratio of $\left(\dfrac{T_1 - T_2}{T_1 T_2} \right)$. The entropy change of the process in an isolated system will be greater, the greater the difference between the two temperatures. When q is positive (i.e. heat is gained), and $(T_1 - T_2)$ and $T_1 T_2$ are also positive, then the entropy change for a real irreversible process in a closed system must also be positive.

The following sign rule applies to entropy changes in such systems: When

$$T_1 > T_2 \quad \Delta S_{irr} > 0 \qquad \ldots (3.15)$$

the entropy change of a real process is greater than zero. When

$$T_1 = T_2 \quad \Delta S_{rev} = 0 \qquad \ldots (3.16)$$

dynamic equilibrium exists between the two vessels and there is no net heat transfer. When

$$T_1 < T_2 \quad \Delta S_{irr} \leqslant 0 \qquad \ldots (3.17)$$

the entropy change is negative, showing that the process proceeds in a reverse direction to that shown in Fig. 3.3.

These conclusions reached from the simple consideration of flow of heat in a closed system of two vessels are extremely important, in so far that they show that the sign of entropy change shows the direction of flow of heat energy. Since according to the First Law heat energy is only one form of energy, therefore the above conclusions regarding entropy change can also be applied to the transfer of any other form of energy. Thus from (3.16) it follows that the entropy change in a closed system will be zero for a process at equilibrium, and positive if the process proceeds in the considered direction. The magnitude of the entropy change is therefore a measure of the irreversibility* of a process, while its sign denotes the direction of a process. The following examples will illustrate the use of entropy change as a measure of irreversibility.

Example 1

Calculate whether melting of ice without change in temperature of the system is a reversible or irreversible process when the ice is dropped into water at 273°K. The latent heat of fusion of ice is 1,436 cal g mole^{-1} and assume its temperature of fusion to be 273°K.

The entropy change of fusion ΔS_f by definition is the heat absorbed reversibly divided by the temperature of fusion.

$$\Delta S_f = \frac{q_{rev}}{T_f} = \frac{\text{Latent heat of fusion}}{\text{Absolute temperature of fusion}} = \frac{1,436}{273} \quad \ldots (3.18)$$

However, the net change in entropy for the system (ΔS_{syst}) is the sum of the change of entropy of the process $(\Delta S_{process})$ and the change in entropy of the surroundings (ΔS_{surr}), i.e. the water. Thus

$$\Delta S_{syst} = \Delta S_{process} + \Delta S_{surr} = \Delta S_f + \Delta S_{surr} \quad \ldots (3.19)$$

---

* See Section 2.3, page 29.

Since the ice gained 1,436 cal on fusion then the surroundings must have lost 1,436 cal. Thus

$$\Delta S_{surr} = \frac{\text{heat absorbed reversibly}}{\text{absolute temperature of the change}} = \frac{-1,436}{273} \quad \ldots(3.20)$$

Substituting (3.18) and (3.20) into (3.19) we obtain:

$$\Delta S_{syst} = \frac{1,436}{273} - \frac{1,436}{273} = 0$$

Thus the ΔS of the system equals zero; therefore according to equation (3.16) the system is under reversible conditions, and ice and water are at equilibrium. On average the mass of ice and water will remain constant.

It is also worth noting that the sign of the entropy change of melting is positive, and the sign of the entropy change of the surrounding material (i.e. water) is negative. Since this is an equilibrium process, it is therefore clear that the signs of entropy changes for single components of the complete system do not signify the direction of the process under consideration. This point will become clearer from the following example.

Example 2

Calculate the entropy change of a closed system in which 143·6 g of water at 10°C are added to a calorimeter containing 18 g of ice at 0°C. Assume that the heat content of the calorimeter is negligible and the molar heat capacity of water is 18 cal g mole^{-1}. Calculate the entropy change of this process, assuming that all the ice will melt, and from the sign of the entropy change of the system deduce whether the process will in fact occur, i.e. is a **real process**.

This problem is shown diagrammatically in Fig. 3.4. Since the water is at a higher temperature than ice, i.e. $T_1 > T_2$, there will be heat energy flow from water to ice. The ice will at first use this heat for fusion, then any remaining heat will be used up for heating the water obtained from the fusion of ice. As the water loses heat energy to the ice its temperature will continuously fall.

The equilibrium temperature will be eventually achieved when the temperature of the water obtained from the fusion of the ice becomes the same as that of the water which was added.

In this example the quantity of ice and the quantity of added water were so chosen that the final temperature will be that of fusion of ice, i.e. 273°K.

Thus the final temperature of the system will be 273°K. Since this system is contained in a calorimeter, the system will neither gain nor

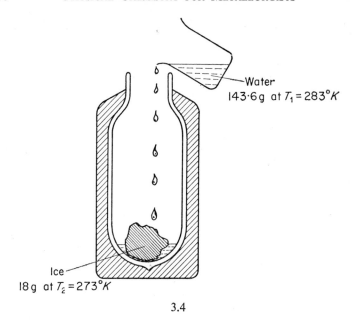

Water
143·6g at $T_1 = 283°K$

Ice
18g at $T_2 = 273°K$

3.4

lose heat energy, i.e. the system is for all practical purposes an isolated or closed system.

From equation (3.19)

$$\Delta S_{\text{system}} = \Delta S_{\text{process}} + \Delta S_{\text{surr}}$$

Consider the process to be fusion of ice; then for n g mole of ice

$$\Delta S_{\text{process}} = \frac{nL_f}{T_f} = \frac{1,436}{273}$$

$$\Delta S_{\text{process}} = 5·26 \text{ entropy units (e.u.)}$$

$\Delta S_{\text{surr}} =$ the sum of entropy changes of 143·6 g of water from $283° - 273°K$

Since

$$\Delta S_T = \frac{q_{\text{rev}}}{T} = \frac{C_p}{T} \text{ at constant } T \text{ and pressure}$$

$$\Delta S_{\text{surr}} = n \int_{T_1}^{T_2} \frac{C_p}{T} dT = \frac{143·6}{18} \int_{283}^{273} \frac{18}{T} dT = 143·6 \int_{283}^{273} \frac{dT}{T}$$

$$\therefore \quad \Delta S_{surr} = 143 \cdot 6 \log_e \frac{273}{283} = 143 \cdot 6 \times 2 \cdot 303 \log_{10} \frac{273}{283}$$

$$\therefore \quad \Delta S_{surr} = -5 \cdot 159 \text{ e.u.}$$

Thus

$$\Delta S_{syst} = \Delta S_{process} + \Delta S_{surr} = +5 \cdot 26 + (-5 \cdot 159)$$
$$= 0 \cdot 101 \text{ e.u.}$$

Answer

The entropy change of this system considered from the point of view of fusion of ice gives a positive value. Using the relation shown in equation (3.14) it follows that, because the sign of the entropy change is positive, the process is irreversible, and that ice will melt spontaneously under these conditions.

There are two main points which emerge from these two examples:

(i) The entropies of fusion in both examples were the same, namely $5 \cdot 26$ cal g mole^{-1} deg^{-1}, but the first was an equilibrium process while the second was irreversible.

(ii) One cannot use therefore the sign of the entropy change for the process alone as an indication of its direction, but all the entropy terms of the system have to be considered.

In these two examples we have only two entropy terms, one of which was always $\oplus$ve, the other $\ominus$ve; however, in more complicated systems there may be many entropy terms. The signs of these separate entropy terms for an irreversible process in a closed system can be positive, zero or negative.

3.2.3 *Calculation of Entropy Change from Heat Capacities*

From Clausius' mathematical definition of entropy change

$$\Delta S = \frac{q_{rev}}{T}$$

it follows that the entropy change at the temperature T is the ratio of heat taken up isothermally and reversibly to the absolute temperature at which the processes proceed at constant pressure, and since their specific heats C_p have exactly the same units as entropy, i.e. cal g mole^{-1} deg^{-1}, therefore for a limiting case of an infinitesimal process the entropy change can be expressed by the following equation:

$$\frac{dq_{rev}}{dT} = C_p \qquad \qquad \dots(3.21)$$

And the entropy change of an element is

$$dS = \frac{dq_{\text{rev}}}{T} \qquad \ldots(3.22)$$

Thus from equations (3.21) and (3.22)

$$dS = \frac{C_p\, dT}{T} \qquad \ldots(3.23)$$

Equation (3.23) is a general differential equation of change in entropy and if we assume that S_0 is the entropy at absolute zero, then the entropy of a substance at T can be calculated from

$$S_T = S_0 + \int_0^T \frac{C_p\, dT}{T} \qquad \ldots(3.24)$$

Since

$$\Delta S = S_{T_2} - S_{T_1}$$

then in this case

$$\Delta S = S_T - S_0 = \int_0^T \frac{C_p\, dT}{T} \qquad \ldots(3.25)$$

This equation is true for an element in which, between absolute zero and the temperature T, there is no phase transformation or change in state.

Equation (3.23) can be graphically integrated by plotting $\dfrac{C_p}{T}$ against T and measuring the area under the curve (Fig. 3.5). If however any phase changes occur in the temperature range considered,

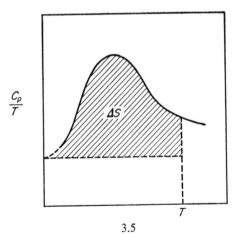

3.5

such as transformation t, fusion f, or evaporation e, their effect on the entropy change must be taken into account. All these changes are thermodynamically reversible, and thus the entropy of transformation ΔS_t, the entropy of fusion ΔS_f, and the entropy of evaporation ΔS_e can be calculated.

Equation (3.25) allows us to calculate the entropy change from absolute zero to the temperature T at which the element is in the gaseous state. Thus if T_t is the temperature of transformation and L_t is the heat of transformation, T_f and L_f the temperature and latent heat of fusion, and T_e and L_e the appropriate temperature and latent heat of evaporation, then using equation (3.25) ΔS_T is given by:

$$\Delta S_T = \int_0^{T_t} \frac{C_p'}{T} dT + \frac{L_t}{T_t} + \int_{T_t}^{T_f} \frac{C_p''}{T} dT + \frac{L_f}{T_f} +$$

$$+ \int_{T_f}^{T_e} \frac{C_p'''}{T} dT + \frac{L_e}{T_e} + \int_{T_e}^{T} \frac{C_p''''}{T} dT \quad \ldots(3.26)$$

where

$$\frac{L_t}{T_t} = \Delta S_t; \quad \frac{L_f}{T_f} = \Delta S_f; \quad \frac{L_e}{T_e} = \Delta S_e$$

and C_p' denotes the heat capacity of the crystalline modification between $0°$ and T_t, C_p'' between T_t and T_f and so on.

Equation (3.26) is very seldom used in the form given above since many standard entropies are known, and they are tabulated in some standard books.[6]

Equation (3.26) then becomes much simpler, and for an entropy change at temperature T at which the metal is molten it is:

$$\Delta S_T = \Delta S_{298} + \int_{298}^{T_t} \frac{C_p}{T} \cdot dT + \int_{T_t}^{T_f} \frac{C_p'}{T} \cdot dT + \frac{L_f}{T_f} + \int_{T_f}^{T} \frac{C_p''}{T} \cdot dT$$

$$\boxed{\text{These terms represent the entropy increase from 298°K to the temperature } T} \quad \ldots(3.27)$$

Example

Calculate the entropy change for pure iron from 0 to 2,000°K. The standard entropy of iron at 298°K is $6·49 \pm 0·03$ entropy units (e.u.).

$$C_{p_{(\alpha)}} = 3·04 + 7·58 \times 10^{-3}T + 0·60 \times 10^5 T^{-2} \text{ (for temperature range from 298 to 1,033°K)}$$

$$L_{(\alpha \to \beta)} \simeq 0$$

$$C_{p_{(\beta)}} = 11·13 \text{ (for temperature range from 1,033 to 1,183°K)}$$

$L_{t_{(\beta \to \gamma)}}$ = 215 cal g atom^{-1} at the transformation temperature 1,183°K

$C_{p_{(\gamma)}}$ = 5·80 + 1·98 × 10^{-3}T (for temperature range from 1,183 to 1,673°K)

$L_{t_{(\gamma \to \delta)}}$ = 165 cal g atom^{-1} at 1,673°K

$C_{p_{(\delta)}}$ = 6·74 + 1·60 × 10^{-3}T (for temperatures from 1,673 to 1,812°K)

L_f = 3,670 cal g atom^{-1}

$C_{p_{(l)}}$ = 9·77 + 0·40 × 10^{-3}T

$$S_{2,000°K} = 6·49 + \int_{298}^{1,033} \left(\frac{3·04 + 7·58 \times 10^{-3}T + 0·60 \times 10^{5}T^{-2}}{T} \right) dT +$$

$$+ \int_{1,033}^{1,183} \frac{11·13}{T} dT + \frac{215}{1,183} + \int_{1,183}^{1,673} \left(\frac{5·80 + 1·98 \times 10^{-3}T}{T} \right) dT +$$

$$+ \frac{165}{1,673} + \int_{1,673}^{1,812} \left(\frac{6·74 + 1·60 \times 10^{-3}T}{T} \right) dT + \frac{3,670}{1,812} +$$

$$+ \int_{1,812}^{2,000} \left(\frac{9·77 + 0·40 \times 10^{-3}T}{T} \right) dT$$

$$= 24·98 \text{ cal deg}^{-1} \text{ g atom}^{-1}$$

The above equation with all the substituted values of heat content, temperature functions, and the entropies of transformation becomes very cumbersome, and subsequent integration and summation of the terms is very tedious. We are therefore very fortunate to have tables available[7] giving the difference between the entropies at a temperature S_T and the standard entropies $S_{298·15}$.

To illustrate the use of these tables[7] the heat content and entropy of iron is shown in Table 3.1. The appropriate values will be taken from the table to calculate our previous example.

The entropy change $\Delta S_{2,000}$ for iron can be computed using the data in this table. Thus:

$$\Delta S_{2,000} = 6·49 + 18·58 = 25·07 \text{ cal deg}^{-1} \text{ g atom}^{-1}$$

Answer: The entropy change for pure iron from absolute zero to 2,000°K is 25·07 cal deg^{-1} g atom^{-1}.

TABLE 3.1

$T°K$	$H_T - H_{298.15}$ cal g mole^{-1}	$S_T - S_{298.15}$ cal deg^{-1} g mole^{-1}
400	640	1·84
500	1,320	3·36
600	2,045	4·68
700	2,830	5·89
800	3,705	7·04
900	4,695	8·21
1,000	5,900	9·48
1,033	6,410	9·98
1,033	6,410	9·98
1,100	7,225	10·74
1,183	8,080	11·49
1,183	8,295	11·69
1,200	8,435	11·79
1,300	9,260	12·45
1,400	10,110	13·08
1,500	10,975	13·68
1,600	11,865	14·25
1,673	12,525	14·66
1,673	12,690	14·76
1,700	12,945	14·91
1,800	13,900	15·45
1,812	14,015	15·52
1,812	17,685	17·54
1,900	18,610	18·04
2,000	19,665	18·58
2,200	21,790	19·59

3.2.4 *Entropy and the Degradation of Energy in Real Processes*

While considering reversible and irreversible processes (p. 29) it became clear that the work done by the expanding gas depended on the conditions of expansion, and varied from zero to 826·3 cal g mole^{-1}. The final condition of the gas did not depend upon how the expansion was carried out. As the process is isothermal, $p_1v_1 = p_2v_2$ where p_1, v_1 are the initial pressure and volume, and

p_2, v_2 the final pressure and volume. Equation (31.7) gives the stored energy of a perfect gas:

$$E = \tfrac{3}{2}RT = \tfrac{3}{2}p_1v_1 = \tfrac{3}{2}p_2v_2$$

Thus the initial energy of the gas E_1 is the same as the energy of the gas after expansion.

It is therefore clear that, when a gas undergoes an expansion at a constant temperature, then its total stored energy will remain unaltered, but that its available energy for doing useful work will become less and eventually, when pressure approaches zero, it will tend to zero.

Since the total energy remains constant and its capacity for doing work decreases, then the energy must consist of at least two factors. Mathematically this fact can be expressed by a product of two variables, one that decreases on expansion and the other which increases. For example for a given mass of a gas the product $p \times v$ consists of such factors; the pressure on expansion will decrease, while the volume will increase, and the product will be constant at a constant temperature. Thus

$$\text{energy} = \text{pressure} \downarrow \times \text{volume} \uparrow$$

where the directions of arrows indicate a decrease $\downarrow$ and an increase $\uparrow$.

In general one can write

$$\text{energy} = \text{intensity factor} \times \text{capacity factor} \quad \ldots(3.28)$$

Larmor[8] considered that the energy factors in general were of two kinds, (i) (for example pressure, electromotive force, temperature, etc.) **intensive properties** which are independent of the mass of the system, and (ii) (volume, etc.) **extensive properties** that depend on the quantity of mass and its conditions.

From the definition of intensive and extensive properties it is clear that the capacity factor in equation (3.28) will have extensive properties.

From Clausius' definition of entropy change

$$\Delta S = \frac{q_{rev}}{T} \quad \text{it follows that} \quad q_{rev} = T\Delta S \quad \ldots(3.29)$$

In equation (3.29) q_{rev} represents a quantity of heat energy absorbed at constant temperature by a system, and it is expressed by the product of two factors, the temperature and the entropy change. Temperature is here the intensive property of matter and is independent of the mass of matter, since it expresses its state. From equation (3.29) it follows therefore that the entropy change ΔS must be a capacity factor, and it is a measure of degradation of energy.

Thus we write:

Heat energy = temperature × change in entropy

Energy = intensity factor × capacity factor

Some other examples of energy and their factors[9]:

Electrical = electromotive force × quantity of electricity

Mass of gas = pressure × volume

Work = force × distance

Kinetic = velocity × momentum

3.2.5 *Entropy and the Thermodynamic Absolute Temperature Scale*

While considering the properties of perfect gases, it was shown that the temperature can be measured by means of expansion of a perfect gas, and if degrees of temperature are measured in Celsius units, then absolute zero is −273°C. This absolute scale is based on the knowledge of the value of the coefficient of expansion (α_v) of a perfect gas. However, as our techniques of measuring are improved, so the value (α_v) is being determined more accurately, and the value for absolute zero has to be modified.

Kelvin in 1852 suggested that the equation obtained by Carnot from his cycle can be used for measuring absolute temperature.

$$\frac{q_1}{T_1} + \frac{q_2}{T_2} = 0$$

where q_1 and q_2 are the reversible heats absorbed at temperatures T_1 and T_2 respectively in a cyclic process. Kelvin defined the temperature interval between the freezing point of water at 1 atm pressure and the normal boiling point of water to be equal to 100 degrees.

Since $T_1 = T_2 + 100$, equation (3.5) becomes then

$$\frac{q_1}{T_2 + 100} + \frac{q_2}{T_2} = 0 \qquad \ldots (3.30)$$

where q_2 is the heat absorbed at the freezing point and q_1 at the boiling point of water.

The values q_1 and q_2 can be found experimentally by subjecting a body to a reversible Carnot cycle between boiling water at 1 atm and melting ice at the same pressure: q_1 will be the heat extracted from the boiling water and q_2 the heat given up to the ice.

Equation (3.30) can be rewritten as follows:

$$-\frac{q_1}{q_2} = \frac{T_2 + 100}{T_2}$$

The value of $-\dfrac{q_1}{q_2}$ is found to be

$$1\cdot3661 = \frac{T_2 + 100}{T_2} \qquad \ldots(3.31)$$

The equation (3.31) contains only one unknown, and when solved the value of T_2 is found to be $273\cdot15$.

From the above description it follows that this temperature is absolute, since it is independent of the state of particular substances and can be measured by solids, liquids, and gases, providing a reversible cyclic process can be devised.[10]

3.2.6 *Entropy and Randomness*

In subsection 3.2.1 dealing with entropy changes of expanding gases it was shown (see equation (3.11)) that the entropy change (ΔS) resulting from volume changes of a perfect gas is given by

$$\Delta S = R \log_e \frac{v_2}{v_1}$$

where v_1 and v_2 are the initial and final volumes of 1 g mole of a perfect gas respectively. This equation shows clearly that, when a perfect gas expands, the entropy change accompanying this process must have a positive value, since the volume ratio v_2/v_1 is greater than unity; conversely it must have a negative value when it is less than unity on compression. Since during an expansion of a perfect gas no other entropy terms occur,* it can be concluded that the expansion of a gas is a natural process (occurring spontaneously), because its entropy change is greater than zero, i.e. $\Delta S > 0$ (see p. 64). This fact was noted by the many scientists who attempted to give a physical meaning to the entropy of a system. Statistical mechanics was found to be useful in this respect, since, similarly to thermodynamics, it deals with systems consisting of many particles. Kelvin[11] and Boltzmann[12] have shown the relationship between entropy and probability. According to this theory a system undergoing a spontaneous process changes from a state of lesser to a state of greater probability. Thus when a system is in the state of equilibrium its probability is maximum. Boltzmann deduced the following equation showing the relation between *entropy* and *probability:*

$$S = k \log_e w \qquad \ldots(3.32)$$

where S is the entropy of a system, w is the total number of ways in which a particular state of the system may be realised, and k is Boltzmann's constant. Since there are many more ways of realising

---

* In imperfect systems other entropy terms can occur originating in attractive forces between molecules, changes in bond structure, etc.

disordered as compared with ordered states, therefore disorder is much more probable than order. Einstein[13] using equation (3.32) has shown that the entropy change accompanying the expansion of gases from a volume v_1 to v_2 is given by

$$S = R \log_e \frac{v_2}{v_1}$$

This equation is identical with that previously derived from classical thermodynamics (see p. 62), thus showing that the expansion of gases is a natural (spontaneous) process, because on expansion the system becomes more disordered. The principle of **maximum disorder (randomness)** has subsequently been extended to calculations of entropy based upon (i) spectroscopic data and (ii) molecular-constant data.

The calculation of entropies from spectroscopic data is restricted at present to the gaseous state. In these calculations it is assumed that the *total entropy S* of a gas is the sum of entropies due to its *translational energy S_t, rotational energy S_r, vibrational energy S_v,* and contributions due to *electronic energies S_e.*

The calculation of entropy from molecular constants may be used for the more complicated gases for which spectroscopic data have not yet been obtained. The data required are the moments of inertia, the fundamental vibration frequencies of the molecule, and the quantum weights and separations of the considered electronic levels. In these calculations the gas molecules are assumed to be rigid ones, whose entropy is again the sum of translational S_t, rotational S_r, vibrational S_v, and electronic S_e contributions to entropy. Thus we have

$$S = S_t + S_v + S_e + S_r \qquad \ldots (3.33)$$

(Lumsden[14] by applying statistical mechanical considerations to alloys has, for example, derived the following equation for calculating the effect of temperature and concentration on ΔG for the formation of lead-zinc liquid alloys.

$$\Delta G = RT[N_{Pb} \log_e N_{Pb} + N_{Zn} \log_e N_{Zn} +$$
$$+ (N_{Pb} + N_{Zn}) \log_e (N_{Pb} + N_{Zn})] +$$
$$+ \frac{1 \cdot 6^{0 \cdot 5} N_{Pb} N_{Zn}(5{,}000 - 0 \cdot 52T)}{(1 \cdot 6 N_{Pb} + N_{Zn})} +$$
$$+ \frac{3 \cdot 2^{0 \cdot 5} N_{Pb} N_{Zn}(3{,}215 - 2 \cdot 79T)}{(3 \cdot 2 N_{Pb} + N_{Zn})} -$$
$$- \frac{1 \cdot 6(N_{Pb})^2(N_{Zn})^2(5{,}000 - 0 \cdot 52T)^2}{8RT(1 \cdot 6^{\frac{1}{2}} N_{Pb} + N_{Zn})^3}$$

where N_{Pb} and N_{Zn} are the mole fractions of lead and zinc respectively. The first term gives the ideal free energy of mixing, while the second term represents the attraction effects of neighbouring atoms in the alloy, and the third the effects of more distant ones. The fourth term is a correction term for the departure of randomness of distribution of the atoms, assuming the number of nearest neighbours in each pure liquid to be eight.

The above equation shows that the statistical approach leads to very complicated mathematical expressions, even though approximations were made in its derivation. However this equation has recently been found useful by Hultgren and others[15] for the calculation of free energy-concentration diagrams at certain temperatures, where it predicted remarkably well the behaviour of this system.)

The following example is chosen to illustrate the physical meaning of entropy and randomness and its influence on the spontaneity of a process.

Example

Calculate the entropy of evaporation ΔS_e for 1 g atom of liquid iron. Use the following data in your calculation; density of liquid iron = 6·88 g/cc; atomic weight = 55·85; boiling point = 3,070°C; atomic volume of perfect gas = 22,400 cc at s.t.p.

Assume that the vapour of iron at one atmosphere pressure obeys the perfect gas equation.

Using equation (3.33) we have:

$$\Delta S_{e_{(Fe)}} = R \log_e \frac{v_{vap}}{v_{liq}} = 4 \cdot 575 \log_{10} \frac{v_{vap}}{v_{liq}}$$

$$v_{vap} \text{ at } 3{,}070°C = \frac{22{,}400 \times (273 + 3{,}070)}{273} = 22{,}400 \times 11 \cdot 81 \text{ cc}$$

$$v_{liq} = \frac{55 \cdot 85}{6 \cdot 88} \text{ cc}$$

Substituting these values into equation (3.33) we have

$$\Delta S_{e_{(Fe)}} = 4 \cdot 575 \log_{10} \frac{22{,}400 \times 11 \cdot 81}{\dfrac{55 \cdot 85}{6 \cdot 88}} = 20 \cdot 61 \text{ cal deg}^{-1} \text{ g atom}^{-1}$$

Answer: The entropy of evaporation (ΔS_e) for iron, calculated from equation (3.33), was found to be +20·61 e.u.

This value is seen to be lower than that of 24·3 e.u. given in Table 3.2 and calculated from the experimental values of its atomic heat of evaporation L_e and its normal boiling temperature T_e. The lower value obtained from equation (3.33) can be accounted for by the fact that this equation is only true for systems in which the initial and final states are the same. In this example v_1 referred to the liquid and v_2 to the vapour. It is therefore clear that during the process of evaporation, besides the entropy change due to a change in volume, there is an entropy change associated with the energy required to overcome the attractive inter-atomic forces still existing in the boiling iron; the entropy of evaporation may thus be regarded as the difference between the states of order of a liquid and its vapour. Since in the majority of cases metallic vapours behave almost as perfect gases, their state of order may be considered to be the same. Similarly the states of order of the majority of liquid metals at their normal boiling points may be considered to be the same. It is therefore clear that the entropy of evaporation for most metals should be the same for all practical purposes. This conclusion reached by the statistical approach thus provides a theoretical basis for the validity of **Pictet Trouton's Rule** for a large number of substances. This rule states that the ratio of latent heat of evaporation L_e to the temperature of normal boiling point T_e is constant, and is approximately 22 cal deg^{-1} g mole^{-1}. Table 3.2 shows some values of ΔS_e for various metals.

TABLE 3.2

Metal	L_e cal g atom^{-1}	$T_e°$K	$\Delta S_e = \dfrac{L_e}{T_e}$ cal deg^{-1} g atom^{-1}
Ag	60,000	2,470	24·3
Bi	41,100	1,830	22·5
Cd	23,900	1,038	22·8
Fe	81,300	3,343	24·3
Hg	14,100	630	22·4
Na	23,700	1,155	20·5
Zn	28,800	1,180	24·4

From Kubaschewski & Evans, *Metallurgical Thermochemistry*, 2nd edition, Pergamon Press Ltd., London, 1958.

3.3 SUMMARY

(i) From the Carnot Cycle it follows that in a reversible cyclic process the energies q_1 and q_2 absorbed at T_1 and T_2 are not equal, but the ratios $\dfrac{q_1}{T_1}$ and $\dfrac{q_2}{T_2}$ are numerically equal.

(ii) Because of the fundamental significance of the ratio $\left(\dfrac{q_{rev}}{T}\right)$ Clausius denoted it by the symbol ΔS and called it a change in entropy.

(iii) The value of the sum of entropy changes in a closed system (i.e. of constant mass and energy) depends on the equilibrium state of the system, and for a system at equilibrium

$$\sum \frac{q_{rev}}{T} = 0 = \Delta S_{process} + \Delta S_{surr} = \Delta S_{system}$$

Thus the change in entropy of the surroundings is numerically equal but opposite in sign to that of the process.

(iv) The entropy change of an irreversible closed system is positive. Thus

$$\Delta S_{system} = \oplus ve = \Delta S_{process} + \Delta S_{surr}$$

(v) The entropy change of an irreversible process $\Delta S_{process}$ may be positive, zero, or negative. The sign of $\Delta S_{process}$ is therefore of no value by itself in indicating the direction of a real process.

(vi) Entropy units for a given mass of a system are cal deg^{-1}, and therefore are not energy units.

(vii) From the equation

$$-\left(\frac{q_1}{q_2}\right) = \left(\frac{T_2 + 100}{T_2}\right)$$

the absolute value of T_2 can be calculated, providing the ratio $-\dfrac{q_1}{q_2}$ is determined. This absolute thermodynamic temperature scale was proposed by Kelvin and is called therefore the Kelvin scale. This absolute thermodynamic temperature scale is more fundamental than that derived from the expansion of gases, since it is applicable to solids, liquids and gases.

(viii) Energy is a function of the product of two factors, the intensity factor (independent of the mass of the system), and the capacity factor (dependent on the mass of the system). Temperature is the intensity factor and the entropy change the capacity factor for heat energy.

REFERENCES

1 BUTLER, J. A. V., *Chemical Thermodynamics*, fourth edition, p. 47, Macmillan & Co. Ltd., London, 1948.
2 CLAUSIUS, R., *Ann. Phys.*, 1850, **79**, 368.
3 THOMSON, W., *Trans. Roy. Soc. Edin.*, 1854, **21**, 123.

4 CLAUSIUS, R., *Ann. Phys.*, 1865, **125**, 353.
5 GLASSTONE, S. and D. LEWIS, *Elements of Physical Chemistry*, second edition, p. 98, Macmillan and Co. Ltd., London, 1960.
SWALIN, R. A., *Thermodynamics of Solids*, p. 15, John Wiley & Sons Ltd., London, 1962.
6 KUBASCHEWSKI, O. and E. L. EVANS, *Metallurgical Thermochemistry*, second edition, Pergamon Press Ltd., London, 1958.
7 KELLEY, K. K., *Contributions to the Data on Theoretical Metallurgy*, U.S. Bureau of Mines, Bulletin 584, U.S. Govt. Printing Office, Washington, 1960.
8 LARMOR, *Theory of Heat*, 1875, p. 194.
9 For further examples see PARTINGTON, J. R., *An Advanced Treatise on Physical Chemistry*, Vol. I, pp. 148 and 159, Longmans, Green & Co. Ltd., London, 1949.
10 *Thermodynamics*, Proceedings of the Symposium on Thermodynamics, Fritzens–Wattens, 1959, Butterworth & Co. (Publishers) Ltd., London, 1961.
BOCKRIS, J. O., J. L. WHITE and J. D. MACKENZIE (Eds.), *Physico-chemical Measurements at High Temperatures*, pp. 6–47, Butterworth & Co. (Publishers) Ltd., London, 1959.
11 KELVIN, W. T., *Nature*, 1874, **9**, 441; *Proc. Roy. Soc. Edin.*, 1875, **8**, 325; *Phil. Mag.*, 1892, **33**, 291.
12 BOLTZMANN, *Wien Ber.*, 1877, **76**, II, 373; *ibid.* 1878, **78**, II, 7; *Compt. Rend.*, 1906, **142**, 513.
13 EINSTEIN, A., *Ann. Phys.*, 1905, **17**, 132.
14 LUMSDEN, J., *Thermodynamics of Alloys*, Institute of Metals, London, 1952.
15 HULTGREN, R, R. L. ORR, P. D. ANDERSON and K. K. KELLEY, *Selected Values of Thermodynamic Properties of Metals and Alloys*, John Wiley and Sons Ltd., London and New York, 1963.

CHAPTER IV

The Helmholtz and Gibbs Free Energies

4.1   INTRODUCTION

In the introduction to the previous chapter it was mentioned that the Second Law of Thermodynamics was the outcome of attempting to make practical use of the First Law in two main ways. One of these arose from the dream of scientists of that time to be able to predict from already available thermochemical data whether a hitherto untried chemical or physical process was possible. Intuitively, from mechanics, Berthelot and Thompson considered that exothermic reactions (accompanied by heat evolution) must be spontaneous, since the system after the process was completed must possess less energy than before. This theory that enthalpy can be taken as an indication of the direction of a process was disproved by the fact that reactions were possible in which heat was evolved or absorbed (exothermic and endothermic reactions). Therefore it is clear that enthalpy change cannot be chosen as a function that allows us to predict the possibility of a process.

It has already been shown (3.2.3) that the entropy change of a system allows us to predict the direction of a process, and thus it is a measure of the spontaneity of a process, i.e.

$$[\Delta S_{system} = \Delta S_{process} + \Delta S_{surroundings}]$$

is a function which in some cases may confront us with practical difficulties in determining the entropy change of the surroundings. The second difficulty, in so far as the scientists of the second half of the nineteenth century were concerned, was the fact that entropy change was not a function which gave the answer in energy units. It was therefore advantageous to obtain a function which would be expressed in terms of energy (calories), and whose value would immediately foretell whether a given process was thermodynamically possible.

The advantage of such a function (or functions) would be great, since it would be complementary to the other branches of science concerned with energies in our world of matter, and thus would be comparable with electrical, mechanical, and chemical energies. The functions which were subsequently proposed, and which have been found to fulfil these requirements, are the **Gibbs and Helmoltz Free Energies.**

4.2   THE DERIVATION OF HELMHOLTZ AND GIBBS FREE ENERGIES

These two functions can be regarded either as (i) the combination of the First and Second Laws of Thermodynamics, or (ii) as the expression of the basic equation of entropy change in a closed system in terms of energy change.

Let us first consider a system in which a process is carried out at constant temperature T and constant volume v. From the First Law of Thermodynamics the internal energy change ΔU is given by $\Delta U = q_{rev} - w$; q_{rev} is the heat absorbed reversibly at constant temperature, and w is the work done by the system during the process.

From the Clausius definition of entropy change

$$\Delta S = \frac{q_{rev}}{T} \qquad \therefore \ q_{rev} = T\Delta S$$

Substituting the above value of q_{rev} into (2.1) we have

$$\Delta U = T\Delta S - w$$

or

$$-w = \Delta U - T\Delta S \qquad (T, v \text{ constant}) \qquad \ldots(4.1)$$

where $-w = $ The maximum work that can be done by the system during a process

$\Delta U = $ The increase in the internal energy of the system

$T\Delta S = $ Energy used up for internal rearrangements or **bound energy.**

This maximum work function $(U - TS)$ is of such importance that a special name has been given to it; it is known as the **Helmholtz Free Energy** (A). Thus

$$A = U - TS \qquad \ldots(4.2)$$

From this equation it follows that, as the system performs work, we can write

$$-w_{max} = \Delta U - T\Delta S = \Delta A \qquad \ldots(4.3)$$

where ΔA gives the maximum work available at constant temperature and volume when the process is carried out reversibly. The
change in A in a process is determined only by the initial and final
states of the system.

Since many real processes are carried out at constant pressure and
temperature, it is therefore convenient to introduce another function
G which gives the maximum useful external work or **free energy** under
these conditions; when a process proceeds at constant pressure, there
is a possibility that some of the available energy is used up in the
expansion of the system. If the constant external pressure of the
system is p and the volume change of the system Δv, then the free
energy for doing useful work (e.g. mechanical, electrical, etc.) will
be less than that shown in equation (4.3) by the amount of energy
spent on the useless work done against the atmosphere, i.e. $p\Delta v$.

Thus the available energy at constant pressure is

$$-w_{\max} = (-w') - p\Delta v = \Delta A$$

or

$$-w' = \Delta A + p\Delta v$$

or

$$\Delta G = \Delta A + p\Delta v \qquad \ldots(4.4)$$

where $-w' = $ maximum work that can be obtained from a process
at constant pressure and T.

Substituting (4.4) into (4.3) one obtains

$$\Delta G = \Delta U - T\Delta S + p\Delta v \qquad (T, p \text{ constant})$$

or

$$\Delta G = \Delta(U + pv) - T\Delta S$$

thus

$$\Delta G = \Delta H - T\Delta S \qquad \ldots(4.5)$$

The term ΔG is called the **Gibbs free energy change,** and has found
numerous applications in metallurgy. *Although ΔG is called Gibbs
free energy change it was Massieu[1] who first introduced both these
functions and had already shown their general usefulness in the study
of heat transfer.*

Just as ΔA is the maximum work that can be obtained from a
process under conditions of constant volume, so ΔG is the maximum
amount of work that can be obtained for useful purposes under
conditions of constant pressure. The name of free energy is in accord
with the idea that this function measures the available energy, and
in any given process the value of ΔG may be greater or less than that
of ΔA, depending on whether the atmosphere does work on the

system as the process proceeds. The numerical value of free energy for specified amount of reactants measures the useful work obtained from the system in a reversible process. Under any other conditions the work actually obtained from the process will be less than the free energy change.

4.3 THE SIGNIFICANCE OF THE SIGN OF FREE ENERGY CHANGE (ΔG)

In general the function A is very seldom used, and therefore we shall not consider it any further.

Equation (4.4) shows that

$$\Delta G = -w_{max} + p\Delta v = -w'$$

where $-w'$ is the maximum useful work for constant pressure.

When work can be actually performed by a process the value of w' will be positive, and therefore the value of ΔG must be negative since

$$\Delta G = -w'$$

Thus

$$\Delta G < 0$$

for a real process or a spontaneous process (thermodynamically possible process).

When however a system is at equilibrium no work can be obtained from the system and therefore

$$-w' = 0 = \Delta G$$

When a system is not at equilibrium but the value of

$$w' = \ominus\text{ve}$$

and when

$$\Delta G = G_2 - G_1 = \oplus\text{ve}$$

(see Fig. 4.1 for explanation of the symbols used), then the overall process proceeds in the opposite direction to that shown by the direction of the arrow (Fig. 4.1).

$$\Delta G = G_{products} - G_{reactants} = (H_2 - H_1) - T(S_2 - S_1)$$

or

$$\Delta G = \Delta H - T\Delta S$$

If the value of the free energy change is $\ominus$ve, the reaction will be thermodynamically possible from left to right; if zero, it will be at equilibrium, and if positive, it will be possible in the opposite direction.

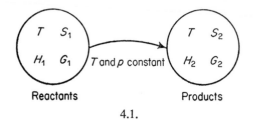

4.1.

For the equilibrium reaction

$$A + B \rightleftharpoons C + D$$

let G_A, G_B, G_C and G_D be the free energies of reactants and products, then if $\Delta G = \ominus$ve

$$A + B \rightarrow C + D$$

if $\Delta G = 0$

$$A + B \rightleftharpoons C + D$$

if $\Delta G = \oplus$ve

$$A + B \leftarrow C + D$$

Where the arrow is $\rightarrow$ it indicates that the reaction proceeds from left to right and $\rightleftharpoons$ indicates a state of equilibrium.

Note: Since it is impossible to determine or calculate the absolute values of either the internal energy or the enthalpy of a system, therefore it is impossible to determine the absolute value of free energy G. We are however able to determine changes in free energies as well as changes in all the other quantities.

Let us now consider a real process and let us calculate (i) the Gibbs free energy change of this process at room temperature, and (ii) the entropy change of the closed system, and then compare these two techniques for the determination of direction of the process to illustrate the advantage of using ΔG in preference to the entropy change ΔS.

Example

(i) Consider whether a reaction between sodium and oxygen at room temperature (298°K) and one atmosphere pressure will be a spontaneous process.

This reaction can be represented by the following chemical equation:

$$4Na_{(s)} + O_{2(g)} = 2Na_2O_{(s)} \quad \text{at} \quad 298°K$$

$$\underbrace{0 \qquad\qquad 0}_{G_1} \qquad \underbrace{-183\cdot0 \text{ kcal}}_{G_2}$$

since $\Delta G = G_2 - G_1$ and G_1 and G_2 represent the free energies of the reactants and products respectively.

The free energies of pure elements are taken to be zero, so that the free energy in the formation of a compound from its elements gives the free energy change of the compound formation. Thus

$$\Delta G_{\text{Na}_2\text{O}} = G_2 - G_1 = -183\cdot0 \text{ kcal g mole}^{-1} \text{ of oxygen*}$$

Since the value of $\Delta G_{\text{Na}_2\text{O}}$ is negative, the amount of external work that could be obtained from this system under reversible conditions at 25°C would be equivalent to 183,000 cal for each 32 g of oxygen used in this reaction.

(ii) Let us now calculate the entropy change for this reaction.

$$4\text{Na} + \text{O}_2 \xrightarrow{\Delta S_{298}} 2\text{Na}_2\text{O} \ldots (T; p \text{ constant})$$

The values of S are:

$$\underbrace{4 \times 12\cdot3 + 49\cdot02}_{S_{\text{reactants}}} \qquad \underbrace{2 \times 17\cdot0}_{S_{\text{products}}}$$

$$\Delta S_{\text{Na}_2\text{O}} = S_{\text{products}} - S_{\text{reactants}} = 34 - (49\cdot2 + 49\cdot02)$$

$$\Delta S_{\text{Na}_2\text{O}} = 34\cdot0 - 98\cdot22 = -64\cdot22 \text{ cal deg}^{-1} \text{ g mole}^{-1} \text{ of oxygen}$$

In this case the entropy change of the reaction is negative. However, as previously shown on p. 67, the sign of the entropy change for the process does not give any indication regarding the spontaneity of the process. We have therefore to calculate the ΔS_{system}, that is to say $\Delta S_{\text{process}} + \Delta S_{\text{surroundings}}$.

$\Delta S_{\text{surroundings}}$ is the entropy gained by the surroundings, which is given by the ratio of the heat absorbed to the temperature of the process.

$$\Delta S_{\text{surroundings}} = \frac{-\Delta H_{\text{process}}}{T} = \frac{-(-201,400)}{298} = +675\cdot8$$

Thus

$$\Delta S_{\text{system}} = -64\cdot22 + 675\cdot8 = +611\cdot58 \text{ cal deg}^{-1} \text{ g mole}^{-1} \text{ oxygen}$$

It is seen from this example that the negative value of the Gibbs free energy enables us to conclude at once that the process is thermodynamically possible, whereas in the entropy change calculations the entropy change of the process gave a negative value which was of no value for the required prediction until all the other entropy change values were known. The use of entropy for prediction of

* The free energy change $\Delta G_{\text{Na}_2\text{O}}$ for 1 g mole of $\text{Na}_2\text{O} = -91\cdot5$ kcal.

the direction of a reaction has a further possible disadvantage in the fact that the answer is in entropy units, and it has to be converted into energy units before the possible work obtained from the reaction can be calculated.

The value for the entropy change can be converted into energy by multiplying the entropy change of the system by the temperature of the process. Thus

$$\text{Available energy of the process} = -T\Delta S_{\text{system}}$$

$$\therefore \quad \text{Energy} = -298 \times 611 \cdot 58 = 182,290 \text{ cal g mole}^{-1} \text{ oxygen}$$

Comparing the value of ΔG and $T\Delta S_{\text{system}}$ it is seen that there is a difference of 710 cal. This difference is well within the normal experimental error of the thermochemical data used. This comparison of the ΔG of the process and the value of $T\Delta S_{\text{system}}$ shows that ΔG really gives the negative value of the entropy change of the system multiplied by the absolute temperature of the process. Thus

$$\Delta G = -T(\Delta S_{\text{process}} + \Delta S_{\text{surroundings}})$$

4.3.1   The Meaning of Thermodynamically Possible Process

In the previous section of this chapter it was shown that if the value of the Gibbs free energy change ΔG is negative, the process is thermodynamically possible or is spontaneous. Let us examine the meaning of the expression thermodynamically possible. This can be illustrated by using an example from mechanics. Figs. 4.2 (*a*) and 4.2 (*b*) show water containers placed above the level of C. In Fig. 4.2 (*a*) the water in the container has a potential energy *mgh*. However, due to the

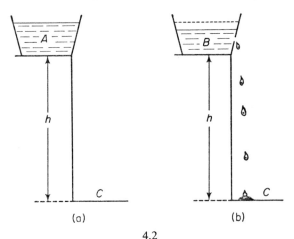

(*a*)   (*b*)

4.2

physical barrier of the walls of the container the water cannot flow down from A → C, i.e. from the higher to the lower level, and thus the potential energy mgh of this water cannot be converted into mechanical, electrical, heat, or other kinds of energy. Fig. 4.2 (b) represents the same system, except for a hole drilled in the container. In this case the water flows spontaneously (i.e. of its own accord, without being subjected by any external forces) to the level C, and *thus conforms to the universal law of the stability of the lowest energy level of a system.*

A thermodynamically possible process is a process which, providing there are no diffusion barriers or other restrictive forces, will proceed of its own accord.

The free energy function is therefore of the utmost practical importance, because when a process is known to be thermodynamically possible and in reality it does not take place, then it is clear that there must be some restrictive forces operating, which have to be overcome* (analogous to drilling a hole in the tank to allow the water to flow down) in order to make the process proceed spontaneously.

Example

The free energy change for the formation of aluminium oxide at 25°C is $-396 \cdot 4$ kcal g mole^{-1} of oxygen, i.e.

$$\tfrac{4}{3} Al + O_2 = \tfrac{2}{3} Al_2O_3, \quad \Delta G_{298} = -396 \cdot 4 \text{ kcal g mole}^{-1} \text{ of oxygen}$$

From the high negative value of the Gibbs free energy it would follow that pure aluminium should be very readily oxidised in air at room temperature. In reality, as we all know, it is used as a protective metallic coating because of its good resistance to oxidation. The physical barrier to oxidation in this case is due to the formation of a very thin aluminium oxide film, which separates physically the reactants and is therefore highly protective. However, any traces of mercury or its salts will destroy this protective oxide film, and aluminium will be oxidised at a very fast rate forming spectacular "whiskers".[2] Here the destruction of the physical barrier is achieved by the physico-chemical action of the mercury vapour.

4.4 DETERMINATION OF GIBBS FREE ENERGY CHANGE (ΔG) FROM THERMAL DATA

The Gibbs free energy change for a process can be determined by many methods, and these will be fully discussed later in this book.

---

* See Fig. 11.1 in which the activation energy is the restrictive force which has to be overcome.

At this stage it may be useful for the reader to know at least one method of calculating the values of ΔG.

ΔG can be calculated very conveniently from the equation which defines the Gibbs free energy change as $\Delta G = \Delta H - T\Delta S$ (T, p constant).

From this equation it follows that providing we know ΔH and ΔS for the given process we can calculate the value of ΔG. To illustrate this let us calculate the free energy change of the aluminothermic reaction at 25°C in which ferrous oxide is reduced by aluminium. Assume that all the reactants and products are always in their pure states (i.e. they are immiscible in each other).

The first step in such a calculation is to write down a balanced equation. Thus

$$\underbrace{2\,Al + 3\,FeO}_{\text{reactants}} \rightarrow \underbrace{Al_2O_3 + 3\,Fe}_{\text{products}}$$

The next step is to find in tables[3] the values of ΔH_{298} and ΔS_{298} of all the species which are usually given for 1 g atom or g mole of each of the the substances. These are

$$2Al + 3FeO \rightarrow Al_2O_3 + 3Fe$$

$$\Delta H_{298} \ldots \quad O \qquad 3(-63 \cdot 2) \quad 400 \cdot 0 \qquad 0$$

$$\Delta S_{298} \ldots 2(6 \cdot 77) \quad 3(14 \cdot 05) \qquad 12 \cdot 2 \quad 3(6 \cdot 49)$$

$$\Delta H_{298(\text{reaction})} = \Delta H_{298(\text{products})} - \Delta H_{298(\text{reactants})}$$

$$= (-400 \cdot 0) - (-189 \cdot 6)$$

$$\Delta H_{298(\text{reaction})} = -210 \cdot 4 \text{ kcal}$$

$$\Delta S_{298(\text{reaction})} = \Delta S_{298(\text{products})} - \Delta S_{298(\text{reactants})}$$

$$\Delta S_{298(\text{reaction})} = (12 \cdot 2 + 19 \cdot 47) - (13 \cdot 54 + 42 \cdot 15)$$

$$\Delta S_{298(\text{reaction})} = -24 \cdot 02 \text{ e.u.}$$

but

$$\Delta G_{298(\text{reaction})} = \Delta H_{298(\text{reaction})} - T\Delta S_{298(\text{reaction})}$$

$$\therefore \qquad \Delta G_{298} = -210{,}400 + 7{,}158$$

$$\Delta G_{298} = -203{,}242 \text{ cal g mole}^{-1} \text{ of } Al_2O_3$$

The value of $-203{,}242$ obtained in this example represents the maximum energy which could be converted into useful work associated with this aluminothermic reaction when carried out at 298°K and 1 atm pressure.

4.5 SOME USEFUL RELATIONS BETWEEN THE GIBBS FREE ENERGY AND OTHER THERMODYNAMIC FUNCTIONS

In the previous sections it was shown that the Gibbs free energy function is defined by $G = H + TS$ (T, p constant).

If we substitute into this equation the expression defining the enthalpy $H = U + pv$, the value of free energy then becomes $G = U + pv - TS$, and the value dG when G is a very small quantity becomes

$$dG = dU + pdv + vdp - TdS - SdT \qquad \ldots(4.6)$$

In a reversible process involving an expansion of a perfect gas

$$dU = q_{\text{rev}} - w = q_{\text{rev}} - pdv$$

Thus

$$dU = TdS - pdv \qquad \ldots(4.7)$$

since the process is reversible, and for very small quantities

$$q_{\text{rev}} = TdS$$

Substituting (4.7) into (4.6) we obtain

$$dG = TdS - pdv + pdv + vdp - TdS - SdT$$
$$dG = vdp - SdT \qquad \ldots(4.8)$$

At constant pressure and variable temperature equation (4.8) gives

$$\left(\frac{\partial G}{\partial T}\right)_p = -S \qquad \ldots(4.9)$$

At constant temperature and variable pressure the equation gives

$$\left(\frac{\partial G}{\partial p}\right)_T = v \qquad \ldots(4.10)$$

Equation (4.9) shows that the change of free energy with temperature at constant pressure gives the entropy of the system with an opposite sign, and the change of free energy with pressure at constant temperature gives the volume of the system. Thus these equations correlate the pressure, volume and temperature with the free energy of a system.

However, previously (4.3) it was shown that it is impossible to determine or calculate the absolute value of free energy. The relationships (4.9) and (4.10) therefore become useful when one deals with a system undergoing a physical or chemical change.

4.3.

Consider a system undergoing a change from $A \to B$ (Fig. 4.3) first at constant pressure and then at constant volume.

Using equation (4.9) we obtain

$$\Delta S_{\text{process}} = S_B - S_A = -\left[\left(\frac{\partial G_B}{\partial T}\right)_p - \left(\frac{\partial G_A}{\partial T}\right)_p\right]$$

$$\Delta S = -\left(\frac{\partial (G_B - G_A)}{\partial T}\right)_p = -\left(\frac{\partial \Delta G}{T}\right)_p$$

$$\therefore \qquad \left(\frac{\partial \Delta G}{\partial T}\right)_p = -\Delta S \qquad \qquad \ldots(4.11)$$

Similarly

$$\left(\frac{\partial \Delta G}{\partial p}\right)_T = \Delta v \qquad \qquad \ldots(4.12)$$

In all these calculations we have assumed that the mass of the system remains constant throughout the process.

From equation (4.11) it follows that the slope of a plot ΔG against T, that is free energy change against temperature, gives the entropy change for the process with an opposite sign (Fig. 4.4):

$$\text{slope} = \frac{y}{x} = -\Delta S$$

The values of these slopes are of great interest to production and theoretical metallurgists and will be discussed in detail later on.

4.6   THE GIBBS-HELMHOLTZ EQUATION[4]

The Gibbs-Helmholtz equation can be conveniently deduced from the partial differentials obtained in the previous section.

Let us consider a process at a constant temperature T and pressure p; then

$$\Delta G = \Delta H - T\Delta S \qquad (T, p \text{ constant})$$

Substituting equation (4.11) into the above equation we obtain

$$\Delta G = \Delta H + T\left(\frac{\partial \Delta G}{\partial T}\right)_p \qquad \qquad \ldots(4.13)$$

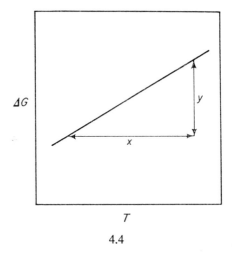

4.4

This equation is known as the Gibbs-Helmholtz equation.[5] It is independent of the entropy term, and therefore permits the evaluation of ΔH of a reaction from the knowledge of free energy change (ΔG) and its temperature coefficient $\left(\dfrac{\partial \Delta G}{\partial T}\right)_p$.

This equation is extremely convenient, when used in conjunction with electrochemical determinations of free energy changes of suitable chemical processes, because they are carried out in thermostats under practically atmospheric pressure. It will be discussed more fully and illustrated in Chapter XIII, p. 271.

The Gibbs-Helmholtz can be written in an alternative form, since

$$\frac{d}{dT}\left(\frac{\Delta G}{T}\right) = -\frac{\Delta G}{T^2} + \frac{1}{T}\cdot\left(\frac{d\Delta G}{dT}\right)$$

therefore

$$\frac{\partial}{dT}\left(\frac{\Delta G}{T}\right)_p = -\frac{\Delta H}{T^2} \quad \text{or} \quad \Delta G = -T\int\frac{\Delta H}{T^2}\,dT + \text{constant}$$

$$\dots(4.14)[6]$$

or

$$\left[\frac{\partial\left(\dfrac{\Delta G}{T}\right)}{\partial\dfrac{1}{T}}\right]_p = \Delta H \qquad \dots(4.15)[7]$$

Thus in equation (4.14) the temperature coefficient of the ratio of free energy change in a chemical or physical process to the temperature at a constant pressure is related to the change in enthalpy.

From equation (4.15) it follows that the slope of $\left(\dfrac{\Delta G}{T}\right)_p$ against $\dfrac{1}{T}$ gives the change in enthalpy ΔH for the process.

REFERENCES

1 *Compt. Rend.*, 1869, **T.1 19**, 858 and 1057.
2 SEARS, C. W., *Acta Met.*, 1955, **3**, 361.
3 KUBASCHEWSKI, O. and E. L. EVANS, *Metallurgical Thermochemistry*, second edition, Pergamon Press Ltd., London, 1958.
4 PARTINGTON, J. R., *An Advanced Treatise on Physical Chemistry*, Vol. I., Longmans, Green & Co. Ltd., London, 1949.
5 Deduced by J. W. GIBBS (1875) and by VON HELMHOLTZ (1882).
6 CALDIN, E. F., *An Introduction to Chemical Thermodynamics*, p. 157, Clarendon Press, Oxford, 1958.
7 MOORE, W. J., *Physical Chemistry*, second edition, p. 2, Longmans, Green & Co. Ltd., London, 1956.

CHAPTER V

The Third Law of Thermodynamics

From the Gibbs-Helmholtz equation

$$\Delta G = \Delta H + T\left(\frac{\partial \Delta G}{\partial T}\right)_p$$

it follows that $\Delta G = \Delta H$ when either

$$T = 0°\text{K} \quad \text{or} \quad \left(\frac{\partial \Delta G}{\partial T}\right)_p = 0$$

providing either T or $\left(\frac{\partial \Delta G}{\partial T}\right)_p$ are not infinite.[1]

T. W. Richards (1902),[2] using an electrochemical method, studied the free energy change and the enthalpy change for a number of chemical reactions, and found that ΔG and ΔH became nearly equal a hundred or more degrees above absolute zero.[3] Nernst in (1906)[4] postulated a 'new heat theorem' or the 'third law of thermodynamics' by concluding that for all reactions of condensed systems, solid or liquid, ΔG and ΔH approach very closely to each other asymptotically, and just above absolute zero they virtually cease to vary with temperature (Fig. 5.1). Since from Kirchhoff's Law

$$\left(\frac{\partial \Delta H}{\partial T}\right)_p = \Delta C_p$$

$$\left(\frac{\partial \Delta G}{\partial T}\right)_p = -\Delta S$$

we may write

$$\lim_{T \to 0} \Delta C_p = 0$$

and

$$\lim_{T \to 0} \Delta S = 0$$

for reactions involving liquids and solids only. The heat energy of solids is mainly in the form of vibratory motion, and, since these

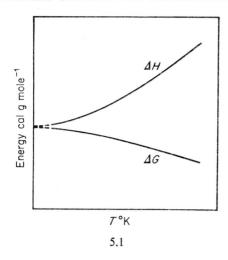

5.1

quanta are large, it follows that at very low temperatures the temperature of solids may be raised without absorbing appreciable heat energy. This is why the heat capacity of all solids approaches zero at very low temperature (see Chapter II, Table 2.3). Planck[5] suggested that the reason why the change of entropy is zero at absolute zero is that the entropy of all pure crystalline substances is zero when $T = 0$.

Thus the Third Law of Thermodynamics may be stated as follows: **at the temperature of absolute zero the entropy of all perfect crystals is zero.**

The third law is generally found to be true within the normal experimental errors; however, there are sometimes some discrepancies.[6]

From this law it follows that, providing the specific heats are known within the range of temperatures under consideration and the substance is crystalline at absolute zero, then the absolute value of entropy S at any temperature can be calculated. Thus

$$S_{298}^0 = \int_0^{T_t} \frac{C_p'}{T} \, dT + \frac{L_t}{T_t} + \int_{T_t}^{298} \frac{C_p''}{T} \, dT \qquad \dots(5.1)$$

where C_p' = the specific heat from absolute zero to T_t

T_t = transformation temperature

L_t = latent heat of transformation

C_p'' = specific heat between T_t and 298°K.

From this law it also follows that the standard entropies S°_{298} of all elements at 25°C must be positive. These values may be found in tables, and can be used for calculations of S at any other temperature.

REFERENCES

1 BUTLER, J. A. V., *Chemical Thermodynamics*, fourth edition, p. 277, Macmillan & Co. Ltd., London, 1948.
2 RICHARDSON, T. W., *Z. physikal. Chem.*, 1902, **42**, 129.
3 ADAM, N. K., *Physical Chemistry*, p. 268, Clarendon Press, Oxford, 1956.
4 NERNST, W. H., *Nachr. Ges. Wiss., Göttingen.* (Math.-Phys. K 1.), p. 1.
5 PLANCK, M., *Thermodynamik*, third edition, p. 279, Veit & Comp., Leipzig, 1911.
6 LEWIS, G. N. and E. L. RANDALL, revised by K. S. PITZER and L. BREWER, *Thermodynamics*, second edition, p. 130, McGraw-Hill Publishing Co. Ltd., London, 1961.

CHAPTER VI

Clausius-Clapeyron Equation

6.1 INTRODUCTION

The Clausius-Clapeyron equation is extremely important in calculating the effects of temperature and pressure changes on the freezing point of solids, boiling point of liquids, and any solid-solid phase transformation. It also enables us to calculate the effect on changes in concentration of solutions on their freezing and boiling temperatures, and is therefore very useful for calculation of phase boundaries of systems which are either immiscible or partially miscible in the solid state. This equation is sometimes regarded as a symbolic form of Carnot's fundamental ideas.[1]

6.2 DERIVATION OF THE CLAUSIUS[3]-CLAPEYRON[2] EQUATION FOR A SINGLE SUBSTANCE

The Clausius-Clapeyron equation as derived here is an example of the application of the consideration of free energy change for a single substance in two different phases at equilibrium.

Let us consider a single solid substance at equilibrium with its liquid, at its temperature of melting, and under one atmosphere of pressure (Fig. 6.1).

There is a natural tendency for molecules to pass from the solid into the liquid and vice versa. The number of atoms passing at any time from one state to the other will depend on the temperature and pressure.

In Chapter IV it was shown that the value of the free energy change indicated the directional tendencies of systems.

Let us assume that the molal free energy of the solid at constant temperature and pressure is G_A and of the liquid G_B; then if $G_A > G_B$ the solid metal can decrease its free energy by dissolving, i.e. if

$G_A > G_B$ solid → liquid; solid melts, since $\Delta G = \ominus$ve

$G_A = G_B$ solid ⇌ liquid; equilibrium, since $\Delta G = 0$

$G_A < G_B$ solid ← liquid; liquid solidifies, since $\Delta G = \oplus$ve

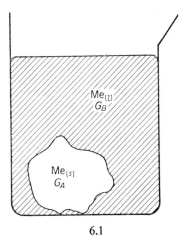

6.1

The condition for a dynamic equilibrium between the solid and the liquid metals is

$$G_A = G_B$$

and

$$dG_A = dG_B$$

The change in the free energy of either phase may be caused by the change in temperature and pressure of the phases. Thus

$$dG = f(T, p)$$

Mathematically the effects of temperature and pressure may be expressed as total differentials of dG_A and dG_B with respect to T and p. Thus

$$dG_A = \left(\frac{\partial G_A}{\partial T}\right)_p \cdot dT + \left(\frac{\partial G_A}{\partial p}\right)_T \cdot dp$$

and

$$dG_B = \left(\frac{\partial G_B}{\partial T}\right)_p \cdot dT + \left(\frac{\partial G_B}{\partial p}\right)_T \cdot dp$$

Since at equilibrium

$$dG_A = dG_B$$

$$\therefore \left(\frac{\partial G_A}{\partial T}\right)_p \cdot dT + \left(\frac{\partial G_A}{\partial p}\right)_T \cdot dp = \left(\frac{\partial G_B}{\partial T}\right)_p \cdot dT + \left(\frac{\partial G_B}{\partial p}\right)_T \cdot dp$$

Substituting equations 4.11 and 4.12 we have

$$-S_A \, dT + v_A \, dp = -S_B \, dT + v_B \, dp$$

On rearranging the terms it becomes

$$(v_B - v_A) \, dp = (S_B - S_A) \, dT$$

$$\therefore \qquad\qquad \Delta v \cdot dp = \Delta S \, dT$$

or

$$\frac{dp}{dT} = \frac{\Delta S}{\Delta v} \qquad\qquad \ldots(6.1)$$

The fusion of a metal is a thermodynamically reversible process, therefore entropy of fusion is given by

$$\Delta S_f = \frac{q_{\text{rev}}}{T} = \frac{L_f}{T_f} \qquad\qquad \ldots(6.2)$$

Thus (6.1) becomes on substitution of (6.2)

$$\frac{dp}{dT} = \frac{L_f}{T_f(v_B - v_A)} \qquad\qquad \ldots(6.3)$$

where q_{rev} = quantity of heat absorbed during fusion of 1 g mole of the substance

L_f = latent heat of fusion of 1 g mole or atom of a substance

v_B = its volume in the liquid state

v_A = its volume in the solid state

This equation is known as the Clausius-Clapeyron equation, and has been deduced here for a single chemical substance undergoing a change from one phase to another. This equation will also be applicable to liquid-vapour, solid-vapour transformation, and for transformations between two crystalline substances. In each case the appropriate latent heat and the volume changes have to be substituted into this equation. In every case L is the heat absorbed during the process and Δv is the accompanying volume change.

Example

Calculate (i) the elevation of the boiling point of zinc when the external pressure is 2 atmospheres, and (ii) the depression of the freezing point when the external pressure is 50 atmospheres. The latent heat of evaporation $L_e = 27\cdot3 \pm 04$ kcal g mole^{-1}, and the normal temperature of boiling T_e is 907°C. The corresponding latent heat of fusion L_f is 1.74 ± 0.03 kcal g mole^{-1}, and the normal temperature of fusion $T_f = 419.5°C$. The density of solid zinc is 7.0 g/cc and that of liquid zinc is 6.48 g/cc at 1 atm pressure.

(i) Using the Clausius-Clapeyron equation for this problem we have

$$\frac{dp}{dT} = \frac{\Delta p}{\Delta T} = \frac{L_e}{T_e(v_g - v_l)}$$

where v_g is the volume of 1 g atom of zinc vapour

v_l is the volume of 1 g atom of the liquid

To solve this problem we have also to know the values of the volume of 1 g atom of zinc in the vapour and liquid states. The volume occupied by 1 g atom of a perfect gas at s.t.p. is 22,400 cc. The volume occupied by 1 g atom of liquid zinc =

$$= \frac{65.38}{6.48} = 10.09 \text{ cc}$$

The volume of one g atom of zinc vapour at 907'C =

$$= \frac{22,400(907 + 273)}{273} \text{ cc}$$

Substituting these values into the Clausius-Clapeyron equation we obtain

$$\Delta T = \frac{\Delta p T_e(v_g - v_l)}{L_e} = \frac{1 \times 1.01325 \times 10^6 \times (907 + 273)^2 \times 22,400}{27,300 \times 4.18 \times 10^7 \times 273}$$

Thus

$$\Delta T = 100°C$$

The elevation of the boiling point of zinc subjected to an increase of the external pressure from 1 atm to 2 atm of pressure is 100°C.

(ii) Since the volumes of 1 g atom of zinc in the liquid and solid state are not given, they must be calculated from the atomic weight of zinc and its density in the two states. From physics we know that volume is equal to mass over density. Thus

$$v = \frac{\text{mass}}{\text{density}} \text{ and in this problem } v_l = \frac{65.38}{6.48}; \; v_s = \frac{65.38}{7.0}$$

Substituting these values into the main equation we get

$$T = \frac{50 \times 692.5 \times \left(\frac{65.38}{6.48} - \frac{65.38}{7.0}\right) \times 1.01325 \times 10^6}{1,740 \times 4.1845 \times 10^7}$$

$$\therefore \quad \Delta T = 0.432°C$$

The depression of the freezing point of liquid zinc subjected to 50 atmospheres of pressure is 0·432°C.

6.2.1 Duhring's Rule for the Estimation of the Vapour Pressures of an Element[4]

Duhring's Rule enables us to calculate the vapour pressure of an element from an empirical formula. According to this rule **the ratio of the absolute temperatures at which the vapour pressure of two similar substances are the same is a constant.** To illustrate this rule consider the case of zinc and cadmium. Their normal respective boiling temperatures are

$$T_{B_{Zn}} = 1,180°K$$

$$T_{B_{Cd}} = 1,038°K$$

Example

The vapour pressure of zinc at the temperature of 610°K is equal to 10^{-5} mmHg.

Calculate the temperature at which the vapour pressure of cadmium will be the same.

Using Duhring's Rule

$$\frac{T_{B_{Cd}}}{T_{B_{Zn}}} = \frac{1,038}{1,180} = \frac{T_{Cd}}{610}$$

Answer: $T_{Cd} = 535°K$.

6.2.2 Solid-Solid Equilibrium

The Clausius-Clapeyron equation also allows us to calculate the effect of pressure on solid-solid transformation temperatures.

Let us consider for example the effect of pressure on the transformation of $Fe_\beta \rightarrow Fe_\gamma$: $\Delta H_{1,183} = 215$ cal g atom^{-1} of iron, and multiplication by 0·0241 is required to convert to the units cc atm.

The molal volume change $= \dfrac{55·85}{7·633} - \dfrac{55·85}{7·571} = 0·060$ cc g atom^{-1}

$$\frac{\Delta T}{\Delta p} = \frac{1,183 \times 0·060 \times 0·02421}{215} = 0·0082 \text{ deg atm}^{-1}$$

Answer: One atmosphere of pressure alters the transformation point by 0·0082°C.

6.2.3 Integration of Clausius-Clapeyron Equation

The form of the Clausius-Clapeyron equation which has been used up till now enables us to calculate only the changes in either pressure with temperature or the latent heat of solid-solid, solid-liquid, solid-gas, and liquid-gas transformations. This equation in its present form does not allow us to calculate the absolute value of pressures and temperatures for a given system. This equation becomes of a much wider application when transformed into a form suitable for integration. In this section more suitable forms of this equation will be deduced.

The First Way of Integrating this Equation. Let us consider first a case in which the following three assumptions are made:

(i) In the liquid-gas transformation the volume of a g atom of the final phase is so much greater than that of the initial phase, that the liquid volume may be neglected. This assumption is reasonable for example in the case of iron, where

$$v_{\text{liquid iron}} = 10 \text{ cc g atom}^{-1}$$

and

$$v_{\text{vapour iron}} = 22{,}400 \text{ cc g atom}^{-1}$$

(ii) The metallic vapour behaves ideally, i.e. so that $pv = RT$. This had been shown to be true for metallic vapours since the ratio $\dfrac{C_p}{C_v}$ for various metals is 1·67 (see p. 12).

(iii) The latent heat of transformation is constant over the range of pressures and temperatures considered.

Using the first assumption the Clausius-Clapeyron equation

$$\frac{dp}{dT} = \frac{L}{T(v_B - v_A)}$$

where v_A = initial volume

v_B = final volume

L = latent heat of transformation of 1 g mole of a substance

then becomes

$$\frac{dp}{dT} = \frac{L}{T \cdot v_B}$$

and since from (ii)

$$v_B = \frac{RT}{p_B}$$

then

$$\frac{dp}{dT} = \frac{L p_B}{R T^2} \qquad \qquad \ldots (6.4\ (a))$$

From assumption (iii) the equation can be written in a form suitable for integration

$$\int_{p_1}^{p_2} \frac{dp}{p} = \int_{T_1}^{T_2} \frac{L}{R} \frac{dT}{T^2}$$

where p_1 and p_2 are the initial and final pressures respectively, T_1 and T_2 the corresponding absolute temperatures.

On integration we obtain:

$$\left[\log_e p \right]_{p_1}^{p_2} = - \frac{L}{R} \left[\frac{1}{T} \right]_{T_1}^{T_2}$$

$$\log_e \frac{p_2}{p_1} = \frac{L}{R} \left[\frac{1}{T_1} - \frac{1}{T_2} \right] = \frac{L}{R} \left[\frac{T_2 - T_1}{T_1 T_2} \right] \quad \ldots (6.4 \ (b))$$

This equation allows us to calculate:

(a) the latent heat of the process, providing that p_2, p_1 and T_2, T_1 are known (see Fig. 6.2),

(b) the variation of the boiling point with change in vapour pressures providing p_1, p_2 and T_1 are known, or

(c) the value of p_2 providing T_1, T_2 and L are known within this temperature range.

Note: p_1 is the normal pressure for vapours (1 atm).

Equation (6.4 (a)) gives on integration

$$\log_e p = - \frac{L}{RT} + C$$

where $C = $ a constant

This form of equation is very useful, because when comparing it with the general equation for a straight line

$$y = mx + c$$

we can see that, if $\log_e p$ is plotted against $\frac{1}{T}$, the slope of the resulting straight line is equal to $- \frac{L}{R}$. Fig. 6.2 shows such plots for a number of metals of metallurgical interest. These plots are very useful in vacuum metallurgy. For example, in vacuum melting of high strength steels, manganese, which has a relatively high vapour pressure (see Fig. 6.2), has *either* to be added to the molten bath under an increased pressure of inert gas, *or* during the late stages of the vacuum refining process its loss has to be made good.

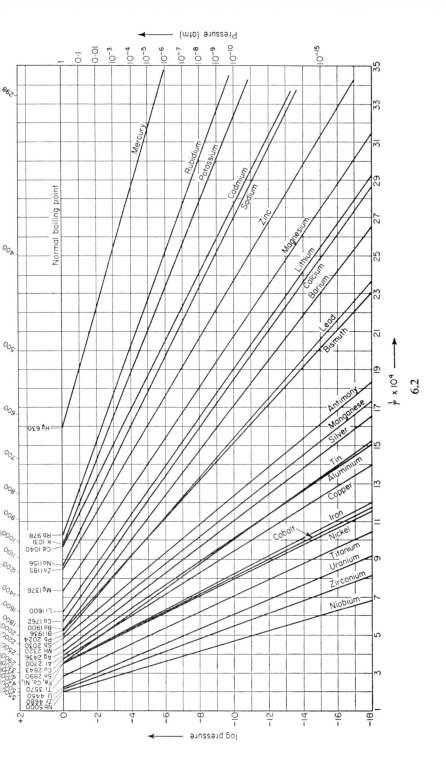

6.2

The Second Way of Integrating this Equation. Assume that in this case

(i) $v_{gas} \gg v_{liquid}$ or v_{solid},

(ii) the latent heat varies with temperature.

solid
or
liquid
gas

ΔH = heat of the transformation

Using the Kirchhoff's equation

$$\left(\frac{\partial \Delta H}{\partial T}\right)_p = \Delta C_p$$

we have

$$\Delta H = \int \Delta C_p \, dT \quad \text{or} \quad \Delta H = \Delta C_p \, T + A$$

Thus the Clausius-Clapeyron equation on substitution of this value for ΔH becomes

$$\frac{dp}{dT} = \frac{\Delta H p}{RT^2} \quad \text{or} \quad \int \frac{dp}{p} = \int \frac{\Delta H}{RT^2} \, dT$$

Thus

$$\int \frac{dp}{p} = \int \left(\frac{\Delta C_p T}{RT^2} + \frac{A}{RT^2}\right) . \, dT \qquad \ldots (6.5)$$

On integration the equation becomes

$$\log_e p = \frac{\Delta C_p}{R} \log_e T - \frac{A}{RT} + \text{a constant} \qquad \ldots (6.6)$$

The use of this form of Clausius-Clapeyron equation is necessary in cases where C_p varies considerably over the given range of temperatures. It is beyond the scope of this book to illustrate the use of this equation.

REFERENCES

1 PARTINGTON, J. R., *An Advanced Treatise on Physical Chemistry*, Vol. I, pp. 181–182, Longmans, Green & Co. Ltd., London, 1949.
2 CLAPEYRON, B. P. E., *J. de L'École Polytechnique*, 1834, **14**, 153.
3 CLAUSIUS, R., *Ann. Phys.*, 1850, **79**, 368.
4 DARKEN, L. S. and R. W. GURRY, *Physical Chemistry of Metals*, p. 303, McGraw-Hill Publishing Co. Ltd., London, 1953.

CHAPTER VII

Thermodynamics and Chemical Equilibria

7.1 INTRODUCTION

In any chemical reaction the reacting species (e.g. atoms, molecules, ions, etc.) are called the reactants, and the resulting species products.

Let us consider a reaction in which A and B are the reactants and C and D are the products. The chemical reaction can then be expressed by a chemical equation $A + B \rightleftarrows C + D$, where the upper arrow separating the reactants and products represents the forward and the lower arrow the reverse reaction. It is probable that all the chemical reactions take place in both directions, but in some cases the reverse reaction is so small that the forward reaction is said to proceed to completion, i.e. $A + B \rightarrow C + D$. In the majority of cases the extent to which the reaction proceeds depends on the temperature. For instance, at room temperature when two parts of hydrogen react with one part of oxygen (reaction being induced by an electric spark) there is a complete conversion of the reactants into products. If the same reaction is carried out for example at 2,000°C it is found that it does not proceed to completion, and even after a prolonged time the proportions of hydrogen, oxygen, and water vapour remain constant, provided the temperature and pressure are not altered. The reaction thus reaches a state of chemical equilibrium, and can be described by the following equation:

$$2H_2 + O_2 \rightleftarrows 2H_2O$$

There are two possible reasons for this equilibrium; either (i) the chemical reaction has ceased completely and the composition of the system remains constant, or (ii) rates of the forward and the reverse reactions become equal and a **dynamic equilibrium** is reached. Since at the same temperature and pressure the same ratio of reactants to products is obtained when we start with the pure products alone (e.g. H_2O at 2,000°C), it can be concluded that the equilibrium is dynamic.

7.2 THE LAW OF MASS ACTION AND THE EQUILIBRIUM CONSTANTS

The Law of Mass Action was formulated in a very general form by C. M. Guldberg and P. Waage.[1,2] This states that **the velocity of a reaction at a given temperature is proportional to the product of the active masses of the reacting substances.**

To illustrate this law let us consider an equilibrium reaction

$$A + B \leftrightharpoons C + D$$

where products C and D are formed from reactants A and B. According to this law the rate of the forward reaction is proportional to the product of the active masses of A and B. Thus the forward rate is proportional to [A][B] where [A] and [B] are concentrations in g moles per litre, or

$$v_1 = k_1 . [A][B]$$

Similarly the rate of the reverse reaction is

$$v_2 = k_2 . [C][D]$$

where v_1 = rate of the forward reaction

        v_2 = rate of the reverse reaction

k_1 and k_2 = proportionality constants

Since the equilibrium is a **dynamic** one in which the rate of the forward reaction is equal to the rate of the reverse reaction, then we have

$$v_1 = v_2$$

or

$$k_1[A][B] = k_2[C][D]$$

and thus

$$\frac{k_1}{k_2} = \frac{[C][D]}{[A][B]} = K$$

where K = the equilibrium constant of the reaction at constant temperature

In general for any reversible reaction, e.g.

$$aA + bB \rightleftharpoons cC + dD$$

$$K_c = \frac{[C]^c[D]^d}{[A]^a[B]^b} \qquad \qquad ...(7.1)$$

These concentration terms refer to the values at equilibrium. K_c is the concentration equilibrium constant at a constant temperature.

The value of K_c is temperature dependent. The equilibrium constant is always written with the resultants in the numerator and the reactant concentrations in the denominator. The significance of the constants a, b, c and d will be appreciated by considering the chemical reaction described by C. L. de Berthollet (1801),[3] which occurs in solution,

$$Na_2CO_3 + CaCl_2 \rightleftharpoons CaCO_3 + 2NaCl$$
$$aA \qquad bB \qquad cC \qquad dD$$

Here the values of a, b and c are equal, and the value of d is two.

These values denote the number of molecules shown in a balanced chemical equation of the reaction.

Thus for this example

$$K_c = \frac{[C]^c[D]^d}{[A]^a[B]^b} = \frac{[CaCO_3]^1 \times [NaCl]^2}{[Na_2CO_3]^1 \times [CaCl_2]^1}$$

Since K_c is constant at a given temperature, it follows that, if the concentration of, say, sodium chloride is increased, then the concentration of calcium carbonate must automatically decrease to form sodium carbonate and calcium chloride, until a dynamic equilibrium is once again reached.

In general three equilibrium constants may be used in reactions, according to the ways in which concentrations are expressed. These are (i) K_p the pressure equilibrium constant, (ii) K_c the concentration equilibrium constant, and (iii) K_N the molal equilibrium constant. Their use depends on the system under investigation. Generally speaking all reactions can be subdivided into **homogeneous (one phase only)** and **heterogeneous (more than one phase)**.

7.2.1 *Equilibrium Constants in Gaseous Reactions*

All three equilibrium constants may be used in gaseous reactions.

The pressure equilibrium constant K_p is expressed in terms of the partial pressures of the gaseous reactants and products.

For example in the reaction $aA + bB \rightleftharpoons cC + dD$ if the partial pressures at equilibrium are p_A, p_B, p_C and p_D respectively, then, providing each gas obeys the ideal gas law, the following relationship holds between their partial pressures at equilibrium:

$$K_p = \frac{p_C^c \cdot p_D^d}{p_A^a \cdot p_B^b} \qquad \qquad \ldots(7.2)$$

7.2.2 The Relationship between K_p and K_c

The concentration equilibrium constant K_c can be obtained by substituting into the equation (7.1) the values C_A, C_B, C_C and C_D, the concentration terms of the gases at equilibrium. Thus

$$K_c = \frac{C_C^c C_D^d}{C_A^a C_B^b} \qquad \ldots (7.3)$$

The relationship between K_c and K_p can then be obtained for perfect gases from the equation of state; since $pv = RT$ for 1 g mole of each gas, and $C = \dfrac{1}{v}$ (i.e. the number of g moles per unit volume).

$$\therefore \qquad p \times \frac{1}{C} = RT \quad \text{or} \quad p = RTC$$

where C = concentration of a gas in a mixture of gases.

For the reactants A, B, etc. the partial pressure is given by

$$p_A = RTC_A \quad \text{and} \quad p_B = RTC_B, \text{ etc.}$$

Replacing each of the partial pressure terms in equation (7.2) we have

$$K_p = \frac{(C_C RT)^c (C_D RT)^d}{(C_A RT)^a (C_B RT)^b} = \frac{(C_C^c)(C_D^d)(RT)^{(c+d)}}{(C_A^a)(C_B^b)(RT)^{(a+b)}}$$

$$K_p = \frac{C_C^c C_D^d}{C_A^a C_B^b} (RT)^{(c+d)-(a+b)} = \frac{C_C^c C_D^d}{C_A^a C_B^b} (RT)^n$$

where $n = (c + d) - (a + b)$ or the total number of g moles of products minus the total number of g moles of reactants; or

$$K_p = K_c (RT)^n \qquad \ldots (7.4)$$

It is clear from this equation that when the total number of molecules of reactants is equal to the total number of molecules of products, then $K_p = K_c$ since when $n = 0$ then $(RT)^n = (RT)^0 = 1$; however, when $n \neq 0$ then $K_p \neq K_c$.

7.2.3 The Relationship between K_p and K_N

The partial pressure of any gas in a mixture of gases is given by the product of the total pressure and the mole fraction of that gas. The mole fraction of a gas is equal to the number of g moles of the gas divided by the total number of g moles in the mixture.

Let p_A be the partial pressure of gas A, and n_A its number of g moles in the mixture. Let P be the total pressure of the mixture and N the total number of g moles of all the gases in the mixture.

Then

$$p_A = \frac{n_A}{N} P; \quad p_B = \frac{n_B}{N} P$$

$$p_C = \frac{n_C}{N} P \quad \text{and} \quad p_D = \frac{n_D}{N} P$$

where

$$N = n_A + n_B + n_C + n_D$$

For a reaction $aA + bB \rightleftharpoons cC + dD$,

$$K_p = \frac{p_C^c \cdot P_D^d}{p_A^a \cdot P_B^b} = \frac{n_C^c \cdot n_D^d}{n_A^a \cdot P_B^b} \cdot \frac{P^{(c+d)}}{P^{(a+b)}}$$

$$\therefore \qquad K_p = K_N \cdot P^{(c+d)-(a+b)} = K_N \cdot P^n \qquad \ldots(7.5)$$

where

$$n = (c + d) -\!\cdot (a + b)$$

It is clear from this equation that when the number of molecules on the left-hand side is equal to that on the right-hand side then $K_p = K_N = K_c$. Otherwise K_N will depend on the total pressure of the system. This molal equilibrium constant for gases is the only constant that enables us to calculate the effect of pressure on the equilibrium of gases at a constant temperature.

7.3 THE VAN'T HOFF ISOTHERM[4]

The majority of chemical reactions are studied at constant temperature and pressure. The **Van't Hoff Isotherm** is therefore extremely useful, since it correlates the Gibbs free energy change for a reaction at a given temperature with its equilibrium constants (K_p, K_c, K_N), the initial conditions of reactants, and the final conditions of the products. This equation is therefore used either to calculate the equilibrium constants when ΔG is known or ΔG from the equilibrium constants. It also leads to the definition of the standard free energy change $\Delta G°$. The modern trend in thermodynamics is to derive this equation via the chemical potentials. However, it is felt that its derivation using a hypothetical *reaction box* offers some advantages to metallurgists, by making the physical meaning of this equation more clear when using it for calculations involving high temperature reactions. It also enables more emphasis to be given to the significance of a certain correction term in this equation.

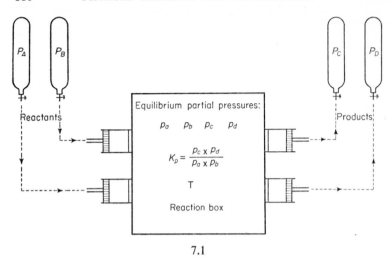

7.1

Consider a chemical reaction between two ideal gases A and B (reactants) which are allowed to react at a constant temperature to form C and D (products). This reaction may be written as follows:

$$A + B \rightleftharpoons C + D$$

Let the initial pressures of the gases A and B, kept separately, be P_A and P_B (Fig. 7.1).

Let us assume that the final pressures of the products considered separately from each other are P_C and P_D. The reaction box can be imagined as an enormous container containing a very large amount of the various gases at temperature T and already at equilibrium. Consider for convenience that the reaction is carried out in the following four distinct steps.

First Step. Take one g mole of gas A at the initial pressure P_A and bring it isothermally under reversible conditions to p_a, the partial pressure of this gas in the enormous reaction box. Using equation (2.10) but substituting pressures for volumes we find that the Gibbs free energy change of the process is given by

$$\Delta G_{1_A} = -w = RT \log_e \frac{p_a}{P_A}$$

Change also under the same conditions the pressure of 1 g mole of gas B from $P_B \rightarrow p_b$. We have then

$$\Delta G_{1_B} = RT \log_e \frac{p_b}{P_B}$$

The free energy change for the two gases during this step is given by

$$\Delta G_1 = \Delta G_{1_A} + \Delta G_{1_B} = RT \log_e \frac{p_a p_b}{P_A P_B}$$

Second Step. Now introduce each of the two gases under reversible isothermal conditions into the reaction box.* Since the pressures of either of the gases A or B will not be altered, and since they are ideal, no work is done during this step, and thus there is no change in free energy,

$$\Delta G_{II} = 0$$

Third Step. Remove separately one g mole of gas C and D from the box under reversible and isothermal conditions without actually changing their pressures (p_c and p_d). This is similar to the second step and thus

$$\Delta G_{III} = 0$$

Fourth Step. Change the pressures of one g mole of C and D reversibly and isothermally from the equilibrium pressures p_c and p_d to P_C and P_D, that is to the final pressures of the products of this process. In a similar way to the first step the free energy change is given by

$$\Delta G_{IV} = RT \log_e \frac{P_C P_D}{p_c p_d}$$

The total free energy change during this reaction is the sum of the free energy changes of the four steps. Thus

$$\Delta G = \Delta G_I + \Delta G_{II} + \Delta G_{III} + \Delta G_{IV}$$

Substituting for ΔG_I and ΔG_{IV} we have

$$\Delta G = RT \log_e \frac{p_a p_b}{P_A P_B} + RT \log_e \frac{P_C P_D}{p_c p_d}$$

rearranging the terms we obtain

$$\Delta G = RT \log_e \frac{p_a p_b}{p_c p_d} + RT \log_e \frac{P_C P_D}{P_A P_B}$$

Since the equilibrium constant of this reaction is given by

$$K_p = \frac{p_c p_d}{p_a p_b}$$

* Either by a suitable diffusion mechanism or by any other physical means.

therefore the term of the above equation includes K_p when the sign of the term is changed. Thus

$$\Delta G = -RT \log_e \frac{p_c p_d}{p_a p_b} + RT \log_e \frac{P_C P_D}{P_A P_B} \qquad \ldots(7.6)$$

or

$$\Delta G = -RT \log_e K_p + RT \log_e \frac{P_C P_D}{P_A P_B} \qquad \ldots(7.7)$$

Equation (7.7) has been known since 1886 as the Van't Hoff Isotherm.

Let us consider equation (7.7) in more detail. This equation consists of two terms. The first term contains R, T and K_p, which are all constants at a constant temperature T. The second term contains the initial pressures P_A and P_B of the reactants and the final pressures P_C and P_D of the products. Since these pressures can possess any value from very low to very high, it is clear that the second term is a variable one, which depends entirely on the conditions at which a reaction is carried out.

Thus we can write

$$\Delta G = \text{a constant value} + \text{a variable value} \qquad \ldots(7.8)$$

This equation is applicable to any reaction.

7.3.1   The Gibbs Standard Free Energy Change of a Process $\Delta G°$

From equation (7.8) it can be seen that the value of ΔG or the Gibbs free energy change of a reaction at a constant temperature T depends on the value of the second term. The value of free energy change at temperature T for a reaction in which all the reactants and products are in their standard states (unit activity or 1 atmosphere pressure) is known as the standard free energy change.

Thus from (7.7)

$$\Delta G = -RT \log_e K_p + RT \log_e \frac{1 \times 1}{1 \times 1}$$

and since $\log_e 1 = 0$, therefore

$$\Delta G = -RT \log_e K_p = \Delta G°$$

where $\Delta G°$ denotes the standard free energy change for a reaction occurring at a constant temperature T.

The Van't Hoff Isotherm may then be rewritten as

$$\Delta G = + \Delta G^{\circ} + RT \log_e \frac{P_C P_D}{P_A P_B} \qquad \dots(7.9)$$

| a constant term at a constant temperature | a variable term called the "correction term" |

For a reversible reaction in which various numbers of g moles of reactants and products take part, as in the equation

$$aA + bB \rightleftharpoons cC + dD$$

then the second term in the isotherm becomes

$$RT \log_e \frac{P_C^c \cdot P_D^d}{P_A^a \cdot P_B^b}$$

Thus equation (7.9) becomes

$$\Delta G = \Delta G^{\circ} + RT \log_e \frac{P_C^c P_D^d}{P_A^a P_B^b} \qquad \dots(7.10)$$

7.4 THE EFFECT OF TEMPERATURE ON THE EQUILIBRIUM CONSTANT OF A REACTION; VAN'T HOFF'S ISOCHORE

In many industrial processes it is necessary to know how the equilibrium constant of a reaction varies with temperature. From this knowledge it is possible to balance the economics of temperature requirements and the optimum yield of a process. **Van't Hoff's isochore** allows us to calculate the effect of temperature on the equilibrium constant.

Consider an equilibrium reaction

$$aA + bB \rightleftharpoons cC + dD$$

The free energy change of this reaction at the temperature T is given by equation (7.10)

$$\Delta G = -RT \log_e K_p + RT \log_e \frac{P_C^c \cdot P_D^d}{P_A^a \cdot P_B^b}$$

On differentiating this equation with respect to temperature at constant pressure, and assuming that K_p is temperature dependent, we have

$$\left(\frac{\partial \Delta G}{\partial T}\right)_p = -R \log_e K_p - RT \left(\frac{\partial \log_e K_p}{\partial T}\right)_p$$
$$+ R \log_e \frac{P_C^c \cdot P_D^d}{P_A^a \cdot P_B^b} + RT \left(\frac{\partial \log_e \frac{P_C^c P_D^d}{P_A^a P_B^b}}{\partial T}\right)_p$$

The fourth term on the right-hand side is zero, since

$$\log_e \frac{P_C^c P_D^d}{P_A^a P_B^b}$$

is constant at constant pressures. Therefore

$$\left(\frac{\partial \Delta G}{\partial T}\right)_p = -R \log_e K_p - RT \left(\frac{\partial \log_e K_p}{\partial T}\right)_p + R \log_e \frac{P_C^c P_D^e}{P_A^a P_B^b}$$
$$\ldots(7.11)$$

Substituting for $\left(\dfrac{\partial \Delta G}{\partial T}\right)_p$ the value from equation (7.11) into equation (4.13) we have

$$\Delta G = \Delta H + T \left[-R \log_e K_p - RT \left(\frac{\partial \log_e K_p}{\partial T}\right)_p + R \log_e \frac{P_C^c \cdot P_D^d}{P_A^a \cdot P_B^b} \right]$$

Solving the terms in the bracket gives

$$\Delta G = \Delta H - RT \log_e K_p - RT^2 \left(\frac{\partial \log_e K_p}{\partial T}\right)_p + RT \log_e \frac{P_C^c P_D^d}{P_A^a P_D^d}$$

The sum of the second and the fourth term on the right-hand side of this equation is equal to ΔG; thus

$$\Delta H - RT^2 \left(\frac{\partial \log_e K_p}{\partial T}\right)_p = 0$$

or

$$\left(\frac{\partial \log_e K_p}{\partial T}\right)_p = \frac{\Delta H}{RT^2} \qquad \ldots(7.12)$$

and for a very small change in temperature this equation becomes

$$\frac{d \log_e K_p}{dT} = \frac{\Delta H}{RT^2} \qquad \ldots(7.13)$$

This equation is known as the Van't Hoff isochore and is expressed by means of the pressure equilibrium constant K_p and the enthalpy change of the reaction ΔH.

7.4.1   *The Van't Hoff Isochore and Le Chatelier Principle*

The influence of changes in the conditions of a system on the position of its equilibrium can be predicted qualitatively from the principle of Le Chatelier (1884), which can be stated as:

if a constraint be imposed on a system in equilibrium, then the system will undergo readjustments which tend to nullify the constraint.

To illustrate this principle let us consider the effect of temperature on the equilibrium constant of an exothermic reaction

$$Me + O_2 \rightleftharpoons MeO_2 + Q; \Delta H = \ominus ve$$

When the temperature of this reaction is increased, i.e. heat is added into the reaction, then some of the MeO_2 will go into Me and O_2 and thus decrease the amount of heat. It follows therefore that the value of K_p will be less with increased temperature. This qualitative conclusion based on the Le Chatelier principle can be calculated quantitatively from the Van't Hoff isochore.

Let us consider the equation (7.13)

$$\frac{d \log_e K_p}{dT} = \frac{\Delta H}{RT^2}$$

For an exothermic reaction the value of ΔH is negative, therefore the higher the temperature T, the smaller the value of K_p.

7.4.2   *Integration of the Van't Hoff Isochore*

The simplest way of integrating this equation is to assume that the enthalpy change of the given reaction is constant within the considered temperatures. Thus

$$\frac{d \log_e K_p}{dT} = \frac{\Delta H}{RT^2}$$

can be rewritten in the integral form as

$$\int_{K_{p_1}}^{K_{p_2}} d \log_e K_p = \frac{\Delta H}{R} \int_{T_1}^{T_2} \frac{dT}{T^2} \qquad \ldots(7.14)$$

where K_{p_1} and K_{p_2} are the equilibrium constants at temperatures T_1 and T_2.

On integration, the equation (7.14) becomes

$$\log_e \frac{K_{p_2}}{K_{p_1}} = -\frac{\Delta H}{R} \left[\frac{1}{T} \right]_{T_1}^{T_2} = -\frac{\Delta H}{R} \left[\frac{1}{T_2} - \frac{1}{T_1} \right] = \frac{\Delta H}{R} \left[\frac{1}{T_1} - \frac{1}{T_2} \right]$$

$$\therefore \qquad \log_e \frac{K_{p_2}}{K_{p_1}} = \frac{\Delta H}{R} \left[\frac{1}{T_1} - \frac{1}{T_2} \right]$$

This equation is useful when either one value of K_p, e.g. K_{p_1} at the temperature T_1, and the value of enthalpy change ΔH of this reaction are known, since then it is possible to calculate K_{p_2}; or when the ratio $\dfrac{K_{p_2}}{K_{p_1}}$ is known for temperatures T_1 and T_2, from which the value of ΔH can be calculated.

REFERENCES

1 GULDBERG, C. M. and P. WAAGE, *Études sur les affinités chimique*, Brogger and Christie, Christiania, 1867.
2 An interesting account of this law is given by W. J. MOORE, *Physical Chemistry*, second edition, pp. 69–70, Longmans, Green & Co. Ltd., London, 1956.
3 BERTHOLLET, C. L. de, *Essai de statique chimique*, 1801.
4 VAN'T HOFF, *K. Svensk. Vet. Akad. Handl.*, 1886, **21**, No. 17, 1–58.

CHAPTER VIII

Thermodynamics of Solutions

8.1 INTRODUCTION

A **solution** may be defined as a **homogeneous phase composed of different chemical substances, whose concentration may be varied without the precipitation of a new phase.** It differs therefore from a mixture by its homogeneity, and from a compound by being able to possess variable composition. It is worth noting that this definition allows for the existence of gaseous, liquid and solid solutions.

In this chapter, although only liquid solutions will be discussed, most of the thermodynamic considerations will apply also to solid and gaseous solutions.

If a system is composed of only two chemical substances (elements or compounds) it is called a **binary solution.** For example when molten cadmium is added to molten zinc they are miscible in all proportions and they form a binary solution (or system). The substance which is present in the larger quantity is usually called the **solvent** and the substance added to the solvent is the **solute.** Thus, if cadmium is being added to zinc, it is the solute and zinc is the solvent. But it is purely arbitrary in this case, since zinc could be added to cadmium and one could obtain exactly the same composition of zinc in cadmium as before.

The composition of the solution can be expressed in a number of ways, but in metallurgy it is usually expressed either as percentage concentration by weight, or as molal or atomic percentage. In aqueous solutions, besides those two already mentioned, molar and molal concentrations are often used.

Percentage by Weight is the ratio of the weight of solute (w_2) to the total weight of both solvent (w_1) and solute expressed on a percentage basis. Thus the

$$\text{percentage of solute} = \left(\frac{w_2}{w_1 + w_2}\right) \times 100 \qquad \ldots(8.1)$$

For example, if a solution contains 25 g of cadmium and 75 g of

117

zinc, then the percentage by weight of cadmium is

$$\left(\frac{25}{25 + 75}\right) \times 100 = 25\%$$

Molecular Percentage or Atomic Percentage is the ratio of the number of g moles of solute to the total number of g moles of all the substances comprising the solution expressed on a percentage basis. To illustrate this way of expressing the concentration let us recalculate the cadmium–zinc alloy in terms of atomic percentage:

$$Cd\text{——}w_2 \text{ (solute)} = 25 \text{ g}$$

$$Zn\text{——}w_1 \text{ (solvent)} = 75 \text{ g}$$

The atomic weight of cadmium $\qquad = 112\cdot41$

The atomic weight of zinc $\qquad\qquad = 65\cdot38$

$\therefore$ The number of g atoms of cadmium $= \dfrac{25}{112\cdot41} = n_{Cd}$

The number of g atoms of zinc $\quad = \dfrac{75}{65\cdot38} = n_{Zn}$

The atomic percentage of cadmium $= \left(\dfrac{n_{Cd}}{n_{Cd} + n_{Zn}}\right) \times 100$

$$= \left(\frac{\dfrac{25}{112\cdot41}}{\dfrac{25}{112\cdot41} + \dfrac{75}{65\cdot38}}\right) \times 100 = 16\cdot25\%$$

The atomic percentage of zinc $\qquad = 83\cdot75\%$

In general the molecular percentage of a component A weighing w_A and molecular weight M_A in a mixture containing w_B of component B and molecular weight M_B is given by

$$\text{Molecular percentage of } A = \left(\frac{\dfrac{w_A}{M_A}}{\dfrac{w_A}{M_A} + \dfrac{w_B}{M_B}}\right) \times 100 \quad \ldots(8.2)$$

Mole Fractions are frequently used in theoretical work because many physical properties of solutions are expressed most simply in terms of the relative numbers of molecules. The mole fraction may be defined as **the number of g moles of a substance divided by the total number of g moles of all the substances comprising the solution.** Thus

$$N_A = \frac{n_A}{n_A + n_B} \quad \text{and} \quad N_B = \frac{n_B}{n_A + n_B}$$

where n_A and n_B are the number of g moles of the components A and B, and N_A and N_B are the mole fractions of A and B in the solution. The sum of the mole fractions of all the components must always be equal to one, e.g.

$$N_A + N_B = \frac{n_A}{n_A + n_B} + \frac{n_B}{n_A + n_B} = \frac{n_A + n_B}{n_A + n_B} = 1$$

There are other ways of expressing concentration of solutions and these are given below*

8.2   IDEAL SOLUTIONS

Ideal solutions have to a certain degree similar properties to ideal gases. They are characterised by the absence of an attractive or repulsive force between the components of the solution, and this results in: (i) no change in internal energy on dilution, (ii) no heat effect on mixing, and (iii) their physical properties being additive. Thus the resulting volume of the solution is simply the sum of the separate volumes of the two liquids, and any particular property can be calculated by taking its average for the components that make up the solution.

In thermodynamics we are frequently concerned with the thermo-dynamic properties of a particular component in a solution, and these properties are expressed by so-called **Partial Molal Quantities,** such as, for example, partial molal volume, entropy, enthalpy, free energy, chemical potential, etc.

8.2.1   *Partial Molal Quantities*

In calculations regarding solutions it is desirable to know how a particular property of the solution varies with the addition of the separate constituents. Since a particular property can be referred only to a particular composition of the solution, the change of

---

* **Molar solutions** contain 1 g mole of solute in one litre of solution. This way of expressing concentration of a solution is mainly used for chemical solutions employed in volumetric analysis and corrosion.

Normal solutions contain 1 g equivalent weight of the solute dissolved in one litre of solution.

Molal solutions contain 1 g mole of the solute in 1,000 g of the solvent.

the property, for example the volume, must be described as a rate of change when an infinitesimal quantity of the constituent is added.

To illustrate the meaning of partial molal quantities let us consider the partial molal volumes of a binary mixture consisting of components A and B. This solution of a definite composition will occupy a definite volume at a constant temperature and pressure. This volume may be imagined to consist of the volume occupied by the A molecules and the volume occupied by B molecules. The volume occupied by one g mole of A in this solution is the partial molal volume of A and is denoted by $\bar{V}_A$. In this concentration the only variable is the composition of the solution, since the temperature and pressure are constant.

This concept of partial molal volumes is expressed mathematically by

$$\bar{V}_A = \left(\frac{\partial V}{\partial n_A}\right)_{T,P,B} \quad \text{and} \quad \bar{V}_B = \left(\frac{\partial V}{\partial n_B}\right)_{T,P,A} \quad \ldots(8.3)$$

Here $\bar{V}_A$ represents the rate of increase in volume of the solution when an infinitesimal amount of dn_A g moles of A is added, and the amount of B, temperature and pressure are kept constant throughout. Using equation (8.3) it is convenient now to calculate the change in volume (ΔV) when small amounts dn_A and dn_B of A and B are added simultaneously to the solution. Thus

$$\Delta V = \bar{V}_A \, dn_A + \bar{V}_B \, dn_B \quad \ldots(8.4)$$

Since the values of $\bar{V}_A$ and $\bar{V}_B$ depend only on the composition of the solution, and, if the constituents are added simultaneously in the same proportion as they are present in the solution, i.e. in the proportion of n_A g moles of A to n_B g moles of B, then

$$V = \bar{V}_A N_A + \bar{V}_B N_B \quad \ldots(8.5)$$

where V is then the volume occupied by one g mole of that solution and N_A and N_B are the mole fractions of A and B in the solution.

Equation (8.5) shows that the volume of one g mole of the solution is equal to the sum of the products of mole fractions and molal volumes of all the constituents (see also page 123).

8.2.2 Gibbs-Duhem Equation

In equation (8.5) the molal volumes and mole fractions vary with concentration, thus on differentiation of equation (8.5) one obtains

$$dV = N_A \, d\bar{V}_A + \bar{V}_A \, dN_A + N_B \, d\bar{V}_B + \bar{V}_B \, dN_B$$

From equation (8.4) it follows that the sum of the second and fourth terms on the right-hand side is equal to dV, therefore

$$N_A \, d\bar{V}_A + N_B \, d\bar{V}_B = 0 \qquad \ldots(8.6)$$

This equation is one form of the Gibbs-Duhem equation expressed in terms of the partial molal volumes. It is frequently rearranged to give

$$d\bar{V}_A = -\frac{N_B}{N_A} \, d\bar{V}_B \qquad \ldots(8.7)$$

The Gibbs-Duhem equation may be used for the calculation of any other partial molal quantities such as entropy, enthalpy, free energy, etc.

Thus the partial molal entropy for component A can be evaluated from the knowledge of the composition of the solution (N_A and N_B) and the value for component B.

Thus

$$d\bar{S}_A = -\frac{N_B}{N_A} \, d\bar{S}_B \qquad \ldots(8.8)$$

Similarly

$$d\bar{H}_A = -\frac{N_B}{N_A} \, d\bar{H}_B \qquad \ldots(8.9)$$

and

$$d\bar{G}_A = -\frac{N_B}{N_A} \, d\bar{G}_A \qquad \ldots(8.10)$$

The partial molal free energy is also called the **chemical potential** and it is denoted by the symbol μ and was first proposed in 1875 by Gibbs.[1]

Thus equation (8.6) in terms of partial molal free energies and chemical potentials becomes

$$N_A \, d\bar{G}_A + N_B \, d\bar{G}_B = 0 \qquad \ldots(8.11)$$

$$N_A \, d\mu_A + N_B \, d\mu_B = 0 \qquad \ldots(8.12)$$

The variation of partial molal free energy or chemical potential with temperature and pressure can be expressed by the same equations as those derived for the free energy change.

Thus from equations (4.9) and (4.10) we have

$$\left(\frac{\partial \bar{G}_A}{\partial T}\right)_{P,B} = \left(\frac{\partial \mu_A}{\partial T}\right)_{P,B} = -\bar{S}_A \qquad \ldots(8.13)$$

$$\left(\frac{\partial \bar{G}_A}{\partial p}\right)_{T,B} = \left(\frac{\partial \mu_A}{\partial p}\right)_{T,B} = \bar{V}_A \qquad \ldots(8.14)$$

and

$$\left(\frac{\partial \overline{H_A}}{\partial T}\right)_{P,B} = \bar{C}_{p_A} \qquad \ldots(8.15)$$

Since the Gibbs-Duhem equation shows that in solutions at equilibrium the sum of the products of the appropriate mole fractions and the partial molal quantities are equal to zero, therefore during thermodynamic calculations it is convenient to use these functions, just as in the calculations of pure substances use is made of the thermodynamic functions.

8.2.3   Integral and Partial Molal Quantities

The difference between the integral and partial molal quantities of a solution can be conveniently illustrated from equation (8.5). Thus in this equation

$$V = \bar{V}_A N_A + \bar{V}_B N_B$$

the value V, which is the total volume of the system containing mole fractions N_A and N_B, is the integral volume, whereas the values $\bar{V}_A$ and $\bar{V}_B$ are the partial molal volumes of A and B. Note that the integral volume does not equal the sum of the partial volumes, i.e.

$$V \neq \bar{V}_A + \bar{V}_B$$

Similarly it can be shown that the free energy change of solution is

$$\Delta G = N_A \Delta \bar{G}_A + N_B \Delta \bar{G}_B = N_A \Delta \mu_A + N_B \Delta \mu_B \quad \ldots(8.16)$$

8.2.4   Graphical Determination of Partial Molal Quantities

In theoretical metallurgy one may be concerned with the determination of partial molal quantities, for example partial molal heat $\bar{H}$, partial molal free energy $\bar{G}$ (which is the same as chemical potential μ), etc. There are several methods which allow us to determine these quantities, either by calculation, or by extrapolation from suitable graphs.[2]

A very convenient method is to plot molal quantities against concentration expressed in mole fractions of one of the components. To obtain the partial molal quantities at any required concentration a tangent is drawn to the curve at this concentration, and the partial

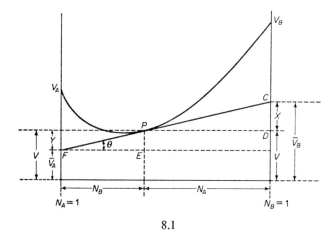

8.1

molal quantities are given by the intersections of the tangent with axis at $N_A = 1$ and $N_B = 1$ (Fig. 8.1).

Since this graphical method has been found convenient, especially in physical metallurgy in the study of the coexistence of phases (see Chap. X) and is known as the tangency rule, it is intended to consider it in some detail. Any of the integral quantities can be used to explain this method, but here partial molal volumes have been chosen since these are easy to imagine. In Fig. 8.1 the volume V of 1 g mole of a binary alloy composed of A and B is plotted against its composition expressed in mole fractions.

V is given by equation (8.5) in terms of mole fractions and partial molal volumes:

$$V = N_A \bar{V}_A + N_B \bar{V}_B$$

at constant T_1, P_1, and

$$N_A + N_B = 1$$

This mathematical expression can be represented in words as follows:

The volume occupied by 1 g mole of the alloy at concentration N_A and N_B	=	Mole fraction of A multiplied by its partial molal volume	+	Mole fraction of B multiplied by its partial molal volume

or

The volume occupied by 1 g mole of the alloy at concentration N_A and N_B	=	The volume occupied in the alloy by the mole fraction of A	+	The volume occupied in the alloy by the mole fraction of B

Thus $N_A \bar{V}_A$ can be regarded as the contribution of the component A to the total volume of the alloy and $N_B \bar{V}_B$ the contribution of the component B.

Rearranging the above equation we have

$$V - N_B \bar{V}_B = N_A \bar{V}_A \qquad \ldots(8.17)$$

Since $\bar{V}_B$ is the rate of change of the volume of the alloy when an infinitesimal amount of B is added and the composition of the alloy remains constant, then

$$\left(\frac{\partial V}{\partial N_B}\right)_{P, T, N_A + N_B = 1} = \bar{V}_B$$

which is the slope of the tangent at the point P in Fig. 8.1. But the slope is given by

$$\tan \theta = \frac{X}{N_A} = \frac{Y}{N_B} \qquad \ldots(8.18)$$

since the triangles PCD and PEF are similar. Substituting (8.18) into (8.17) we obtain

$$V + X = N_B \bar{V}_B$$

$$V - N_B \cdot \frac{Y}{N_B} = N_A \bar{V}_A \quad \text{or} \quad V - Y = N_A \bar{V}_A \qquad \ldots(8.19)$$

The partial molal volume of A is equal to the volume contribution of N_A when $N_A = 1$.

Thus equation (8.19) becomes $V - Y = \bar{V}_A$ or from Fig. 8.1 the intersection of the tangent of the axis $N_A = 1$ gives the partial molal volume of component A. Similarly, the intersection with the axis at $N_B = 1$ of the same tangent gives the value of $\bar{V}_B$.

Let us take a closer look at Fig. 8.1, since it illustrates very clearly the difference between partial molal volumes and molar volumes. Thus V_A is the molar volume of A, that is the volume occupied by 1 g mole of A when it is in its pure state. $\bar{V}_A$ is the partial molal volume that 1 g mole of A occupies in an alloy having a composition N_A and N_B.

$$\therefore \quad \bar{V}_A = V - N_B \left(\frac{\partial V}{\partial N_B}\right) \qquad \bar{V}_B = V + (1 - N_B)\left(\frac{\partial V}{\partial N_B}\right)$$

The determination of partial molal volumes will be illustrated using the cadmium–magnesium binary system at 25°C.

Example

Determine the partial molal volumes of cadmium and magnesium in $N_{Mg(0.3)} - N_{Cd(0.7)}$ and in $N_{Cd(0.4)} - N_{Mg(0.6)}$ alloys at 25°C using the data given in the following table[3]:

N_{Mg}	V_{Cd-Mg} ideal cm³ g mole⁻¹	ΔV cm³ g mole⁻¹	V_{Cd-Mg} experimental cm³ g mole⁻¹
0·1	13·05	0	13·05
0·2	13·11	−0·2	12·91
0·3	13·17	−0·43	12·74
0·4	13·23	−0·58	12·65
0·5	13·29	−0·64	12·65
0·6	13·35	−0·58	12·77
0·7	13·41	−0·53	12·88
0·8	13·47	−0·4	13·07
0·9	13·53	−0·22	13·31

Figure 8.2 was plotted using the data shown in the above table. The molal volumes of Cd–Mg alloys were plotted against their atomic mole fractions. The partial molal volumes of cadmium and magnesium ($\bar{V}_{Cd}$ and $\bar{V}_{Mg}$ respectively) were obtained from the intersections of the y axis at N_{Cd} and $N_{Mg} = 1$ by the tangents drawn to points A and B (see Fig. 8.2). The $\bar{V}_{Mg(0.3)}$ is found from Fig. 8.2 to be 11·89 cm³ g atom⁻¹, and that for cadmium at $Cd_{(0.7)}$ is 13·1 cm³ g atom⁻¹. Similarly the partial molal volumes for $Mg_{(0.6)}$ is found to be 13·18 cm³ g atom⁻¹, and that for $Cd_{(0.4)}$ is 12·05 cm³ g atom⁻¹.

This example also illustrates very clearly the difference between the meaning of molal volume, partial molal volume and atomic (molar) volume.

8.3   THE VAPOUR PRESSURE OF IDEAL SOLUTIONS—RAOULT'S LAW

One of the most fundamental properties of a substance is the tendency for its atoms or molecules to pass into the surrounding space. The result of this property is the observed vapour pressure of liquids and solids. In Section 8.2 it was mentioned that the vapour pressure of ideal solutions can be calculated simply from the knowledge of the vapour pressures of the pure components and their

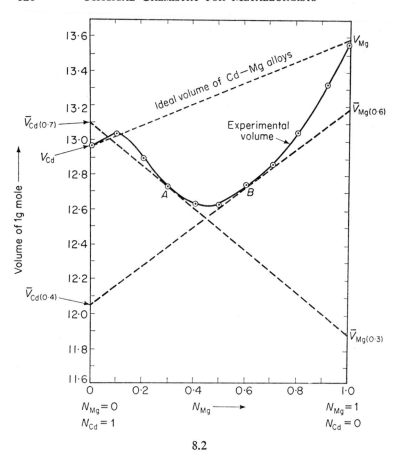

8.2

mole fractions. In an ideal solution therefore the total pressure P is the sum of the partial vapour pressures of the components:

$$P = p_A + p_B + p_C + \ldots + p_N$$

where the p_A, p_B, etc., are the partial vapour pressures of the components A, B, etc.

The partial vapour pressures of each of the components depends on its mole fraction (e.g. N_A for the component A, which is responsible for the vapour pressure p_A).

Raoult's Law. Raoult (1886) showed that for ideal solutions the partial vapour pressure of a component was equal to the product of

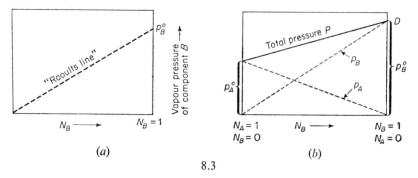

8.3

its mole fraction and the vapour pressure of the pure component at the same temperature.

Thus for a binary mixture consisting of A and B components at a constant temperature

$$p_A = \frac{n_A}{n_A + n_B} \cdot p_A^{\circ}$$

where p_A is the partial vapour pressure of the component A in the solution and p_A° is the vapour pressure of A in its pure state at the same temperature; n_A is the number of g moles of A and n_B the g moles of B in the solution. Since

$$\frac{n_A}{n_A + n_B} = N_A$$

thus

$$p_A = N_A p_A^{\circ} \quad \text{and} \quad p_B = N_B p_B^{\circ}$$

or

$$P = N_A p_A^{\circ} + N_B p_B^{\circ}$$

Figure 8.3 (a) shows **Raoult's Line** for component B in the alloy AB. Fig. 8.3 (b) shows graphically Raoult's relationship between the partial pressures of A and B and the resultant total pressure P. The broken line $N_A D$ is Raoult's vapour pressure line for component B.

8.4 THE ELEVATION OF BOILING POINT BY A NON-VOLATILE SOLUTE

When a solute is added to a solvent the vapour pressure of the solvent is lowered (see Fig. 8.4).

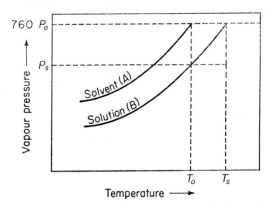

8.4. A = *Vapour pressure temperature curve for the solvent.*
B = *Vapour pressure temperature curve for the solution.*

The normal boiling point is the temperature at which the vapour pressure of the solvent or solution is equal to the atmospheric pressure of 760 mm mercury.

The boiling temperatures for the solvent and solutions at a constant pressure of 1 atmosphere are denoted in Fig. 8.4 by T_O and T_S respectively. The temperature difference $T'_S - T_O = \Delta T$ gives the elevation of the boiling point of the solvent.

Raoult's law enables us to express the relationship between depression of the vapour pressure and the concentration of the solution. For the system under consideration the vapour pressure composition curve at a constant temperature is shown in Fig. 8.5. If n_A and n_B are the number of g moles of A and B respectively, then

$$N_A = \frac{n_A}{n_B + n_A} \quad \text{and} \quad N_B = \frac{n_B}{n_B + n_A}$$

The difference in the pressure between the solvent and the solution is equal to $p^\circ_A - p_S$. From the similarity of triangles $p^\circ_A C p_S$ and $p^\circ_A B A$ it follows that

$$\frac{p^\circ_A - p_S}{p^\circ_A} = \frac{N_B}{N_A + N_B} = N_B$$

since

$$N_A + N_B = 1$$

The effect of the decrease in the vapour pressure of this solution dp and the change in the temperature of boiling dT can be evaluated

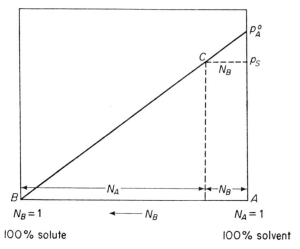

8.5. $A = Solvent.$ $B = Non-volatile\ solute.$

from the Clausius-Clapeyron equation

$$\frac{dp}{dT} = \frac{L_e}{T(v_v - v_l)} \qquad \ldots(8.20)$$

where L_e is the molar latent heat of evaporation of the solvent; v_v and v_l are the volumes of 1 g mole of the solvent in the vapour and in the liquid states respectively.

Since the volume of the liquid v_l is much smaller than that of the vapour, it may be neglected. For dilute solutions one can also consider that the latent heat of evaporation is independent of solute concentration, and is equal to that for the pure solvent. It is also assumed that the vapour obeys the ideal gas law. Thus

$$\frac{dp}{dT} = \frac{L_e}{Tv_v}$$

but since $v_v p = RT$

$$\therefore \qquad v_v = \frac{RT}{p}$$

Then

$$\frac{dp}{dT} = \frac{L_e p}{RT^2}$$

$$\therefore \qquad \frac{dp}{p} = \frac{L_e\, dT}{RT^2} \qquad \ldots(8.21)$$

Let the vapour pressure of the pure solvent be p_A° at its normal boiling point T_A°, and let the depressed vapour pressure of the solution be p_S and the new boiling point T_S. Using these values as integration limits in equation (8.21) we obtain

$$\int_{p_S}^{p_A^{\circ}} \frac{dp}{p} = \frac{L_e}{R} \int_{T_A^{\circ}}^{T_S} \frac{dT}{T^2}$$

Integrating,

$$\log_e \left[p \right]_{p_S}^{p_A^{\circ}} = -\frac{L_e}{R} \left[\frac{1}{T} \right]_{T_A^{\circ}}^{T_S}$$

we obtain

$$\log_e \frac{p_A^{\circ}}{p_S} = \frac{L_e}{R} \left[\frac{1}{T_A^{\circ}} - \frac{1}{T_S} \right]$$

or

$$\log_e \frac{p_A^{\circ}}{p_S} = \frac{L_e}{R} \left[\frac{T_S - T_A^{\circ}}{T_A^{\circ} \cdot T_S} \right] = \frac{L_e}{R} \cdot \frac{\Delta T}{T_A^{\circ} T_S} \qquad \ldots(8.22)$$

This gives

$$\Delta T = \frac{R}{L_e} T_A^{\circ} \cdot T_S \cdot \log_e \frac{p_A^{\circ}}{p_S} \qquad \ldots(8.23)$$

This equation correlates the vapour pressures of the solvent and solution and the latent heat of evaporation of the solvent L_e with the elevation of the boiling point of the solution (ΔT).

However, in practice it is of more interest to correlate the concentration of the solution with its boiling point. Fig. 8.5, which shows the Raoult's vapour pressure concentration curve for a solution, allows us to correlate the mole fraction concentration of the solution with its vapour pressure. But, before we attempt to do that, let us rearrange the left-hand side of the equation (8.22) into the more useful form of

$$\log_e \frac{p_A^{\circ}}{p_S} = \log_e \left(1 + \frac{p_A^{\circ} - p_S}{p_S} \right)$$

Now since $\log_e (1 + x) = x$ when x is small—then the above equation becomes

$$\log_e \left(1 + \frac{p_A^{\circ} - p_S}{p_S} \right) = \frac{p_A^{\circ} - p_S}{p_S}$$

since the solution is very dilute therefore $p_S = p_A^{\circ}$ and thus

$$\log_e \frac{p_A^{\circ}}{p_S} = \frac{p_A^{\circ} - p_S}{p_A^{\circ}} \qquad \ldots(8.24)$$

From Fig. 8.5 it follows that

$$\frac{p_A^\circ - p_S}{p_A^\circ} = \frac{N_B}{N_A + N_B} = N_B = \log_e \frac{p_A^\circ}{p_S}$$

Equation (8.22) can now be written as

$$\log_e \frac{p_A^\circ}{p_S} = N_B = \frac{L_e}{R}\left(\frac{1}{T_A^\circ} - \frac{1}{T_S}\right) \qquad \ldots (8.25)$$

And since we have assumed that the solution is very dilute then $T_A^\circ = T_S$ and $T_A^\circ T_S = (T_A^\circ)^2$. The equation (8.25) then becomes

$$N_B = \frac{L_e}{R} \times \frac{\Delta T}{(T_A^\circ)^2} \qquad \ldots (8.26)$$

or

$$\Delta T = N_B \times \frac{R}{L_e} \times (T_A)^2 \qquad \ldots (8.27)$$

for very dilute solutions.

8.5 DEPRESSION OF FREEZING POINT AND SIMPLE APPLICATION TO A LIQUIDUS LINE

The amount by which the freezing point of a solution is depressed below that of the pure solvent for a given solute concentration can be calculated from the vapour pressure of the solution and solvent at the normal freezing point of the solvent and the latent heat of fusion of the solvent. Let us consider a graph showing the vapour pressures of the solvent and solution (Fig. 8.6).

The curve AB represents the variation of vapour pressure of the solid solvent with increasing temperature. BC represents the vapour pressure of the solvent. AED represents the vapour pressure curve of the solution at a constant concentration.

The point of intersection of the vapour pressure curves of the solvent and the solid gives the temperature of fusion T_f, and p_1° is the normal vapour pressure of the pure solvent. The vapour pressure of the solution at that temperature is p_3. The temperature of freezing of the solution T_1 is the temperature of intersection of the vapour pressure curves of the solid and the solution, and the vapour pressure of the solution is then p_2.

The variation of the vapour pressure of the solid with temperature is expressed by the simplified Clausius-Clapeyron equation

$$\frac{dp}{p} = \frac{L_s}{R}\frac{dT}{T^2}$$

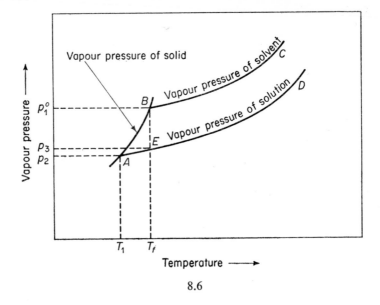

8.6

where L_s = molecular latent heat of sublimation of the solid:

$$\text{solid} \xrightarrow{\;L_s\;} \text{vapour}$$

Assuming that the metallic vapour obeys the ideal gas law and that the latent heat remains constant between T_1 and T_f, equation (8.21) can be integrated between the limits p_2 and p_1°, and thus an expression is obtained correlating the temperature T_1 and T_f with the respective vapour pressures.

Thus

$$\int_{p_2}^{p_1^\circ} \frac{dp}{p} = \frac{L_s}{R} \int_{T_1}^{T_f} \frac{dT}{T^2}$$

$$\therefore \qquad \log_e \frac{p_1^\circ}{p_2} = - \frac{L_s}{R} \left[\frac{1}{T_f} - \frac{1}{T_1} \right]$$

$$\therefore \qquad \log_e \frac{p_1^\circ}{p_2} = \frac{L_s}{R} \left[\frac{1}{T_1} - \frac{1}{T_f} \right] \qquad \qquad \dots(8.28)$$

Assuming then that the same equation holds for the solution, that its vapour pressure changes from p_2 to p_3 for an increase in temperature from T_1 to T_f, and that the latent heat of evaporation of the solvent is L_e, then

$$\int_{p_2}^{p_3} \frac{dp}{p} = \frac{L_e}{R} \int_{T_1}^{T_f} \frac{dT}{T^2}$$

∴

$$\log_e \frac{p_3}{p_2} = -\frac{L_e}{R} \left[\frac{1}{T_f} - \frac{1}{T_1} \right]$$

∴

$$\log_e \frac{p_3}{p_2} = \frac{L_e}{R} \left[\frac{1}{T_1} - \frac{1}{T_f} \right] \qquad \ldots(8.29)$$

By subtracting equation (8.29) from (8.28) one obtains a relationship involving only p_1 and p_3, which can be related to the depression of the vapour pressure of the solvent on addition of solute.

Thus

$$\log_e \frac{p_1^\circ}{p_2} - \log_e \frac{p_3}{p_2} = \frac{L_s}{R} \left[\frac{1}{T_1} - \frac{1}{T_f} \right] - \frac{L_e}{R} \left[\frac{1}{T_1} - \frac{1}{T_f} \right]$$

on rearranging we obtain

$$\log_e \frac{p_1^\circ}{p_3} = \left(\frac{L_s - L_e}{R} \right) \left[\frac{1}{T_1} - \frac{1}{T_f} \right] \qquad \ldots(8.30)$$

The value of the difference between the latent heat of sublimation and evaporation for a given substance can be shown to be equal to the latent heat of fusion by applying Hess's Law.

Thus

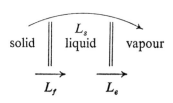

$$\text{solid} \quad \| \quad \text{liquid} \quad \| \quad \text{vapour}$$

Thus from Hess's Law it follows that $L_s = L_f + L_e$ or

$$L_s - L_e = L_f \qquad \ldots(8.31)$$

Substituting (8.31) into (8.30) we obtain

$$\log_e \frac{p_1^\circ}{p_3} = \frac{L_f}{R} \left[\frac{1}{T_1} - \frac{1}{T_f} \right] \qquad \ldots(8.32)$$

From Fig. 8.5 remembering that $p_A^\circ = p_1^\circ$ and $p_S = p_3$ it follows that

$$\log_e \frac{p_1^\circ}{p_3} = \log_e \left(\frac{N_A + N_B}{N_A} \right) = \log_e \left(1 + \frac{N_B}{N_A} \right) \quad \ldots(8.32\text{A})$$

When the mole fraction of B (N_B) is small, that is to say, the solution is very dilute, then

$$\log_e \left(1 + \frac{N_B}{N_A} \right) = \frac{N_B}{N_A} \simeq \frac{N_B}{N_A + N_B} \simeq N_B \quad \text{and} \quad T_f \simeq T_1$$

Equation (8.32) becomes then

$$N_B = \frac{L_f}{R} \left[\frac{1}{T_1} - \frac{1}{T_f} \right] = \frac{L_f}{R} \cdot \frac{\Delta T}{(T_f)^2}$$

or

$$\Delta T = N_B \cdot \frac{R}{L_f} \cdot (T_f)^2 \qquad \qquad \ldots (8.33)$$

When N_B becomes larger the assumption $N_A = N_A + N_B$ is no longer true; thus

$$\Delta T = \frac{N_B}{N_A} \cdot \frac{R}{L_f} \cdot (T_f)^2 \qquad \qquad \ldots (8.34)$$

At even greater concentrations the left-hand side of equation (8.32) has to be written as shown in equation (8.32A), and then we have

$$\log_e \frac{p_1^\circ}{p_3} = \log_e \left(\frac{N_A + N_B}{N_A} \right) = \frac{L_f}{R} \left[\frac{1}{T_1} - \frac{1}{T_f} \right]$$

Since $N_A + N_B = 1$, therefore

$$\log_e \frac{1}{N_A} = \frac{L_f}{R} \left[\frac{1}{T_1} - \frac{1}{T_f} \right] \quad \text{or} \quad \log_e N_A = \frac{L_f}{R} \left[\frac{1}{T_f} - \frac{1}{T_1} \right] \quad \ldots (8.35)$$

In these equations ΔT represents the lowering of the freezing point of the pure solvent to that of the solution containing a mole fraction N_B of the solute; L_f is the molar latent heat of fusion of the solvent.

It is worth noting that in the derivation of these equations it was assumed that Raoult's Law was obeyed, and that the latent heats of the solutions were the same as those of the pure solvent and independent of temperatures. Obviously in many cases, especially for more concentrated solutions, these assumptions may not be true. The following example will illustrate the usefulness of the equations (8.33) and (8.34) in the calculation of the liquidus curve of the Bi–Pb binary alloy.

Example
Calculate the liquidus line of the bismuth–lead equilibrium phase diagram on the bismuth rich side. The normal freezing point of

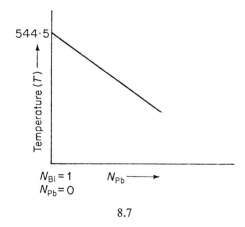

8.7

bismuth is $544 \cdot 5°K$ $(T_{f_{Bi}})$, and its atomic latent heat of fusion 2,600 cal g atom^{-1} $(L_{f_{Bi}})$. Assume that there is no solid solubility of lead in bismuth, and that they are completely soluble in their liquid states. Let us tentatively draw the diagram (Fig. 8.7). At low concentrations of lead in bismuth equation (8.33) should be applicable and as there is no solid solubility, thus the latent heat of fusion will remain constant, while the depression of the vapour pressure of the molten bismuth will be small.

Let us first calculate the depression of the freezing point for a solution containing $N_{Pb} = 0 \cdot 1$. Since $L_{f_{Bi}} = 2,600$ cal g atom^{-1}, $T_{f_{Bi}} = 544 \cdot 5°K$, and $R \simeq 2$ cal deg^{-1} g atom^{-1}, then on substitution of these values into equation (8.33) we have

$$\Delta T = 0 \cdot 1 \times \frac{2}{2,600} \times (544 \cdot 5)^2 = 22 \cdot 8°K \text{ or C}$$

This result shows that when the mole fraction of lead in bismuth is $0 \cdot 1$, which means there is 10 atomic per cent of lead in the solution, then the freezing point of this solution will be lower by $22 \cdot 8°$ either Kelvin or Centigrade, since the magnitude of one degree on either scale is identical.

Equation (8.33) is linear for a given system, and the value of ΔT depends only on the molal concentration of N_{Pb}. From this one calculation therefore all the other points can now be calculated using the equation shown below. Thus

$$\Delta T_{N_{Pb_x}} = X \cdot 22 \cdot 8° \qquad \qquad \ldots(8.36)$$

where X denotes the mole fraction of Pb in the bismuth–lead alloy.

A series of freezing points have been calculated from equation
(8.36) for various lead concentrations and are shown in Table 8.1.
For comparison, values obtained from equation (8.34) are also
included in this table.

TABLE 8.1

Values obtained from equations (8.33) and (8.36)

N_{Pb}	0·05	0·1	0·15	0·2	0·25	0·3	0·4
ΔT	11·4	22·8	34·2	45·6	57·0	68·4	91·2
T_x	533·1	521·7	510·3	498·9	487·5	476·1	453·3

Values obtained from equation (8.34)

N_{Pb}	0·05	0·1	0·15	0·2	0·25	0·3	0·4
N_{Bi}	0·95	0·9	0·85	0·8	0·75	0·7	0·6
ΔT	11·99	25·3	40·1	57·0	75·9	97·6	152
T_x	532·5	519·2	504·4	487·5	468·6	446·9	392·5

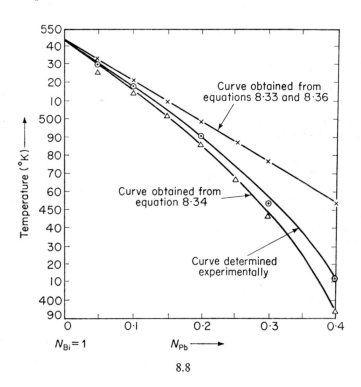

8.8

The calculated values for the depression of freezing points using the two different equations (8.33) and (8.34) are plotted, together with the values obtained experimentally, in Fig. 8.8. From the graph it is clear that the values calculated from equation (8.33) are very close to the experimental ones when N_{Pb} does not exceed 0·15; however, at higher concentrations the deviations become larger and at $N_{Pb} = 0·4$ the difference amounts to about 40°C. If on the other hand equation (8.34) is used, it is seen to be applicable over a much greater concentration range of the solutions, and even at $N_{Pb} = 0·3$ the calculated values are only 9 degrees, and at $N_{Pb} = 0·4$ about 16 degrees below the experimental ones.

From this simple application of the Clausius-Clapeyron equation for the calculation of the liquidus line it can be concluded that both these equations are useful, providing they are not used indiscriminately in the higher concentration range. Equation (8.34) was found to be applicable in this case to a wider range of concentrations; however, this is not necessarily so in other systems. More applications of these equations will be given in Chapter X when discussing the application of thermodynamics to phase diagrams.

8.6 CHEMICAL POTENTIAL OF IDEAL SOLUTIONS

The general equation of the free energy change of a system with temperature and pressure $dG = vdp - SdT$ did not take into account any variations in free energy due to concentration changes. The total free energy of a system must vary when small amounts of constituents dn_A, dn_B, etc., are introduced into a homogeneous solution. Thus the free energy of a system is dependent on four different variables or $G = f(T, P, V, n_i)$ where n_i denotes the addition of n molecules of a constituent i. The change in the free energy of the system can then be expressed by means of the total differential using any three of the four variables. Let us express any infinitesimal free energy change in terms of a change in temperature, pressure and composition. Then

$$dG = \left(\frac{\partial G}{\partial T}\right)_{P,n_j} dT + \left(\frac{\partial G}{\partial p}\right)_{T,n_j} dp + \sum \left(\frac{\partial G}{\partial n_i}\right)_{P,T} dn_i$$

Substituting into this equation the values for $\left(\frac{\partial G}{\partial T}\right)_P$ and $\left(\frac{\partial G}{\partial p}\right)_T$ (page 89) we obtain

$$dG = -S\,dT + V\,dp + \sum \left(\frac{\partial G}{\partial n_i}\right)_{P,T} dn_i \quad \ldots(8.36\text{A})$$

The coefficient $\left(\dfrac{\partial G}{\partial n_i}\right)_{P,T}$, first introduced by Gibbs, is called the **chemical potential** and is denoted by the symbol μ. Thus

$$\left(\frac{\partial G}{\partial n_i}\right)_{P,T} = \mu_i$$

Equation (8.36A) now becomes

$$dG = -S\,dT + V\,dp + \Sigma\mu_i\,dn_i \qquad \ldots(8.37)$$

At constant temperature and pressure the first two terms in equation (8.37) are equal to zero. If the system is at equilibrium then $dG = 0$ and thus

$$\Sigma\mu_i\,dn_i = 0 \qquad \ldots(8.38)$$

To illustrate the physical meaning of the term *chemical potential* let us consider the change in free energy (dG) of a system produced by the addition of dn_A of component A at constant pressure and temperature. The change in free energy of the system is given then by

$$dG = \mu_A\,dn_A = \bar{G}_A\,dn_A$$

where $\bar{G}_A$ is the partial molal free energy of the component A.

From this equation it follows that the chemical potential of either 1 g atom or 1 g mole of a substance dissolved in a solution of a definite concentration is its partial molal free energy. Thus

$$\left(\frac{\partial G}{\partial n_A}\right)_{P,T} = \bar{G}_A = \mu_A$$

8.6.1   *Calculation of Chemical Potentials in Ideal Solutions*

From the relationship $\Sigma\mu_i\,dn_i = 0$ (8.38) it is possible to predict whether a system will be at equilibrium under any specified conditions of temperature, pressure and concentration. In order to be able to use this equation it is necessary to obtain a relationship between the chemical potential and some easily measurable property of the system.

Let us consider first the possibility of calculating the chemical potential of a single gas in an ideal gaseous mixture, and then apply this result to other states of matter.

For a single substance it has already been shown that

$$\left(\frac{\partial G}{\partial p}\right)_T = V$$

It follows, therefore, that for a very small change of pressure dp, $dG = V\,dp$, but since $\bar{G} = \mu$ for 1 g mole of A then $d\mu = V\,dp$ and for 1 g mole of perfect gas

$$V = \frac{RT}{p}$$

so that

$$d\mu = RT\frac{dp}{p}$$

Integrating this expression we obtain

$$\mu = RT\log_e p + c \qquad \ldots(8.39)$$

where c is the integration constant.

At a pressure of 1 atm the first term on the right-hand side of this equation becomes zero, and the chemical potential is thus equal to the integration constant; under these conditions it is called **the standard chemical potential,** and is represented by the symbol μ°. μ° is a constant at a constant temperature but its actual value nearly always alters with the temperature. Equation (8.39) becomes then

$$\mu = \mu^\circ + RT\log_e p \qquad \ldots(8.40)$$

In a perfect gaseous mixture each component can be regarded as a separate entity, and therefore equation (8.40) is applicable to any component, providing the appropriate partial pressure of the component is taken. Thus the chemical potential of a component A in a gaseous mixture exerting partial vapour pressure p_A can be calculated from the equation

$$\mu_A = \mu_A^\circ + RT\log_e p_A$$

$$\therefore \qquad \Delta\mu_A = RT\log_e p_A \qquad \ldots(8.40\text{A})$$

Similarly for the component B we have

$$\Delta\mu_B = RT\log_e p_B \qquad \ldots(8.40\text{B})$$

Since $\Delta\mu$, similarly to the change in free energy of a system, is an extensive property, that is it depends on the quantity or mass of the system, therefore the total free energy change associated with the formation of 1 g mole of the composition of N_A and N_B (thus containing N_A g mole of the constituent A and N_B g mole of the constituent B) is the sum of the products of appropriate change in chemical potentials multiplied by the mole fractions of the components; thus

$$\Delta\mu_{\text{sol}} = \Delta G_{(1\text{ g mole solution})} = N_A \cdot \Delta\mu_A + N_B \cdot \Delta\mu_B \quad \ldots(8.41)$$

or, substituting for $\Delta\mu_A$ and $\Delta\mu_B$;

$$\Delta G_{(sol)} = RT(N_A \log_e p_A + N_B \log_e p_B)$$

and since

$$\left(\frac{\partial \Delta G}{\partial T}\right)_p = -\Delta S$$

therefore

$$\Delta S_{(sol)} = -R(N_A \log_e p_A + N_B \log_e p_B) \qquad \ldots(8.42)$$

Gibbs introduced the concept of chemical potential when he was considering the coexistence of various phases at equilibrium. This quantity can be regarded therefore as the **free energy change of solution** associated with dissolution of N_A g mole of the gas A and N_B g mole of the gas B in a mixture of A and B gases of the composition N_A and N_B. Thus equation (8.40) correlates the chemical potential of a gas at an arbitrary standard state with that at any other concentration in a gaseous mixture. This form of equation may also be used for liquid solutions, for, if a solution at a given temperature T is at equilibrium with its vapour, then the chemical potentials of each component in the gaseous phase and in the liquid phase must be equal. The partial pressure p_A of the component A in a binary solution of A and B can therefore be expressed in terms of its mole fraction N_A, since from Raoult's Law

$$p_A = N_A p_A^\circ$$

or

$$N_A = \frac{p_A}{p_A^\circ}$$

From (8.40) we obtain

$$\mu_A - \mu_A^\circ = \Delta\mu = \bar{G}_A - \bar{G}_A^\circ = RT \log_e \frac{p_A}{p_A^\circ} = RT \log_e N_A$$
$$\ldots(8.43)$$

where $\bar{G}_A^\circ$ is the free energy of one g mole of the component A in its standard state. Equation (8.43) then becomes for 1 g mole of a binary solution A and B and consisting of N_A and N_B mole fractions respectively

$$\Delta G = RT(N_A \log_e N_A + N_B \log_e N_B)$$

This equation[1] is applicable to liquid as well as to solid solutions.

8.6.2 *Activity, Fugacity and Chemical Potential in Non-Ideal Solutions*

From accurate measurements of the vapour pressures at constant temperature it was observed that binary solutions obeyed Raoult's

Law only at low concentrations, that is when the mole fraction of the solvent was approaching one. Otherwise some of these systems showed positive deviations (Fig. 8.9), and others negative deviations (Fig. 8.10). Since during the derivation of the thermodynamic formulae we have always assumed until now that the systems obeyed Raoult's Law and that the metallic vapours conformed to the ideal gas laws, it is clear that, in order to make these equations useful, corrections have to be made for the positive and negative deviations. Obviously this equation can still be used for dilute solutions, since from Figs. 8.9 and 8.10 it can be seen that at very low concentrations of the solute the solutions do in fact obey Raoult's Law.

Another difficulty was pointed out by Lewis[5] regarding the use of equation (8.40) for the calculation of the chemical potential of a gas approaching zero pressure, since the second term would then tend to a negative infinite value.

For this reason Lewis[5] proposed a new function which he called **fugacity** and which he related to the vapour pressure of a component in a way similar to that in which the perfect gas thermometer scale is related to any actual gas thermometer.[2]

The fugacity was therefore made equal to the vapour pressure when the vapour is a perfect gas and may be regarded as a "corrected" pressure.

It was shown that for ideal gaseous systems

$$G_{p_2} - G_{p_1} = \Delta G = RT \log_e \frac{p_2}{p_1}$$

where $\Delta G =$ the change in free energy of a gas when 1 g mole is expanded from pressure p_1 to p_2

$G_{p_1} =$ free energy of the system at p_1

$G_{p_2} =$ free energy of the system at p_2

dividing both sides by RT we obtain

$$\frac{G_{p_2}}{RT} - \frac{G_{p_1}}{RT} + \log_e p_1 = \log_e p_2$$

or

$$\log_e p_2 = \frac{G_{p_2}}{RT} + \log_e p_1 - \frac{G_{p_1}}{RT}$$

According to Lewis instead of p_2 and p_1 fugacity has to be used; thus

$$\log_e f_2 = \frac{G_{p_2}}{RT} + \log_e f_1 - \frac{G_{p_1}}{RT}$$

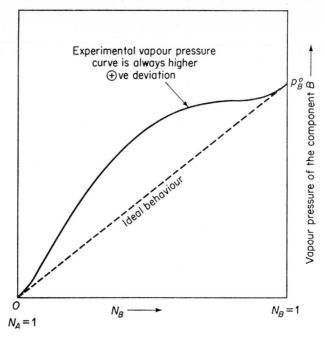

8.9. *Positive deviation: the experimental curve is always higher*

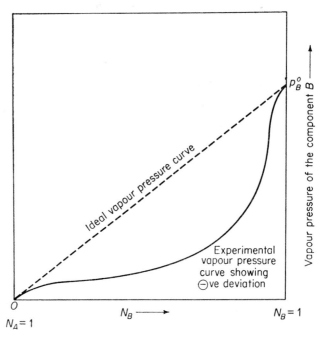

8.10. *Negative deviation: the experimental curve is always lower*

But in the limit at low pressure $f = p$, thus the above equation becomes

$$\log_e f_2 = \frac{G_{p_2}}{RT} + \lim_{p_1 \to 0} \left(\log_e f_1 - \frac{G_{p_1}}{RT} \right)$$

The second term on the right-hand side is constant at a constant temperature, and so on differentiation the above equation becomes

$$d \log_e f_2 = \frac{dG_{p_2}}{RT} \quad \text{at constant } T \qquad \ldots(8.44)$$

Equation (8.44) defines the fugacity and for any general case it can be written as

$$d \log_e f = \frac{dG}{RT} \qquad \ldots(8.45)$$

or

$$\Delta G = RT \log_e \frac{f}{f^\circ}$$

where f is the fugacity in a solution and f° in the standard state. This definition applies not only to real gases but also to liquids and solids[6] in equilibrium with their vapours.

The choice of the standard state is a matter of convenience, and for gases we usually take a gas at one atmosphere pressure to be in its standard state. For liquids and solids the fugacities of pure substances at a given temperature and one atmosphere external pressure are taken as standard states. However, in most cases of interest to us the partial pressures of solids and liquids are usually low enough for their vapours to be considered to obey the ideal gas laws, and therefore their fugacities are equal to their vapour pressures. Thus for example the standard fugacity f° for a pure metal A at the absolute temperature T and total external pressure 1 atm is equal to p_A°, that is $f_A^\circ = p_A^\circ$. If the partial vapour pressure for this metal in an alloy AB is p_A at the same temperature and total external pressure of 1 atm, then using equation (8.45) we can write

$$\Delta \bar{G}_A = RT \log_e \frac{p_A}{p_A^\circ} \qquad \ldots(8.46)$$

where $\Delta \bar{G}_A$ represents the partial molal free energy change when 1 g atom of pure A is dissolved in B to form an alloy of composition AB, at a constant temperature.

It is found convenient to denote the ratio $\frac{p_A}{p_A^\circ}$ in equation (8.46) by the symbol a which is called **activity**. Thus

$$a_A = \frac{p_A}{p_A^\circ}$$

where a_A is now activity of A in the alloy AB. This concept of activity is extremely useful, since it is now possible to correlate the activity of A and the concentration of A expressed by means of the mole fraction N_A.

From Raoult's Law we have $p_A = p_A^\circ N_A$ and thus for an ideal solution

$$\frac{p_A}{p_A^\circ} = N_A \qquad \ldots(8.47)$$

From equation (8.47) it follows that in an ideal solution the mole fraction of a component is equal to its activity. However, in a solution which departs from ideality the activity does not equal its mole fraction, that is $a_A \neq N_A$, since the vapour pressure of the solution at concentration N_A is different from that which one would expect from the ideal behaviour (see Fig. 8.11).

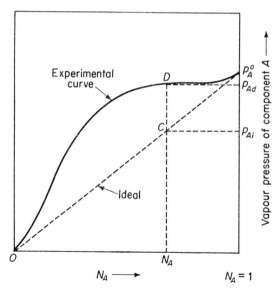

8.11. p_{Ad} = *Determined vapour pressure*. p_{Ai} = *Ideal vapour pressure for N_A mole fraction*

Thus from Fig. 8.11 $p_{Ad} \neq p_{Ai}$ but by definition

$$a_A = \frac{p_{Ad}}{p_A^\circ} \neq \frac{p_{Ai}}{p_A^\circ} = N_A$$

Again for convenience, a new coefficient γ is chosen which correlates the activity with the concentration of A expressed as a mole fraction. Thus

$$a_A = \gamma N_A \qquad \gamma = \frac{a_A}{N_A}$$

$$\gamma = \frac{\dfrac{p_{Ad}}{p_A^\circ}}{\dfrac{p_{Ai}}{p_A^\circ}} = \frac{p_{Ad} \cdot p_A^\circ}{p_{Ai} \cdot p_A^\circ} = \frac{p_{Ad}}{p_{Ai}}$$

The activity coefficient can be thus defined as the ratio of the vapour pressure of a component at a given temperature and concentration of the component to the vapour pressure this component actually would exert under the same conditions of temperature, pressure and concentration, if the solution behaved ideally.

Thus from Fig. 8.11 we see that

$$\gamma_A = \frac{N_A D}{N_A C} > 1$$

It is worth noting that for $\oplus$ve deviations of the vapour pressure curve the activity coefficient is greater than one, for the ideal behaviour it is equal to one, and for $\ominus$ve deviations it is less than one.

Applying the concept of activity we can use the thermodynamic equations for any non-ideal system, providing that in these equations we replace mole fractions by activities and partial pressures by fugacities.

Thus equation (8.45) becomes

$$\Delta \bar{G}_A = \Delta \mu_A = RT \log_e a_A \qquad \qquad \ldots (8.48)$$

and the free energy change of a solution consisting of mole fractions N_A and N_B is given by

$$\Delta G = RT(N_A \log_e a_A + N_B \log_e a_B)$$

similarly:

$$\Delta S = -R(N_A \log_e a_A + N_B \log_e a_B)$$

The Van't Hoff isotherm may be used for calculations involving non-ideal gaseous, liquid or solid solutions. For gases it becomes

$$\Delta G = -RT \log_e K_f + RT \log_e \frac{f_C^c \times f_D^d}{f_A^a \times f_B^b}$$

while for solids and liquids we have

$$\Delta G = -RT \log_e K_a + RT \log_e \frac{a_C^c \times a_D^d}{a_A^a \times a_B^b}$$

where K_a is the equilibrium constant expressed in terms of activities and K_f that expressed in terms of fugacities.

8.6.3 Raoultian and Henrian Activities

Raoultian Activity. In the previous sub-section we have learnt that for non-ideal solutions corrections have to be made for the departure from the ideal Raoult's Law. A new function called **activity** was therefore defined by means of equation (8.48). The pure substance (element or compound) was chosen as the standard state having unit activity. Mathematically this can be represented by $a_A = N_A$ when $N_A = 1$. In general it is found that in the majority of systems when mole fraction N_A tends to unity its activity is equal to its mole fraction. Thus we have, when $N_A \to 1$, then $a_A \to N_A$ in the region of $N_A = 0.9$ to 1 (see Fig. 8.11). In this region of concentrations the component A for all practical purposes obeys the Raoult's Law, and therefore in thermodynamic calculations we may simply substitute the mole fraction values for activities (i.e. the activity coefficient γ_A in the equation $a_A = \gamma_A \cdot N_A$ is taken as unity).

At any other concentrations the activity coefficient γ_A may be greater or less than unity. Since in all these cases the activity co-efficient (γ_A) is related to the Raoultian ideal behaviour line, it is called the **Raoultian Activity Coefficient.**

The activity of any component in a mixture depends upon the environment in which it is present. Forces of attraction or repulsion caused by the environment acting on the substance determine its activity. Let us now consider the physical significance of both Raoult's ideal and non-ideal behaviour of binary systems.

a. Raoult's ideal behaviour. If in a solution composed of substances A and B (atoms or molecules) the attractive forces between A and B are the same as between A and A or between B and B, then the activities of A and B in the solution at all concentrations will be equal to their mole fractions, and the solution is said to be ideal. The system Bi–Sn (see Fig. 8.12) can serve as an example of such a

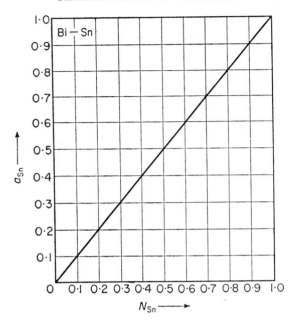

8.12. *From Kubaschewski and Evans,* Metallurgical Thermochemistry, *second edition, Pergamon Press Ltd., 1959.*

solution. Here the net attractive force between Bi and Sn in the solution (denoted by $\leftrightarrow$) can be represented by the following equation:

$$Bi \leftrightarrow Sn = \tfrac{1}{2}(Sn \leftrightarrow Sn + Bi \leftrightarrow Bi)$$

b. Positive deviations. When the net attractive force between the substances A and B is less than between A–A and B–B, then the solution of A and B exhibits positive deviations from Raoult's Law. In these cases the Raoultian activity is always greater than unity except when approaching the concentration of $N_A = 1$. Lead and zinc liquid solutions show such behaviour at temperatures above 1,071°K (see Fig. 8.13). At lower temperatures the activity-mole fraction plots are characterised by a region parallel to the x-axis, that is of constant activity. A constant activity region (see Fig. 10.9) indicates that within this range of concentrations there is a miscibility gap, and the zinc present will be distributed between two liquid phases; for example at 873°K one of composition $N_{Zn} = 0.23$ (lead rich) and the other of $N_{Zn} = 0.98$ (zinc rich) respectively. The heat of solution in systems showing positive deviations is endothermic.

6

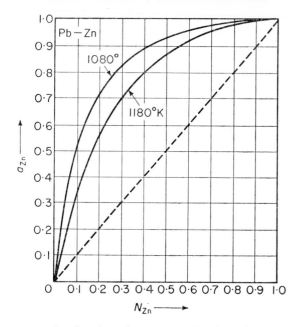

8.13. *From Kubaschewski and Evans,* Metallurgical Thermochemistry, *second edition, Pergamon Press Ltd.,* 1958

c. Negative deviations. Negative deviations occur when the attractive force between the two substances A and B is higher than between A–A and B–B. For example a magnesium–bismuth system shows such a behaviour (see Fig. 8.14). Negative deviations generally indicate a tendency for compound formation. The heat of solution for systems exhibiting negative deviation is usually exothermic.

Henrian Activity and Activity Coefficients. In many calculations it is not necessary to assume the standard state to be the pure substance. From Fig. 8.15 it is clear that in the concentration region of $N_A = 0$ to 0·1, that is to say at low concentrations of the component A, there is a marked difference between the value of N_A and a_A, the activity a is proportional to its mole fraction N_A, and the ratio $\dfrac{a_A}{N_A}$ is constant. This behaviour is analogous to *Henry's Law,* which refers to solubility of gases in liquids, and which states that the amount of dissolved gas by weight in a given volume of liquid at a constant temperature is proportional to its vapour pressure in contact with the liquid, providing there is no chemical reaction

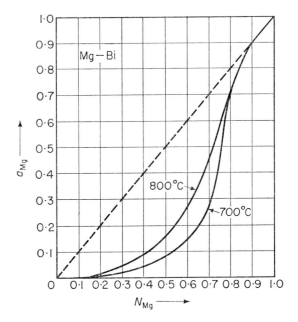

8.14. *From Kubaschewski and Evans,* Metallurgical Thermochemistry, *second edition, Pergamon Press Ltd., 1958*

between the gas and the liquid. Since the vapour pressure of the component A at these low concentrations is proportional (linear) to its mole fraction, it is said to obey Henry's Law. Thus $a_A^H = f_A \cdot N_A$ where a_A^H is the Henrian activity and the proportionality constant (f_A) is the **Henrian activity coefficient**, therefore

$$f_A = \frac{a_A^H}{N_A}$$

Henrian Activity and its Standard Reference States. There are various reference states which may be taken as standards for Henrian unit activity. Thus the Henrian activity may be taken as unity,

(i) when the solute concentration is one per cent by weight,

or (ii) when the concentration is one atomic per cent,

or (iii) when $N_A = 1$,

or (iv) for a molar (M) solution, i.e. when $M_A = 1$.

Because of the existence of these four possibilities it is always necessary to indicate the reference state in any calculation. The following Table 8.2 summarises the differences between Raoultian and Henrian activities and their coefficients.

TABLE 8.2

Activity	Standard State for Unit Activity	Activity Coefficient	Tendency Towards	Uses

Raoult's Law ($N_A = a_A$ when $N_A \to 1$)

| $a_A = \gamma_A \cdot N_A$ | $N_A = 1$: pure substance | $\gamma_A = \dfrac{a_A}{N_A}$ $= \dfrac{p_A}{\overset{\circ}{p}_A}$ | $\gamma_A > 1$: two phases, im- miscibility $\gamma_A < 1$: com- pound formation | Alloys, free energy/con- centration diagrams, vapour pressure calculations |

Henry's Law ($N_A = a_A$ when $N_A \to 0$)

$a_A^H = f_A \cdot \mathrm{Wt}\%$	1% by weight	$f_A = \dfrac{a_A^H}{\mathrm{Wt}\%}$		
$a_A^H = f_A \cdot \mathrm{At}\%$	1 atomic per cent	$f_A = \dfrac{a_A^H}{\mathrm{At}\%}$	$f_A > 1$: compound formation $f_A < 1$: two phases, immiscibility	Often applied in pro- duction processes
$a_A^H = f_A \cdot N_A$	pure sub- stance	$f_A = \dfrac{a_A^H}{N_A}$		
$a_A^H = \gamma_A \cdot M_A$	molar solution	$\gamma_A = \dfrac{a_A}{\text{molarity}}$		Aqueous electrolytes

Example

Using Fig. 8.15 showing the activity concentration curve for the component A, determined from vapour pressure measurements, obtain the relation between the Raoultian and Henrian activity scales.

The relations between the Raoultian and Henrian activity scales are shown in Fig. 8.15. In this case the activity of the component A shows a negative deviation from Raoult's Law. The solution $N_A = 0.2$ has a Raoultian activity of 0.10 and thus

$$\gamma_A = \frac{0.10}{0.2} = 0.5$$

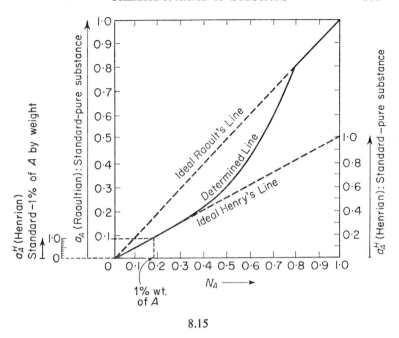

8.15

The Henrian activity value for the same concentration of A must be 0·2, since it lies on the ideal Henry's line, and for the Henrian activity coefficient we have $f_A = 1$. To convert from Henrian to Raoultian activity it is clear that we have to multiply the Henrian activity by 0·5 which is the slope of Henry's line.

Answer: Between $N_A = 0$ and $N_A = 0·35$ a_A (Raoultian) = a_A (Henrian) × 0·5. Solutions of $N_A = 0·35$ begin to deviate positively from Henry's Law and the conversion from Henrian to Raoultian activities requires knowledge of f_A and of the slope of the Henry's Law line.

8.6.4 *Activity Coefficients and Heat of Mixing of Regular Solutions*

In the case of non-ideal solutions the heat of mixing is no longer zero because there are heat changes due to changes in bonding energies. However, in cases where the deviation from ideality is small we can still assume random mixing, and thus the entropy of mixing (ΔS_m) is given by

$$\Delta S_m = -R(N_A \log_e N_A + N_B \log_e N_B)$$

Solutions of this type are called **regular solutions.** Since the free energy of mixing (ΔG_m) can be calculated from

$$\Delta G_m = RT(N_A \log_e a_A + N_B \log_e a_B) = \Delta H_m - T \cdot \Delta S_m$$

and

$$a_A = \gamma_A N_A \quad \text{and} \quad a_B = \gamma_B N_B$$

therefore on substitution we have

$$\Delta G_m = RT(N_A \log_e \gamma_A N_A + N_B \log_e \gamma_B N_B) = \Delta H_m - T \Delta S_m$$

and on rearrangement of this equation we have

$$\Delta H_m = T \cdot \Delta S_m + RT(N_A \log_e N_A + N_B \log_e N_B) + \\ + RT(N_A \log_e \gamma_A + N_B \log_e \gamma_B) \quad \ldots (8.49)$$

since

$$T \Delta S_m = -RT(N_A \log_e N_A + N_B \log_e N_B) \quad \ldots (8.50)$$

On substitution of (8.50) into (8.49) we have

$$\Delta H_m = RT(N_A \log_e \gamma_A + N_B \log_e \gamma_B) \quad \ldots (8.51)$$

Equation (8.51) shows that systems showing positive deviations from Raoult's Law have positive heats of mixing ΔH_m, that is to say the processes are endothermic. Similarly, systems exhibiting negative deviations have exothermic heats of mixing ($\Delta H_m = \ominus \text{ve}$).

8.6.5 *The Use of the Gibbs-Duhem Equation for Determination of Activity*

It is often difficult to measure the activity of both components in a binary mixture. The Gibbs-Duhem equation allows us to calculate the activity of one component, providing the activity of the other component is known. However, before this equation can be applied it has to be transformed into a convenient form. From equation (8.12) we have the following expression for a binary mixture A and B.

$$N_A \, d\mu_A + N_B \, d\mu_B = 0$$

Using equation (8.40A),

$$\mu_A = \mu_A^\circ + RT \log_e a_A$$

Differentiating and remembering that μ_A° is constant at a constant temperature and pressure we have

$$d\mu_A = RT \, d \log_e a_A$$

Substituting the above expressions into each other we obtain

$$RT(N_A \, d \log_e a_A + N_B \, d \log_e a_B) = 0$$

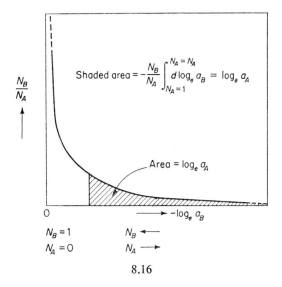

$$\text{Shaded area} = -\frac{N_B}{N_A} \int_{N_A=1}^{N_A=N_A} d\log_e a_B = \log_e a_A$$

Area $= \log_e a_A$

$\frac{N_B}{N_A}$

O $\longrightarrow -\log_e a_B$

$N_B = 1$ $N_B \longleftarrow$
$N_A = 0$ $N_A \longrightarrow$

8.16

Since RT is positive for all values of T except at absolute zero, the above expression is equal to zero when

$$N_A d\log_e a_A + N_B d\log_e a_B = 0 \qquad \ldots(8.52)$$

at $T \neq 0$, and thus on rearrangement we have

$$d\log_e a_A = -\frac{N_B}{N_A} d\log_e a_B$$

and integrating between $N_A = 1$ and $N_A = N_A$, the value on the left-hand side becomes

$$\log_e a_A = -\frac{N_B}{N_A} \int_{N_A=1}^{N_A=N_A} d\log_e a_B \qquad \ldots(8.53)$$

The value of $\log_e a_A$ at the concentration N_A can be obtained from a plot of N_B/N_A against $-\log_e a_B$, where the area under the curve between $N_A = 1$ and the desired value of N_A gives the value of $\log_e a_A$ (see Fig. 8.16). It is worth noting that when $N_A \to 1$, then $N_B/N_A \to 0$ and $-\log_e a_B \to \infty$; and when $N_A \to 0$, then $N_B/N_A \to \infty$ and $-\log_e a_B \to 0$.

REFERENCES

1 GIBBS, J. W., *The Scientific Papers*, Vol. 1, p. 65, Dover Publications, New York, 1961, (*Trans. Conn. Acad.*, 1875, 108–248).
2 LEWIS, G. N. and E. L. RANDALL, revised by K. S. PITZER and L. BREWER, *Thermodynamics*, second edition, pp. 205–212, McGraw-Hill Publishing Co. Ltd., London, 1961.

LUMSDEN, J., *Thermodynamics of Alloys*, pp. 157–160, Institute of Metals, London, 1952.

WEBER, H. C. and H. P. MEISSNER, *Thermodynamics for Chemical Engineers*, second edition, p. 406, Chapman & Hall Ltd., London, John Wiley & Sons, Inc., New York, 1957.

3 V values were extrapolated from RAYNOR, G. V., *The Physical Metallurgy of Magnesium and its Alloys*, Fig. 153, p. 319, Pergamon Press Ltd., London, 1959.

V_{Mg} and V_{Cd} were calculated using data from HODGMAN, C. D. (Ed.), *Handbook of Chemistry and Physics*, 27th edition, pp. 1608–1609, Chemical Rubber Publishing Co., Cleveland.

4 LUMSDEN, J., *Thermodynamics of Alloys*, p. 275, Institute of Metals, London, 1952.

5 LEWIS, G. N., *Proc. Am. Acad.*, 1901, **37**, 40; *Z. Phys. Chem.*, 101, **38**, 205.

6 LEWIS, G. N. and E. L. RANDALL, revised by K. S. PITZER and L. BREWER, *Thermodynamics*, second edition, pp. 244–249. McGraw-Hill Publishing Co. Ltd., London, 1961.

CHAPTER IX

The Effect of Temperature and Pressure on Equilibria in Metallurgical Processes

9.1 INTRODUCTION

In metallurgy we are concerned with many different processes, ranging from pure metallurgy to immersed corrosion. In all these processes, whether they are beneficial (e.g. extraction, fabrication, development of new alloys and materials), or whether they are wasteful (corrosion of metals), we are always concerned to know the answer to the following basic questions:

(i) Is the process possible under the proposed conditions of temperature and pressure; if not, how could it be made possible by altering the temperature and pressure of the system?

(ii) How fast will it proceed in practice?

(iii) What will be the concentrations of reactants and products when equilibrium is reached?

It will be shown in this chapter that in the majority of processes thermodynamics will allow us to answer to the first and last question. The second question however involves the subject of kinetics and will be dealt with in a later chapter.

In this chapter it is intended firstly to show the effect of temperature and pressure on processes consisting of a simple reaction (e.g. oxide formation), then to apply this knowledge to more complicated systems in which a number of reactions are possible, such as the case when various metals are competing for oxygen. It may be useful to mention at this stage that in many high temperature metallurgical processes, the kinetic considerations (question (ii)) may be of lesser importance, since under these conditions the majority of reactions are usually fast.

In thermodynamics there are quite a few relationships which could be used in the theoretical consideration of equilibria and the effect of temperature and pressure on equilibrium constant. The Van't Hoff isotherm and isochore both include K_p in their equations, and theoretically either of them could be used for such calculations. In metallurgy, however, Van't Hoff's isochore has proved to be extremely convenient, since, besides allowing us to calculate the effect of temperature change on the equilibrium constant, it is also useful in considerations regarding the effect of pressure on equilibria. This equation will also be applied in electrometallurgy for the deduction of the Nernst equation.

9.2 CALCULATION OF EQUILIBRIUM CONSTANTS FROM STANDARD FREE ENERGY CHANGES

From the value of the standard free energy change for a reaction it is possible to calculate its equilibrium constant, using the Van't Hoff isotherm $\Delta G_T^\circ = -RT \log_e K_{p_T}$.

Thus for the equilibrium reaction of the type

$$Me + O_2 \rightleftharpoons MeO_2$$

the equilibrium constant

$$K_p = \frac{a_{MeO_2}}{a_{Me} \cdot p_{O_2}}$$

or when substituted into the isotherm one obtains

$$\Delta G_T^\circ = -RT \log_e \frac{a_{MeO_2}}{a_{Me} \cdot p_{O_2}} \qquad \ldots (9.1)$$

In reactions in which the metal Me and the oxide MeO_2 can be considered to be pure solids or pure liquids, their activities are taken to be equal to unity. Thus

$$a_{MeO_2} = a_{Me} = 1$$

These systems are called **condensed systems,** and their equilibrium constants can be expressed in terms of partial pressures of the gaseous components. Thus the equation becomes

$$\Delta G_T^\circ = -RT \log_e \frac{a_{MeO_2}}{a_{Me} p_{O_2}} = -RT \log_e \frac{1}{p_{O_2}} = RT \log_e p_{O_2} \ldots (9.2)$$

where T = the absolute temperature,

p_{O_2} = the equilibrium partial pressure of the oxide at temperature T.

$= p_{total}$ if this is the only gas present.

$$P_{tot} = P_a + P_b + P_c + \cdots = \Sigma \text{ partial pressures}$$
$$= P_a \quad \text{if } P_b = P_c = etc = 0.$$

Equation (9.2) being of a general form is therefore applicable to any oxidation reaction in which oxygen is the only gaseous component. This equation allows us to calculate the oxygen equilibrium pressure of an oxide, and it finds numerous applications in metallurgy.

Example

From the given values of Gibbs standard free energy changes of silica (SiO_2) at 500°, 1,000° and 1,500°C calculate its oxygen equilibrium pressures at these temperatures.

(i) $\Delta G^\circ_{500} = -175,000$ cal g mole^{-1},

(ii) $\Delta G^\circ_{1,000} = -153,000$ cal g mole^{-1},

(iii) $\Delta G^\circ_{1,500} = -131,000$ cal g mole^{-1}.

The chemical reaction between silicon and oxygen is given by

$$Si + O_2 = SiO_2$$

From equation (9.1) we have

$$\Delta G^\circ_T = -RT \log_e \frac{a_{SiO_2}}{a_{Si} \cdot p_{O_2}}$$

Taking pure silica (SiO_2) and pure silicon (Si) as standard states we have

$$a_{SiO_2} = a_{Si} = 1$$

Thus

$$\Delta G^\circ_T = -4 \cdot 575T \log_{10} \frac{1}{p_{O_2}} = 4 \cdot 575T \log_{10} p_{O_2}$$

or

$$\log_{10} p_{O_2} = \frac{\Delta G^\circ_T}{4 \cdot 575T}$$

(i) $\qquad \log_{10} p_{O_2} = \dfrac{-175,000}{4 \cdot 575 \times (500 + 273)} = -49 \cdot 48$

Answer: $\therefore \quad p_{O_2} = 3 \cdot 0 \times 10^{-50}$ atm.

(ii) $\qquad \log_{10} p_{O_2} = \dfrac{-153,000}{4 \cdot 575 \times 1,273} = -26 \cdot 27$

Answer: $\therefore \quad p_{O_2} = 5 \cdot 37 \times 10^{-27}$ atm.

(iii) $\qquad \log_{10} p_{O_2} = \dfrac{-131,000}{4 \cdot 575 \times 1,773} = -16 \cdot 15$

Answer: $\therefore \quad p_{O_2} = 7 \cdot 1 \times 10^{-17}$ atm.

From the calculated values of oxygen equilibrium pressure it can be seen that silica will be stable in any vacuum apparatus.

The value of the standard free energy change ΔG_{298}° can be obtained from the free energy change equation derived in Chapter VII, that is

$$\Delta G_T^{\circ} = \Delta H_T^{\circ} - T\Delta S_T^{\circ}$$

In earlier chapters it was shown how ΔH_T° and ΔS_T° at the temperature T can be calculated from a knowledge of the specific heats of reactants and products and their variation with temperature. It was shown that the value of ΔH° and ΔS° did not change markedly with temperature, providing there was no change in the state of the constituents. It is however worth noting that the variation of the standard free energy change may be considerable, since in the second term the entropy change has to be multiplied by the absolute temperature.

Since the enthalpy change at any temperature T can be calculated from the equation

$$\Delta H_T = \Delta H_{298}^{\circ} + \int_{298}^{T} \Delta C_p \, dT,$$

providing there are no changes in the states of reactants and products (see p. 49), and similarly the standard entropy change is

$$\Delta S_T^{\circ} = S_{298} + \int_{298}^{T} \frac{\Delta C_p}{T} \, dT$$

where the values of ΔC_p are expressed as empirical functions of temperature, it therefore follows that the variation of the value ΔG° with temperature may also be expressed by means of an empirical equation. There are tables available which give the coefficients for these functions and thus enable us to calculate the free energy change at any temperature for various metallurgical reactions.

9.3 STANDARD FREE ENERGY

In many metallurgical processes such as extraction, refining, manufacture and treatment, welding, etc., we may be confronted with very complicated systems involving a number of possible reactions. The thermodynamic approach enables us to predict the feasibility of a proposed process, and thus may contribute to a considerable saving in its cost.[1]

In 1944 Ellingham[2] compiled diagrams of standard free energy changes against temperature for oxides and sulphides. This graphical method of presentation proved to be extremely convenient, since often it was found to convey far more information at a glance than tedious calculations or examination of lengthy tables to eliminate thermodynamically impossible reactions. Since then many more similar diagrams have been published, and because of their simplicity they have been equally well accepted by development metallurgists as by process metallurgists. They have thus brought closer together the approaches of theoretical and process metallurgists.

It is the purpose of this section to explain the nature and to show the advantages and disadvantages of this type of diagram. It is worth mentioning that, although these Ellingham diagrams are generally used, there are others, for example, Pourbaix[3] diagrams, which, although not so popular for high temperature considerations, have been useful in theoretical work on corrosion of metals.

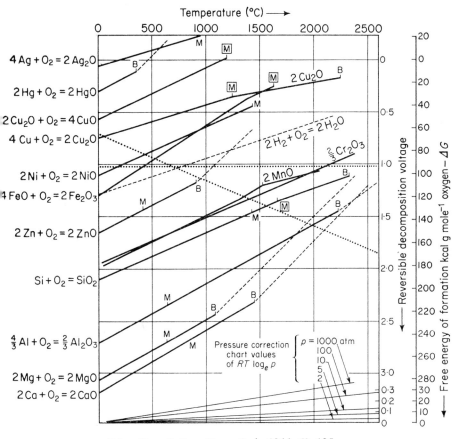

9.1.   *From* J. Soc. Chem. Ind., 1944, **63**, 125

9.3.1   General Description of Ellingham Diagrams

The general diagrams drawn by Ellingham showed a plot of negative standard free energy change $-\Delta G^\circ$ in kilocalories, against temperature T in degrees centigrade for a number of oxides and sulphides. A scale of reversible electrochemical potential E° was also included (see Fig. 9.1), since $\Delta G^\circ = -nFE^\circ$, where n is the number of electrons involved in the appropriate chemical equation, F is the Faraday constant and is equal to 96,460 coulombs per g equivalent, and E° is the standard reaction potential (see chapter on electrochemistry). A pressure correction chart giving correction values of standard free energy change ΔG° for variation in the partial pressures from standard conditions (1 atm) for any gases participating in the reactions under consideration was also included. This pressure correction part of the diagram was calculated from Van't Hoff's isotherm

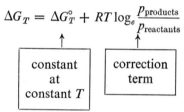

where p_{products} is the product of the final partial pressures of the products and $p_{\text{reactants}}$ is the product of the initial partial pressures of the reactants (see page 112).

The Ellingham diagrams were extended by Richardson,[4] who added the nomographic scales (see Fig. 9.2) which allow equilibrium gas compositions to be read directly at any temperature for a number of reactions.

Thus the free energy/temperature diagram for oxides gives scales for equilibrium oxygen pressures as well as the CO/CO_2 and H_2/H_2O ratios; while for sulphides the diagram includes scales giving the equilibrium sulphur pressures and the H_2S/H_2 ratio. An explanation of the derivation and uses of these scales is given on page 170.

9.3.2   Properties of a Single Standard Free Energy Change/Temperature Line

a. Linearity and Errors in ΔG_T°. In this sub-section it is intended to examine in detail the nature and properties of a hypothetical free energy–temperature line for the oxide formation of the type

$$Me_{(s)} + O_{2(g)} \rightarrow MeO_{2(s)}$$

negative value for $\Delta S°$, and vice versa. From our previous consideration (page 78) it is clear that for various reactions the slopes may
be positive, negative or zero, since the condition which determines
whether the reaction is possible is that the total entropy change of
a process, ΔS_{system}, must be positive. Since

$$\Delta S_{system} = \Delta S_{surroundings} + \Delta S_{process}$$

then $\Delta S_{process}$ can still be $\oplus$ve or $\ominus$ve or zero for real processes.
Referring to Fig. 9.3 it can be seen that there is a sudden change in
the slope of the line at point B. This denotes that at this point a
phase change of either reactant or products must have occurred.
Usually the contribution of the entropy of fusion

$$\Delta S_f = \frac{L_f}{T_f}$$

is small, and changes in this would hardly be noticeable. However,
the contribution made by the entropy of evaporation is appreciable
and accounts for the change in slope above B.

c. *The Decomposition Temperature of the Oxide* (T_D). From Van't
Hoff's isotherm it follows that for the reaction

$$Me_{(s)} + O_{2(g)} \rightarrow MeO_{2(s)}$$

the standard free energy change at temperature T is given by

$$\Delta G_T° = -RT \log_e \frac{a_{MeO_2}}{a_{Me} \cdot p_{O_2}}$$

Since MeO_2 and Me are pure solids, therefore

$$a_{MeO_2} = a_{Me} = 1$$

Thus

$$\Delta G_T° = -RT \log_e \frac{1}{p_{O_2}} = 4\cdot575T \log_{10} p_{O_2} \qquad \ldots(9.3)$$

When $\Delta G_T° = 0$, then the right-hand side of the above equation is
zero when either $T = 0$ or p_{O_2} is equal to 1 atmosphere. The intersection of the free energy change/temperature line with the temperature axis when $\Delta G° = 0$ gives the temperature at which the oxygen
equilibrium pressure p_{O_2} is equal to the standard pressure of 1
atmosphere. This temperature is known as the decomposition
temperature of the oxide and is denoted in Fig. 9.3 as T_D.

d. *The Standard Enthalpy Change* $(\Delta H°)$. From the equation

$$\Delta G° = \Delta H° - T\Delta S°$$

it follows that at zero absolute temperature $\Delta G° = \Delta H°$. Thus, by extrapolating the free energy change line to the position of $T = 0$, then $\Delta H°$ values can be read off directly from the $\Delta G°$ axis (see Fig. 9.3).

e. Range of Stability of the Metallic Oxide. According to the second law of thermodynamics, when the value of $\Delta G°$ is negative the formation of the oxide is thermodynamically possible, that is the oxide is stable. When however the $\Delta G°$ value is positive, then the oxide is unstable. It is therefore clear that in the range of temperatures at which the free energy change line is below the line of $\Delta G° = 0$ the oxide is stable; above this line it is unstable (see Fig. 9.3: at temperature T_D MeO$_2$ oxide is unstable).

f. The Effect of External Pressure of Oxygen on the Stability of the Oxide. The effect of oxygen pressure on the free energy of formation of the metallic oxide can be calculated using Van't Hoff's isotherm.

Thus

$$\Delta G_T = \Delta G_T° + RT \log_e \frac{p_{\text{products}}}{p_{\text{reactants}}}$$

(For explanation see page 112.) Since in the reaction

$$Me_{(s)} + O_{2(g)} \rightarrow MeO_{2(s)}$$

all the substances are solids except for the oxygen, then we can write

$$\Delta G_T = \Delta G_T° + RT \log_e \frac{1}{p_{O_2}} = \Delta G_T° - 4\cdot575T \log_{10} p_{O_2}$$

$$\ldots(9.4)$$

In equation (9.4) the first term $\Delta G_T°$ is constant at a constant temperature, and its value can be found from Fig. 9.3. The second term is variable, since it includes the external pressure of oxygen which can have any value. Thus for values of p_{O_2} greater than one atmosphere $\log p_{O_2}$ will be positive, and the value of this term will be negative, which means that the overall value of the free energy change at this temperature will be more negative, and so the oxide will be more stable. Using a similar argument it is clear that, when the value of p_{O_2} is less than one atmosphere, the second term will be positive, and the overall free energy change ΔG_T less negative, so that the oxide will be less stable as a result of this decreased oxygen pressure. When the oxygen pressure in contact with the solid oxide drops to below the value of the equilibrium oxygen pressure of the oxide, the oxide will become unstable and may decompose.

Let us now consider two examples, firstly where the outside oxygen pressure is less than 1 atm, and secondly where it is greater than 1 atm.

Example 1

Calculate by how much the free energy change for the oxide formation will alter when the external pressure of oxygen is equal to 10^{-6} atm at a temperature of $1,000°K$.

Using equation (9.4) we have

$$\Delta G_{1,000} = \Delta G^\circ_{1,000} - 4\cdot575 \times 1,000 \times \log_{10} 10^{-6}$$

which when solved gives

$$\Delta G_{1,000} = \Delta G^\circ_{1,000} + 27{,}450 \text{ cal}$$

This calculation shows that, when the oxide is in contact with an atmosphere containing 10^{-6} atm of oxygen, its free energy change becomes less negative by 27,450 cal g mole^{-1} of oxygen. This result shows that an oxide whose $\Delta G^\circ_{1,000}$ value is numerically less than 27,450 cal g mole^{-1} of oxygen will always be unstable at this pressure, since its $\Delta G_{1,000}$ will become positive.

Example 2

Consider the effect of an external oxygen pressure of 10 atm at $1,000°K$ on the stability of an oxide. Using again equation (9.4), we have

$$\Delta G_{1,000} = \Delta G^\circ_{1,000} - 4\cdot575 \times 1,000 \times \log_{10} 10$$

$$\therefore \quad \Delta G_{1,000} = \Delta G^\circ_{1,000} - 4{,}575$$

Thus the correction term in this case amounts to $-4{,}575$ cal g mole^{-1} of oxygen, and therefore the point on the free energy temperature oxide line (Fig. 9.3) will be lowered by this amount. The oxide will therefore be more stable, since its free energy temperature line will now be lower (Fig. 9.3).

In general it can be concluded that an increase in the oxygen pressure in this type of reaction, where the gaseous term is on the left-hand side of the chemical equation, favours the formation of the oxide, while a reduction in pressure decreases the stability of the oxide.

This possibility of predicting quantitatively the effect of pressure on the stability of oxides and other compounds is of the greatest industrial and research value, since it allows us either to calculate the conditions under which an oxide or compound becomes unstable (e.g. in vacuum work, welding, inert atmospheres, etc.) or it allows us to calculate what pressure is required to enable certain compounds to remain stable (e.g. in pressure leaching, formation of carbonyls, etc.).

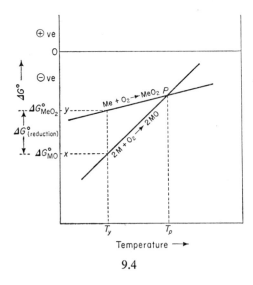

9.4

9.3.3 *Interpretation of Two or More Free Energy Change/Temperature Lines taken Together*

Figure 9.4 shows two plots of ΔG° against T for the formation of two hypothetical oxides MeO_2 and MO. For comparison the ΔG° values are plotted in both cases for 1 g mole of oxygen, and *not* for 1 g mole of the oxide.

a. Relative Stability of the Oxides. The slopes of the lines (Fig. 9.4) are different, and therefore the lines cross at the point P and temperature T_p. At temperatures below T_p the line for the 2MO oxide formation is below that for MeO_2, and therefore in this region the MO oxide is more stable. At the temperature T_p both these oxides have the same oxygen equilibrium pressure, and therefore they coexist. Above this temperature the MeO_2 oxide is the more stable one. It follows therefore that below the temperature T_p the MeO_2 may be reduced by M, providing that suitable conditions can exist.

Thus we have

$$MeO_2 + 2M \xrightarrow{\text{below } T_p} 2MO + Me$$

Above that temperature the reverse will be true, and

$$2MO + Me \xrightarrow{\text{above } T_p} MeO_2 + 2M$$

b. The Standard Free Energy Change of the Reduction Reaction.
At any given temperature the standard free energy change for the
above reactions can be read directly from the diagram. For example,
at temperature T_y the standard free energy change of the reduction
of MeO_2 by the metal M is given by the distance between the two
ΔG° lines at this temperature.

This can be shown as follows, since for

$$2M + O_2 \rightarrow 2MO \qquad \ldots \Delta G^\circ_{MO_{Ty}} = X$$

and for

$$Me + O_2 \rightarrow MeO_2 \qquad \ldots \Delta G^\circ_{MeO_{2Ty}} = Y$$

On subtracting we have

$$2M + MeO_2 \rightarrow 2MO + Me \qquad \ldots \Delta G^\circ_{reduction} = X - Y$$

Here ΔG° for the reduction reaction is therefore the difference
between the two respective standard free energy changes at T_y.

It must be pointed out that values obtained for the free energy
change will not be very accurate if the free energy difference is small.
To illustrate this fact, let us consider the following example.

Assume that the values of ΔG°_{MO} and $\Delta G^\circ_{MeO_2}$ at T_y are
-102 ± 2 kcal g mole^{-1} and -98 ± 2 kcal g mole^{-1} oxygen
respectively.

The $\Delta G^\circ_{reduction} = -102 - (-98) = -4 \pm 4$ kcal g mole^{-1}
oxygen.

In this example it would clearly be very unwise to draw any definite
conclusions regarding the possibility of this reduction reaction,
since the possible experimental error is $\pm 100\%$ of the standard free
energy change value for this reduction.

c. Reversion of Stability. Above the equilibrium temperature T_p
MeO_2 becomes more stable, since its line is then below that of MO.

The possibility of choosing at a glance the appropriate temperature
which allows a reversible reaction to take place in the required
direction is one of the most useful properties of these diagrams.
Consider for example the line of carbon monoxide in the free energy–
temperature diagram for oxide formation; its usefulness to extraction
metallurgists is apparent, since it will be seen that below 600°C
neither water vapour nor ferrous oxide can be reduced with coke
under standard conditions. However, above 1,500°C it is clear from
the diagram that all the iron oxides, chromium oxide, manganese
oxide, and many others can now be reduced by coke. This greater
power of reduction by coke at higher temperatures is brought about
by the negative slope of the $\Delta G^\circ/T$ line (see Fig. 9.6) of carbon
monoxide.

d. The Effect of Pressure on the Direction of Equilibrium at a Constant Temperature. The effect of pressure on the position of the free energy/temperature line can be calculated from Van't Hoff's isotherm. According to this equation

$$\Delta G_T = \Delta G_T^\circ + 4\cdot 575T \log_{10} Q$$

constant term	correction term

where

$$Q = \frac{\left.\dfrac{p}{a}\right|\text{products}}{\left.\dfrac{p}{a}\right|\text{reactants}} \quad \begin{array}{l} p = \text{pressure} \\ a = \text{activity} \\ c = \text{concentration (when applicable)} \end{array}$$

The effect of pressure on the free energy change will depend on the type of reaction, and in general one can consider three possible cases, which will now be discussed.

(i) Where the equation for the oxide formation contains the gaseous term on the left-hand side only, for example

$$Me_{(s)} + O_{2(g)} \rightarrow MeO_{2(s)}$$

Since the activities of pure solids are unity, then

$$\Delta G = \Delta G_0 + 4\cdot 575T \log_{10} \frac{1}{p_{O_2}}$$

or

$$\Delta G = \Delta G_0 - 4\cdot 575T \log_{10} p_{O_2}$$

From this equation it is clear that for increasing external oxygen pressure above 1 atmosphere the position of the free energy line (see Fig. 9.5) is lowered, while for pressures lower than 1 atmosphere its position will become higher. It must be noted that the slope of the line is different at different pressures.

(ii) Where the equation for the oxide formation contains the gaseous term on the right-hand side only, for example

$$FeO_{(s)} + C_{(s)} \rightarrow Fe_{(s)} + CO_{(g)}$$

Let us assume that FeO and Fe are pure substances and therefore their activities are unity.

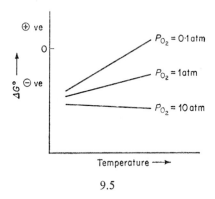

9.5

Thus

$$\Delta G = \Delta G^\circ + 4\cdot575T \log_{10} p_{CO} \qquad \ldots(9.5)$$

From this equation it follows that at carbon monoxide pressures p_{CO} higher than 1 atmosphere $\Delta G > \Delta G^\circ$, so that the position of the new free energy line will be above the standard one, while at pressures p_{CO} less than one atmosphere the reverse will be true. This is well illustrated in Fig. 9.6.

(iii) Where the equation for the oxide formation contains the gaseous terms on both sides: for example in the reaction

$$2CO_{(g)} + O_{2(g)} \rightarrow 2CO_{2(g)}$$

The ΔG for this reaction will depend on the ratio of $p^2_{CO_2}$ to $p^2_{CO} \times p_{O_2}$ and

$$\Delta G = \Delta G^\circ + 4\cdot575T \log_{10} \frac{p^2_{CO_2}}{p^2_{CO} \times p_{O_2}}$$

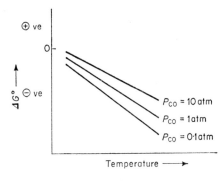

9.6

When the value of the quotient in the correction term is greater than one, then the position of the corrected line is above the $\Delta G°$ line; the reverse is true when its value is less than one.

9.3.4   Derivation and Uses of the Oxygen Nomographic Scale in Richardson's Diagrams

In the standard free energy/temperature diagrams when two lines cross the two systems are then at equilibrium, since their values of $\Delta G°$ are then identical. Thus any two oxide lines at the temperature of their intersection will have the same oxygen equilibrium pressure, if their equilibrium constants depend on the oxygen pressure only. Richardson[4] utilised this property by plotting a series of lines representing the free energy change associated with expansion of oxygen. Thus for an expansion of 1 g mole of oxygen from 1 atmosphere to any pressure p_{O_2} the free energy change

$$\Delta G_{O_2} = RT \log_e p_{O_2} = \Delta \mu_{O_2}$$

The value at constant pressure p_{O_2} is therefore

$$\Delta G_{O_2} = \Delta \mu_{O_2} = 4 \cdot 575 T \log_{10} p_{O_2} \qquad \ldots (9.6)$$

For any constant lower pressures the plot of ΔG_{O_2} against temperature will give a straight line.

At absolute zero temperature the value of ΔG or $\Delta \mu_{O_2}$ becomes zero for all pressures, and so all the lines for the various p_{O_2} values will originate from that one point. Richardson[4] first used this property by showing that a suitable nomographic scale could be obtained from equation (9.6) to allow us to read off directly equilibrium pressures for oxides at given temperatures. Fig. 9.7 shows the construction of the oxygen pressure scale.

Richardson[4] first plotted these p_{O_2} lines on a separate transparent paper which could be superimposed on his original diagrams but later, for convenience and to avoid too many lines on his diagrams, he marked only the point 'O' (Fig. 9.7) on the absolute zero temperature line and the intersections of the oxygen lines with the nomographic p_{O_2} scale around two sides of the diagram. By means of a straight edge one can follow any one of the free energy changes for oxygen potential lines for various pressures of oxygen, and their oxygen pressure values can be read directly on the p_{O_2} scale.

From Fig. 9.7 it is clear that the point of intersection of any of the oxygen lines with a free energy line for any oxide enables the oxygen equilibrium pressure at the temperature corresponding to that point to be read off in the nomographic oxygen pressure scale.

Thus for any oxide at a given temperature it is possible to read off directly its oxygen equilibrium pressure by drawing an imaginary

straight line from the point 'O' through the point where its free
energy line meets the correct temperature co-ordinate, and reading
off the p_{O_2} value where its projection cuts the nomographic scale
outside the diagram.

It will be noticed that nomographic scales for CO/CO_2 and
H_2/H_2O ratios are included in Fig. 9.2, the corresponding reference

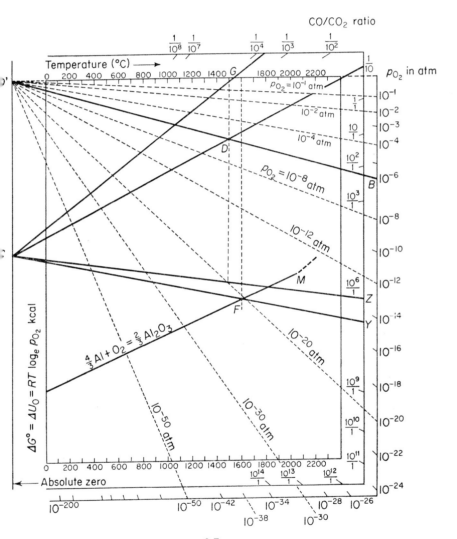

9.7

points being C and H on the absolute zero ordinate. The scales give the pressure ratios instead of the equilibrium pressures. However, these ratios have a fixed relationship to the partial pressure of oxygen.

Writing the equation

$$2CO_{(g)} + O_{2(g)} \rightleftharpoons 2CO_{2(g)}$$

therefore the CO/CO_2 ratio is determined by the oxygen partial pressure and by the value of the equilibrium constant K_p for this reaction at the given temperature T.

$$(K_p)_T = \frac{(p_{CO_2})^2}{(p_{CO})^2 \times p_{O_2}}$$

It is clear that, as p_{O_2} varies, $\dfrac{(p_{CO_2})^2}{(p_{CO})^2}$ must also vary in such a way as to keep K_p constant.

This type of diagram can be used in many fields such as calcining, roasting, reduction processes, decomposition processes, vacuum work, preparation of alloys, welding, etc.

It is beyond the scope of this book to discuss the application of these diagrams to these processes as they will be dealt with in further text books in this series. However, it is intended here to show a few simple uses of these nomographic scales.

Example 1

Determine from Fig. 9.7 the CO/CO_2 ratio at 1,500°C when the partial pressures of oxygen are: (i) 1 atm, (ii) 10^{-6} atm, (iii) 10^{-20} atm.

To solve this example first consider Fig. 9.7 which shows the oxygen line 'O'B at $p_{O_2} = 10^{-6}$ atm. Point D gives the intersection of this line with the perpendicular drawn to the temperature axis at 1,500°C. Produce a line from C, the reference point for carbon, through the point D, and the intersection of this line with the CO/CO_2 nomographic line gives us the equilibrium ratio of CO/CO_2, which for this example is found to be 1/10. Similarly the equilibrium ratio of CO/CO_2 at 1,500°C and 1 atm pressure is obtained by producing a line from C through point G on Fig. 9.7. This line intersects the CO/CO_2 line at the point $CO:CO_2 = 1:10^4$. From line CZ we find that at $p_{O_2} = 10^{-20}$ atm the equilibrium CO/CO_2 ratio at 1,500°C is $10^6:1$.

Example 2

Obtain from Fig. 9.7 the equilibrium oxygen pressure for aluminium oxide at 1,620°C, and also determine the equilibrium ratio of CO/CO_2 at this temperature.

When a ruler is positioned through 'O' and the point F corresponding to 1,620°C on the 2/3 Al_2O_3 line, it intersects the p_{O_2} scale at $p_{O_2} = 10^{-20}$ atm.

Similarly a line from C through the same point intersects the CO/CO_2 ratio line between $10^6/1$ and $10^7/1$ (point Y). To find the exact equilibrium CO/CO_2 an interpolation has to be made between $10^6/1$ and $10^7/1$ bearing in mind that the scale is logarithmic. Since in this case the intersection point is 1/5 of the distance between these two reference points, that is 0·2, therefore by taking antilog of 0·2 we obtain 1·585 or 1·6 for the position of intersection, and the answer is $CO/CO_2 = 1·6 \times 10^7/1$.

It follows from the value of the equilibrium oxygen pressure that pure aluminium oxide will be stable at 1,620°C in atmospheres containing as little as 10^{-20} atm of oxygen. However, below this value it would become unstable. Since it is most improbable that our system would ever contain less than this amount of oxygen, pure aluminium oxide under these conditions always remains a stable oxide.

It is also clear from this diagram that the equilibrium ratio of CO/CO_2 is so large that even 'pure' carbon monoxide will most probably contain more CO_2 than that indicated by the equilibrium ratio, and therefore pure alumina would not be reduced by what we normally call 'pure' CO at this temperature.

9.3.5   Disadvantages of the $\Delta G°/T$ Diagrams

Although there are many advantages of plotting $\Delta G°$ against T for various compounds, it has always to be remembered that in using these diagrams

(i) the free energy changes shown refer to *standard states* only;

(ii) the assumption is made that the oxides, sulphides, etc., are *compounds of definite composition*, and, although in practice this may not be so, at least for many oxides this assumption is true;

(iii) we do not take into account the possibility of the distribution of reactants and products between the different phases (e.g. solid or liquid solutions);

(iv) the possibility of the formation of intermetallic compounds between the products and reactants is not taken into account;

(v) they indicate *only* whether processes are thermodynamically possible, and do not give any information regarding the rate of the processes under consideration.

Nevertheless, in spite of some of the above shortcomings, these diagrams have been found very useful in metallurgy because of their simplicity in use and the speed with which answers can be obtained to many problems.

REFERENCES

1 EVANS, J. W., *Research*, 1958, **11,** 12.
2 ELLINGHAM, H. J. T., *J. Soc. Chem. Ind.*, 1944, **63,** 125.
3 POURBAIX, M. S. N. and C. M. RORIVE-BOUTE, *Disc. Farad. Soc.*, 1948, **4,** 139–154.
4 RICHARDSON, F. D. and J. H. E. JEFFES, *J.I.S.I.*, 1948, **160,** 3 261.
5 RICHARDSON, F. D. and J. H. E. JEFFES, Contribution to discussion *Disc. Farad. Soc.*, 1948, **4,** 218.

CHAPTER X

Application of Thermodynamics to Simple Equilibrium Phase Diagrams

10.1 INTRODUCTION

Thermodynamics has proved to be useful to physical metallurgists mainly for three reasons: it allows them to predict the maximum number of possible phases in a given system, it enables them to calculate simple equilibrium phase diagrams from a very limited thermodynamic data, and finally it provides us with a convenient tool for rechecking parts of phase diagrams, especially when the conventional experimental methods for the determination of certain boundary conditions give widely differing results. In this chapter it is intended first to deduce the Gibbs' phase rule, and then to apply it to a very simple eutectic system (Bi–Cd), whose liquidus lines in the equilibrium phase diagram will be calculated using the Clausius-Clapeyron equation. This is followed by the application of thermodynamics to a system completely different to the first one, that is, where the two components are miscible over the whole range of concentrations in the solid and liquid states. Finally an illustration of the principles and application of the tangency rule is given by determination of the liquidus and solidus curves for the NiO–MgO equilibrium phase diagram, and the prediction of the coexistence and composition of two liquids in the lead–zinc system.

10.2 THE DERIVATION OF THE GIBBS' PHASE RULE

10.2.1 Definition of Terms

When dealing with equilibrium phase diagrams we are frequently confronted with such terms as 'degree of freedom', 'phase' and 'component'. It is therefore imperative to define these terms and to explain their meaning.

A Phase can be defined as any homogeneous and physically distinct part of a system which is separated from other parts of the system by a definite bounding surface.

For example, at 273·16°K, ice, water, and water vapour can co-exist in equilibrium. Here we have three phases. However, if ice should exist in more than one crystalline form, then each form would be a separate phase, since it is clearly distinguishable from the other forms.

In general every solid in a system is a separate phase, but a homogeneous solid solution constitutes a single phase irrespective of the number of chemical components it may contain. Liquid solutions are considered to be single phases but two immiscible liquids constitute two phases, since there is a boundary between them. Gases whether pure or as a mixture always give one phase, since their molecules are intimately mixed together and thus produce a homogeneous mixture.

The number of Components in a system at equilibrium is the smallest number of independently variable constituents by means of which the composition of each phase present can be expressed directly or in the form of a chemical equation. For example when we consider calcium carbonate, it can be expressed by means of the following chemical reaction

$$CaCO_{3(s)} \rightleftharpoons CaO_{(s)} + CO_{2(g)}$$

At equilibrium, according to the above definition, this system will consist of two components, since the third is then fixed by the equilibrium conditions. It is worth noting that the number of phases is three, since there are two solids $CaCO_3$ and CaO and a gas.

The number of Degrees of Freedom is the number of variable factors such as temperature, pressure, and concentration that need to be fixed in order that the condition of a system at equilibrium may be completely defined when referring to its equilibrium phase diagram. The precise meaning of this term will be explained later when describing phase diagrams using the so-called *Phase Rule Equation*.

10.2.2 *Derivation of the Phase Rule Equation*

This derivation is based largely on Gibbs' original derivation[1] given in his paper entitled 'The conditions of equilibrium for heterogeneous masses in contact when uninfluenced by gravity, electricity, distortion of solid masses, or capillary tension'. From this title it is clear that we shall be considering a system consisting of a certain amount of phases and components, and the only external factors influencing the equilibrium will be temperature, pressure and internal concentrations.

Let us consider a system consisting of C components distributed

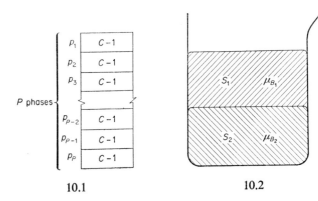

10.1   10.2

between P phases. The composition of each phase is completely known, if we know $C - 1$ concentrations in each phase, since the last concentration can be calculated by difference. Thus to define completely all the phases in terms of their composition we have to know $P(C - 1)$ concentration terms. Fig. 10.1 illustrates this. If we wish to describe the system completely, then, in addition to the composition, the temperature and pressure of the system have to be stated. Assuming that all the phases are at the same temperature and pressure and at equilibrium, then the total number of variables which have to be known is given by

$$P(C - 1) + 2 \qquad \ldots (10.1)$$

Thermodynamics helps us to decide how many of the variables in the above equation can be eliminated. At equilibrium the chemical potential of any one component must be the same in each of the phases, otherwise there would be a net transfer of this component from one phase to another. For example let us consider two immiscible solutions S_1 and S_2 (Fig. 10.2). Each of these solutions contains a certain amount of the component B. Let the chemical potential of the component B in S_1 be μ_{B_1} and in S_2 be μ_{B_2}.

Then at equilibrium at a constant temperature and pressure $\mu_{B_1} = \mu_{B_2}$, since otherwise B would either pass from S_1 to S_2 or vice versa until its chemical potential became the same (see page 186) in each phase.

Thus in our system of C components and P phases we need only know one concentration term for each component to be able to calculate all the concentrations of this component in the other phases from its chemical potential.

Since for the components A, B, . . . C their chemical potentials at equilibrium are given by

$$\mu_{A_1} = \mu_{A_2} = \ldots = \mu_{A_p}$$

$$\mu_{B_1} = \mu_{B_2} = \ldots = \mu_{B_p}$$

$$\cdot \qquad \cdot \qquad \qquad \cdot$$

$$\cdot \qquad \cdot \qquad \qquad \cdot$$

$$\cdot \qquad \cdot \qquad \qquad \cdot$$

$$\mu_{C_1} = \mu_{C_2} = \ldots = \mu_{C_p}$$

therefore the number of concentration terms (variables) that are automatically fixed by the chemical potentials is

$$C(P - 1) \qquad\qquad \ldots (10.2)$$

The total number of variables which must now be specified in order to define the system completely is the difference between equation (10.1) and (10.2). Thus

$$[P(C - 1) + 2] - [C(P - 1)] = C - P + 2$$

The number of degrees of freedom is therefore given by

$$F = C - P + 2 \qquad\qquad \ldots (10.3)$$

and this equation expresses what is known as the **Gibbs' Phase Rule.**

10.2.3   Illustration of the Gibbs' Phase Rule for a One-Component System

Consider for example the phase diagram of water (Fig. 10.3). The line AB separates the regions of solid and vapour, the line BC liquid and vapour, and BD solid and liquid. At any point on the line AB we shall have two phases coexisting in equilibrium, namely the ice and water vapour. Since we have only one component, then according to the phase rule

$$F = C - P + 2 = 1 - 2 + 2 = 1$$

Thus any system represented by a point on this line, and similarly on the other lines CB or DB (except at B), will have only one degree of freedom, which means that we have to define one variable (e.g. temperature or pressure) to be able to fix the position of this point on the appropriate line in the equilibrium phase diagram. Thus at temperature T_1 the pressure corresponding to the point P is immediately read off as p_1. Any separate change in either temperature or pressure of the system at P will alter the number of phases present;

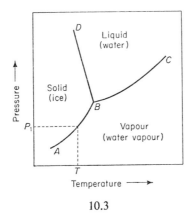

10.3

a lower pressure will convert all the solid into vapour, while increasing the pressure converts all the water vapour into ice. Since in this case the vapour is obtained directly from the solid, this process is known as **sublimation** (see Chapter VI). Thus curve AB represents a set of univariant points, and at point B three phases coexist—solid, liquid and vapour. From the phase rule we have

$$F = 1 - 3 + 2 = 0$$

We therefore have zero degrees of freedom and B is called an **invariant point** or **triple point.** There is only one such point for any substance, and at this point the pressure and the temperature are fixed (known),* since any change in either pressure, or temperature, or in both together will result in the disappearance of one phase.

Any other point outside the lines represents either solid, liquid or vapour. Here from the Gibbs' phase rule we have

$$F = C - P + 2 = 1 - 1 + 2 = 2$$

This system is bivariant, since it has two degrees of freedom, and therefore in order to locate the position of a point representing the system in the diagram two variables, the temperature and the pressure of the system, must be known.

---

* This point is taken as the lower reference point on the Kelvin scale of temperature and is equal to 273·16°K. This point, being invariable, is more reproducible than the normal melting point of ice which on the same scale is equal to 273·15°K.

10.3 CALCULATION OF THE LIQUIDUS LINE OF BISMUTH–CADMIUM EUTECTIC BINARY SYSTEM AND APPLICATION OF THE PHASE RULE TO THIS EQUILIBRIUM PHASE DIAGRAM

The bismuth–cadmium equilibrium phase diagram (Fig. 10.4) is an example of a system in which the two metals are completely miscible in the liquid phase and virtually insoluble in each other in the solid phase. The **Clausius-Clapeyron equation is suitable for calculation of such diagrams,** since the mole fractions of the components in the solid state are equal to their activities. The only data necessary for calculation of the liquidus line of such a system are the normal temperatures of fusion for these two metals and their heats of fusion.

The normal temperature of fusion of bismuth $T_{f_{Bi}}$ is 544·5°K and its latent heat of fusion is 2,600 cal g atom^{-1}. The normal temperature of fusion of cadmium $T_{f_{Cd}}$ is 594°K and its latent heat of fusion $L_{f_{Cd}}$ is 1,450 cal g atom^{-1}. It is also known that these two metals are insoluble in each other in the solid state, but completely soluble in the liquid phase.

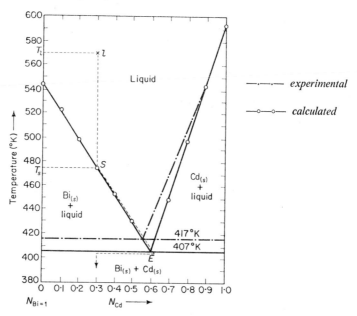

10.4. *Calculated and experimental bismuth–cadmium phase diagrams*

Using the Clausius-Clapeyron equation (Chapter VI) in the form

$$\Delta T = \frac{N_A R T^2}{L_{f_{Bi}}}$$

where N_A = mole fraction of cadmium,

ΔT = depression of normal melting point

let us calculate first the depression of freezing point when cadmium is added to bismuth, and then when bismuth is added to cadmium. Table 10.1 shows the depression of freezing points calculated from this equation.

TABLE 10.1

N_{cd}	0·1	0·2	0·3	0·4	0·5
$\Delta T°K$	22·8	45·6	68·4	91·2	114·0
$T_m°K$	521·7	498·9	476·1	453·3	430
N_{Bi}	0·1	0·2	0·3	0·4	0·5
$\Delta T°K$	48·7	97·4	146·1	194·8	243·5
$T_m°K$	545·3	496·6	447·9	399·2	350·5

From the calculated equilibrium phase diagram of bismuth–cadmium it can be seen that it differs very little from that obtained from experimental results, in so far as the bismuth-rich part of the diagram is concerned. This good agreement is rather surprising, since the above equation should only be applicable up to about $N = 0·15$, as the value $T^2 \neq T^0$. T at high concentrations. It is probable that this effect has been largely offset by variations in the latent heats of fusion of these two metals, which may vary with temperature and concentration, or that the activities of the two metals in the liquid alloys may be different from their molal concentrations.

Let us now consider the application of the phase rule to this binary system. Consider what happens when the liquid solution of composition l at temperature T_l is cooled until the whole alloy becomes solid. When the liquid alloy is cooled and reaches the temperature T_s at the liquidus line, solid bismuth will start being deposited in the solution. Applying the phase rule to the composition l at temperature T_l in the diagram we see that the system consists of one phase. Since there are two components in this system (Cd and Bi), the number of degrees of freedom is given by

$$F = C - P + 2 = 2 - 1 + 2 = 3$$

Since the cooling is being done at a constant pressure (condensed system), $F = C - P + 1$; on substituting numbers for C and P into this equation we have

$$F = 2 - 1 + 1 = 2$$

Thus both the temperature and concentration have to be known, in order to define the precise position of the alloy here denoted by l in the diagram.

When the liquid cools to temperature T_s it meets the liquidus line at S; then $C = 2$ and $P = 2$ (liquid and solid Bi), therefore

$$F = 2 - 2 + 1 = 1$$

and the system is univariant. It is sufficient now to know either the concentration or the temperature T_s to be able to specify the precise position of the system in the diagram.

On further cooling more bismuth is deposited, and thus the liquid becomes richer in cadmium; as a consequence of this the concentration of Cd in the liquid phase increases, and the freezing point falls even further. The composition of the liquid follows the liquidus line SE until it reaches the eutectic point E. At this point the liquidus lines starting from the bismuth and cadmium sides meet. **The eutectic point is thus the lowest point at which these alloys can coexist in the liquid state.**

At the eutectic temperature there are three phases consisting of solid cadmium, solid bismuth, and the liquid alloy. Thus

$$F = 2 - 3 + 1 = 0$$

This point is therefore invariant, since it has zero degrees of freedom; the temperature and concentration are fixed, and any change in either results in a reduction in the number of phases present.

This example illustrates the use of thermodynamics for the calculation of the liquidus for a simple eutectic system, and illustrates also the application of the phase rule in the elucidation of the number of either degrees of freedom or phases that must exist at equilibrium.

It is worth noting that the eutectic point E is invariant only for systems at definite constant pressure. For different pressures its position on the diagram will alter (it is still an invariant point at each pressure), but such variations are usually negligible for changes in pressures amounting to only a few atmospheres.

10.4 THE USE OF FREE ENERGY/CONCENTRATION DIAGRAMS FOR THE CALCULATION OF A SIMPLE EQUILIBRIUM PHASE DIAGRAM

In Section 10.3 the Clausius-Clapeyron equation was used for the calculation of the liquidus line of a binary system in which the two components were completely miscible in the liquid state but completely immiscible in the solid state. In this section it is intended to choose an example for a system in which the two components are completely miscible in all proportions in both the liquid and solid states, and thus form a series of regular liquid and solid solutions. In this case according to our definition of an ideal solution (page 119) one would expect the melting points of these solutions to lie on a straight line from A to B and the liquid composition to be exactly the same as that of the solid.

In practice, however, when the two components have the same type of structure and similar lattice dimensions and thus form a complete series of solid and liquid solutions, these are always characterised by entropies and heats of mixing which can be determined. From these values it is possible to obtain the solidus and liquidus lines either by direct calculations or graphically. Since calculations, except for a few simple cases, are highly complicated, it is not surprising that in physical metallurgy the graphical method is preferred whenever possible.

In this method the free energy change for both the solid solution and the liquid solution phase is plotted against concentration, and by using the tangency rule (see page 124) the points of contact of the common tangent to the two curves gives the composition of the solid and the liquid solutions which are in equilibrium.

Let us apply this rule to the calculation of the liquidus and solidus curves in the NiO and MgO equilibrium phase diagram (Fig. 10.6).

The solidus and liquidus curves in this system must be considered between the temperature of fusion of the component of the lowest melting point (NiO) and that of the highest (MgO), that is between 1,960°C and 2,800°C respectively.[2]

The heats of fusion of these two oxides are approximately known to be 12,500 and 18,500 cal g mole^{-1}.

The free energy change of formation of both the solid solution and the liquid solution at the intermediate temperatures have to be considered. *In every case the standard state for the NiO will be pure liquid and for the MgO pure solid.*

The free energy change on the formation of an ideal solution without any change in phase is given by

$$\Delta G_{(sol)} = \Delta H_{(sol)} - T \cdot \Delta S_{(sol)}$$

Since $\Delta H_{(sol)}$ for an ideal solution is equal to zero, the equation then becomes

$$\Delta G_{(sol)} = - T\Delta S_{(sol)}$$

Using equation (8.42)

$$\Delta S_{(sol)} = -R(N_A \log_e N_A + N_B \log_e N_B)$$

and thus we have

$$\Delta G_{(sol)} = RT(N_A \log_e N_A + N_B \log_e N_B)$$

Let us now consider the formation of a *solid solution from solid MgO and liquid NiO* of the composition $[(NiO)_x(MgO)_y]_s$ which is associated with a free energy change $\Delta G_{(s)}$.

The free energy change equation for this solid solution formation will have to account for the entropy change of mixing of $(NiO)_x$ and $(MgO)_y$ in the solid state; since the final state is a solid, an appropriate term for the latent heat evolved on solidification of $(NiO)_x$, i.e. $(-L_{f_{NiO}} \times N_{NiO})$, and the appropriate entropy change term for its solidification, i.e. $\left[T \times \left(\dfrac{L_{f_{NiO}}}{T_{f_{NiO}}} \right) \times N_{NiO} \right]$ have also to be included. Since MgO remains solid, no correction terms for MgO are necessary.

Thus the general equation for the $\Delta G_{(s)}$ is given by

$$\Delta G_{(s)} = 4 \cdot 575T(N_{NiO} \log_{10} N_{NiO} + N_{MgO} \log_{10} N_{MgO}) -$$

$$- L_{f_{NiO}} \times N_{NiO} + T \times \left(\frac{L_{f_{NiO}}}{T_{f_{NiO}}} \right) \times N_{NiO}$$

and on substituting the values of $T_{f_{NiO}}$ and $L_{f_{NiO}}$ we have

$$\Delta G_{(s)} = 4 \cdot 575T(N_{NiO} \log_{10} N_{NiO} + N_{MgO} \log_{10} N_{MgO}) -$$

$$- 12{,}500N_{NiO} + 5 \cdot 6N_{NiO} \times T \quad \dots (10.4)$$

Similarly the free energy change $\Delta G_{(l)}$ at any temperature T (between $T_{f_{\text{NiO}}}$ and $T_{f_{\text{MgO}}}$) for *the liquid solution* formation is given by

$$\Delta G_{(l)} = 4 \cdot 575T(N_{\text{MgO}} \log_{10} N_{\text{MgO}} + N_{\text{NiO}} \log_{10} N_{\text{NiO}}) +$$

$$+ L_f \times N_{\text{MgO}} - T\left(\frac{L_{f_{\text{MgO}}}}{T_{f_{\text{MgO}}}}\right) \times N_{\text{MgO}}$$

On substituting the numerical values into this equation we obtain

$$\Delta G_{(l)} = 4 \cdot 575T(N_{\text{MgO}} \log_{10} N_{\text{MgO}} + N_{\text{NiO}} \log_{10} N_{\text{NiO}}) +$$

$$+ 18,500N_{\text{MgO}} - 6 \cdot 0T \times N_{\text{MgO}} \quad \ldots(10.5)$$

The values of $\Delta G_{(s)}$ and $\Delta G_{(l)}$ for various mole fractions of NiO and MgO at a temperature of $2,600°K$ have been calculated from equations (10.4) and (10.5) and are presented in Table 10.2.

TABLE 10.2

N_{MgO}	N_{NiO}	$\Delta G_{(l)}$	$\Delta G_{(s)}$
0	1	0	+2,060
0·1	0·9	−1,370	+174
0·2	0·8	−2,005	−852
0·3	0·7	−2,226	−1,714
0·4	0·6	−2,292	−2,216
0·5	0·5	−2,031	−2,551
0·6	0·4	−1,712	−2,628
0·7	0·3	−986	−2,538
0·8	0·2	−265	−2,173
0·9	0·1	+1,110	−1,474
1	0	+3,100	0

In Fig. 10.5 curves were drawn showing the free energy change of formation of the solid solution $\Delta G_{(s)}$ and liquid solution $\Delta G_{(l)}$ against the solidus and liquidus mole fraction composition at the temperature of $2,600°K$.

The common tangent to the two curves AB gives the compositions of the liquid $N_{(l)}$ and the solid $N_{(s)}$ that are at equilibrium at $2,600°$ K. On page 123 it was shown that the intercepts of the tangent on the ΔG axis give the partial molal free energy changes $\Delta \bar{G}_{\text{NiO}}$ and $\Delta \bar{G}_{\text{MgO}}$. Referring to Fig. 10.5, these give the free energy change when 1 g mole of either pure NiO or pure MgO is dissolved in the solid or liquid solution of composition $N_{(s)}$ and $N_{(l)}$. Since the tangent at A and B is common to the curves, therefore the chemical

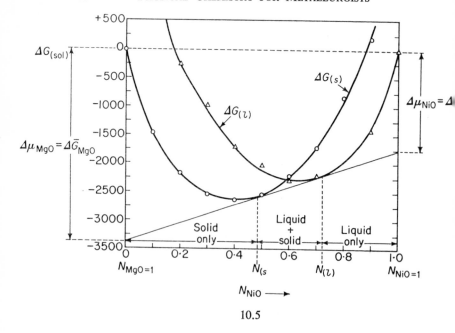

10.5

potential of each component in the liquid and solid phase is the same. Thus

$$\Delta\mu_{NiO(l)} = \Delta\mu_{NiO(s)} \qquad \ldots(10.6)$$

and

$$\Delta\mu_{MgO(l)} = \Delta\mu_{MgO(s)} \qquad \ldots(10.7)$$

Thus equations (10.6) and (10.7) signify that for a transfer of a very small amount of NiO from the solid solution to the liquid solution and vice versa the sum of the chemical potentials will be zero, and therefore *solid and liquid are in a dynamic equilibrium with respect to NiO. The same is true for MgO at these compositions of the liquid and solid phases.*

According to the second law of thermodynamics at a given composition, temperature and pressure it is always the phase or mixture of phases with the lowest free energy that is the most stable. Thus from Fig. 10.5 at the temperature 2,600°K in the range of compositions from $N_{NiO} = 1$ to $N_{NiO} = N_{(l)}$, the value of $\Delta G_{(l)}$ is always lower than $\Delta G_{(s)}$, and therefore the liquid is the only stable phase. In the intermediate range of concentrations between $N_{(l)}$ and $N_{(s)}$ mixtures of the solid and liquid phases have lower free energy than either solid or the liquid phases and therefore both phases can

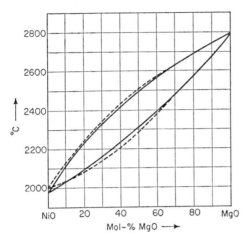

10.6. *From the* Transactions of the British Ceramic Society, 1961, p. 77

coexist. In the range of concentrations from $N_{(s)}$ to $N_{MgO} = 1$, the solidus curve has a lower free energy change of formation than either the liquid or the liquid–solid mixture, and in this concentration range the solid is the only stable phase.

By calculating and plotting such $\Delta G_{(s)}$ and $\Delta G_{(l)}$ curves for various temperatures and drawing common tangents to them, the complete composition of the liquidus and solidus curves of this equilibrium phase diagram can be obtained. Kubaschewski[3] has calculated values for this binary oxide system, and his curves are shown in Fig. 10.6 together with those obtained experimentally.

In this system the agreement between the experimental and the calculated lines is very good, thus indicating that the NiO–MgO binary system is ideal. Similar agreement between theory and experiment was found for the FeO–MnO system,[4] and in general this method is found to give good results for *systems which form regular solid and liquid solutions.*

In the Ag–Au system Wagner[5] had shown a difference between the calculated and the available experimental curves. Subsequently White[6] rechecked experimentally this equilibrium phase diagram and found that the previous experimental data was inaccurate, probably due to the low diffusivity in the solid phase. The Ag–Au system can serve as a simple example where the thermodynamic calculations indicated an inaccuracy in the existing equilibrium phase diagram, which was subsequently corrected by repeating the experimental work.

10.5   FREE ENERGY/CONCENTRATION DIAGRAMS
FOR NON-IDEAL SOLUTIONS

In Chapter VIII it was shown that all the thermodynamic equations deduced for ideal systems can be equally applied to non-ideal systems, providing the concentration terms were replaced by activities. Therefore using the free energy of mixing equation and replacing mole fractions by activities we obtain the relationship

$$\Delta G_m = RT(N_A \log_e a_A + N_B \log_e a_B)$$

This equation is applicable to all cases where there is no change in state either in the solvent or solute; that is to say, either there are liquids to give liquid solution or solids to give solid solutions. According to the values of the activity of the metals A and B forming a binary solution, the curves of ΔG_m against concentrations will be either above or below the ideal one, as shown in Fig. 10.7.

In the binary Pb–Zn system between the temperatures of 590° and 1,070°K the two liquids present, that is lead rich and zinc rich, are not miscible in all proportions. There is therefore in the equilibrium phase diagram (see Fig. 10.8) a two liquid region. Let us use this system as an example for the application of the free energy change of mixing against concentration diagram to explain the type of curves

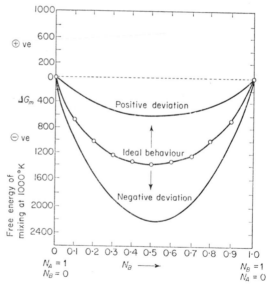

10.7

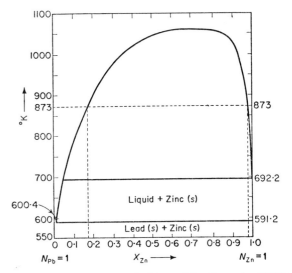

10.8. *From R. D. Rosenthal* et al., *Trans. Met. Soc., April* 1958, *p.* 15, *copyright A.I.M.E.*

we obtain in systems characterised by a miscibility gap and which show positive deviations from ideality.

The equation which we shall use for the calculation of ΔG_{m_T} is

$$\Delta G_{m_T} = RT(N_{Zn} \log_e a_{Zn} + N_{Pb} \log_e a_{Pb}) \quad \ldots (10.8)$$

The activities of zinc in the liquid lead–zinc alloy at different temperatures[7] are shown in Fig. 10.9, and the values taken from the graph are tabulated in Table 10.3. In Fig. 10.9 it can be seen that at the lower concentration the difference between the activity and the mole fraction of zinc in lead is very high, whereas the higher the concentration the lower the departure from ideality (Raoult's Law). Thus in the relationship $a_{Zn} = \gamma N_{Zn}$ at temperature 873°K and for $N_{Zn} = 0.2$ we find $a_{Zn} = 0.97$, and the activity coefficient is then given by

$$\gamma = \frac{a_{Zn}}{N_{Zn}} = \frac{0.97}{0.2} = 4.85$$

Since the activity coefficient is much greater than unity, the system therefore exhibits a positive deviation from the ideal behaviour which indicates that there are considerable repulsive forces between the lead and zinc atoms in the liquid alloy.

Between the zinc mole fraction of 0.23 and 0.98 at 873°K the zinc activity remains constant at 0.988 (Table 10.3).

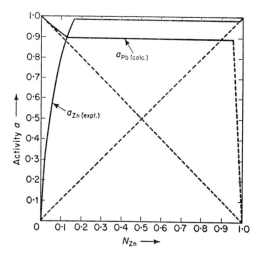

10.9. *From R. D. Rosenthal* et al., Trans Met. Soc., *April* 1958, *p.* 15, *copyright A.I.M.E.*

TABLE 10.3

Activities of Lead and Zinc at 873°K

N_{Pb}	a_{Pb}	N_{Zn}	a_{Zn}
0·005	0·15	0·995	0·997
0·01	0·3	0·99	0·995
0·015	0·45	0·985	0·99
0·02	0·6	0·98	0·988
0·03	0·89	0·97	0·988
0·85	0·89	0·5	0·988
0·9	0·92	0·4	0·988
0·95	0·95	0·2	0·97
—	—	0·154	0·967

From Rosenthal *et al.*, *Trans. Met. Soc.*, April 1958, copyright A.I.M.E.

The equilibrium free energies of mixing ΔG_m of molten lead in molten zinc at a temperature of 873°K were calculated from equation (10.8) using the activity values in Table 10.3. The non-equilibrium free energies of mixing $\Delta G'_m$ for a homogeneous solution of molten lead in molten zinc were calculated from Lumsden's equation (see page 75). Both sets of results are presented side by side in Table 10.4. Plots of these values of ΔG_m against concentration of zinc are

Table 10.4

Equilibrium and Non-equilibrium Free Energies of Mixing ΔG_m for Lead–Zinc System at 873°K.

N_{Zn}	Non-equilibrium $\Delta G'_m$ calculated from Lumsden's Equation in cal g mole^{-1} of alloy					Equilibrium ΔG_m from equation (10·8) in cal g mole^{-1} of alloy
	1st term	2nd term	3rd term	4th term	Total	
0	—	—	—	—	0	0
0·1	−563·5	349·6	42·1	−3·4	−175·2	−173
0·15	—	—	—	—	—	−179
0·2	−868	621·6	80·9	−12·3	−177·8	−173
0·3	−1,059	813·9	110·4	−25	−159·7	−149
0·4	−1,167	1,015	144·3	−38·7	−46·4	−128
0·5	−1,202	1,106	166·1	−44	+26·1	−107
0·6	−1,167	1,113	178	−55·7	+68·3	−93
0·7	−1,059	979·5	176·5	−51·2	+46	−75
0·8	−868	821·5	123·1	−37·2	+39·4	−57
0·9	−563·5	488	102·9	−15	+12·4	−31
0·995	−54·68	28·51	6·87	−0·06	−19·36	−20
0·999	−13·58	5·74	1·39	−0·002	−6·45	−7·7

shown in Fig. 10.10. The tangent drawn to the non-equilibrium $\Delta G'_m$/concentration curve has two points of contact A and B, representing the two compositions of lead rich (N_A) and zinc rich (N_B) alloys which can coexist. According to the tangency rule (see page 123) the chemical potential (or partial free energies) of lead and of zinc is the same for both these metals in both liquid alloys (N_A and N_B). This signifies that when these two liquid alloys are in contact there will be no net transfer of either lead or zinc between the alloys N_A and N_B, and thus they will be at equilibrium (dynamic equilibrium). From Fig. 10.10 it can be seen that in the range of concentrations between N_A and N_B two liquid alloys will exist as separate phases, since the total free energy of their separate phases taken together (given by the straight line A and B) is always lower, thus more stable, than that of complete miscibility given by the non-equilibrium upper curve calculated from Lumsden's equation.

It is interesting to note that the equilibrium free energy/concentration curve follows the tangent to A and B. In general equilibrium free energy curves in the immiscibility region give straight lines. Let us show it to be true in this case. In this case the two alloys of composition N_A and N_B are at equilibrium, and thus the chemical

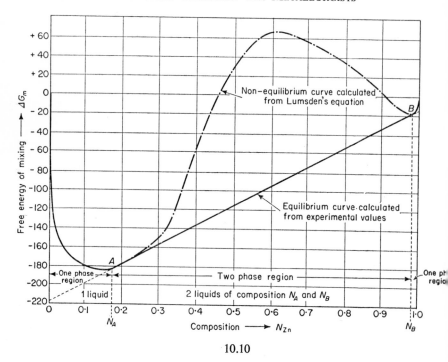

10.10

potential and the activity is the same for both these metals in both liquid alloys. From equation (10.8) we have

$$\Delta G_m = RT(N_{Pb} \log_e a_{Pb} + N_{Zn} \log_e a_{Zn})$$

Since

$$N_{Pb} + N_{Zn} = 1$$

thus

$$N_{Pb} = (1 - N_{Zn})$$

Substituting this value of N_{Pb} into equation (10.8) we have

$$\Delta G_m = RT[(1 - N_{Zn}) \log_e a_{Pb} + N_{Zn} \log_e a_{Zn}]$$

or

$$\Delta G_m = RT \log_e a_{Pb} + RTN_{Zn}(\log_e a_{Zn} - \log_e a_{Pb})$$

or

$$\Delta G_m = RT \log_e a_{Pb} + RTN_{Zn} \left(\log_e \frac{a_{Zn}}{a_{Pb}} \right) \quad \ldots (10.9)$$

Since in (10.9) both the first term and $\log_e \dfrac{a_{Zn}}{a_{Pb}}$ are constant between

$N_{Zn} = N_A$ and N_B, therefore this expression represents a straight line when ΔG_m is plotted against RTN_{Zn}. The slope of this plot gives the value of $\log_e \dfrac{a_{Zn}}{a_{Pb}}$, and the intercept of ΔG_m gives the value of $RT \log_e a_{Pb}$.

Applying the second law of thermodynamics it is clear that within the range of concentrations of zinc from $N_{Zn} = 0$ to $N_{Zn} = N_A$ and $N_{Zn} = N_B$ to $N_{Zn} = 1$, see Fig. 10.10, there is a complete solubility of zinc in liquid lead and the two free energy/concentration curves (equilibrium and non-equilibrium), allowing for the normal errors, overlap.

From this example we can see that, when there are positive deviations in the activity of solutions, then there is a tendency in the system for immiscibility, and this is always shown by an *upward kink* in the *non-equilibrium* free energy/concentration diagrams and by a *straight line* in the *equilibrium* free energy/concentration diagrams. This example also illustrates the application of the tangency rule for the determination of the composition of two liquid alloys which are at equilibrium.

10.5.1 The Two Components form a Compound with a Congruent Melting Point and are Completely Immiscible

If we assume a compound of composition A_xB_y is formed, then the equilibrium phase diagram illustrating this is shown in Fig. 10.11

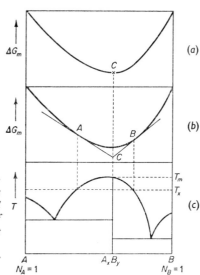

10.11
(a), (b) *Free energy change/concentration diagrams at temperatures T_m and T_x respectively. Points C represent the free energy change of formation of compound A_xB_y at these temperatures.*
(c) *Equilibrium phase diagram for a binary system.*

with the relevant free energy change/concentration diagram at a certain temperature denoted by T_x. At this temperature T_x, which is below the melting point of the compound A_xB_y, its free energy change value must according to the second law of thermodynamics, since it is stable, be below the ΔG_m for the same concentration. The points of contact of tangents to the curves of free energy change of liquid solution formation from the point C give the composition of liquid solutions that can coexist with the solid compound A_xB_y. The composition of these two liquids can be read from the diagrams and are found to be N_A and N_B.

The effect of temperature on the relative position of the free energy curve for liquid solutions and that of the compound are illustrated in the diagram above. At this temperature the point C is on the curve and therefore only one common tangent can be drawn through the point and the curve showing ΔG_m. Thus the composition at equilibrium of the liquid and the solid must be the same, and this is the highest temperature at which the solid can coexist with the liquid. In this case the solid A_xB_y is characterised by a **congruent** melting point.

10.5.2 *The Two Components are Completely Miscible in the Liquid State but only Partially Miscible in the Solid State*

There are many different possibilities for the relative positions of various free energy/concentration diagrams but in all cases the same

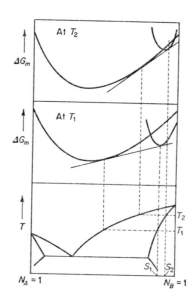

10.12. *The relative positions of the free energy changes with concentration are shown at temperatures T_1 and T_2; S_1 and S_2 represent the solid solutions of A and B respectively*

principles apply as in the previous examples. The main point to remember is that a common tangent to ΔG/concentration curves allows us to obtain the composition of phases at a given temperature whose components have exactly the same chemical potential, that is to say, no net transfer of any one component common to these two phases can take place without an external agency acting on the system (e.g. temperature, pressure, electrical force, change in concentration, etc.).

References

1 GIBBS, J. W., *The Scientific Papers*, Vol. I, p. 65, Dover Publications Inc., New York, 1961, (*Trans. Conn. Acad.*, 1875, 108–248).
2 KUBASCHEWSKI, O. and E. L. EVANS, *Metallurgical Thermochemistry*, second edition, 1958, Pergamon Press, Ltd., London, 1958.
3 KUBASCHEWSKI, O. "Symposium on the Thermodynamics of High Temperature Systems," *Trans. Brit. Cer. Soc.*, 1961, **60,** 67.
4 SCHENK, A., N. G. SCHMAHL, and A. K. BISWAS, *Arch. Eisenhutw.*, 1957, **28,** 517.
5 WAGNER, C., *Acta Met.*, 1954, **2,** 242.
6 WHITE, J. L., *Trans. Met. Soc.* A.I.M.E., 1959, **215,** 178.
7 ROSENTHAL, F. D., *et al.*, *Trans. Met. Soc.* A.I.M.E., 1958, **214,** 156.

CHAPTER XI

Chemical Kinetics

11.1 INTRODUCTION

In the preceding chapters we became acquainted with the basic concepts of thermodynamics and their importance to metallurgy in predicting the possible direction of a reaction, the equilibrium concentrations of reactants and products, and finally the effect of temperature, pressure and concentration on reactions and their equilibria. We have also seen that the application of thermodynamics enables us to calculate various energy changes associated with a process. However, the two main disadvantages of the thermodynamic treatment of processes are that: (i) all the equations which we use in thermodynamics refer to equilibrium conditions and usually refer to ideal behaviour, and (ii) thermodynamics does not allow us to predict the rate of possible reactions. For this reason another theoretical approach has been devised to study this aspect of reactions and is known as **kinetics.**

The field of study covered by the term kinetics, which in general deals with the rate at which processes occur (change of concentration of reactants per unit time), is very wide. Broadly speaking it can be divided into two main branches, firstly the kinetics of physical processes, and secondly that of chemical kinetics. The former deals with the study of the rates of such processes as distillation, physical separation of phases, and the flow of reactants to their place of reaction, which can all be of great interest to metallurgists. Chemical kinetics is mainly concerned with the rates at which certain chemical processes proceed, and until recently has been used very little by metallurgists. In this book we shall confine our discussion to that part of the field of kinetics which deals with chemical kinetics, and reference will only be made to the relevant physical processes in those cases where it is difficult to decide whether chemical kinetic factors or physical factors are the regulating steps in the reactions. The final aim in using the kinetic approach is to elucidate the atomic or molecular mechanism of a reaction, and from this knowledge to control the process with a view to making it possible or more economic.

11.2 KINETICS OF CHEMICAL PROCESSES

The velocity of a chemical process depends on the following four factors:

(i) The nature of reactants and products.
(ii) Temperature.
(iii) Concentration.
(iv) The presence of catalysts.

Let us consider each of these factors in turn and see how they influence the velocity of a chemical process.

11.2.1 *The Nature of Reactants and Products*

The first factor, in so far as the velocity of chemical bond formation is concerned, cannot be predicted completely from basic data. It is true that certain physical properties may indicate the speed of a chemical reaction. For example, the volume ratio of metallic oxide to metal may indicate that a given oxidation reaction will be fast when the oxide is porous, or slow when the oxide is non-porous, thus providing a diffusion barrier to the metal or oxygen. But even in these cases we cannot use such information to predict quantitatively the exact velocity of reactions under these conditions.

Another important factor which influences the overall velocity is the mobility of the reactants, which may control the supply of the reactants to the place of reaction. For instance chemical reactions in the solid phase are usually slow because of the physical factor of diffusion, whereas in liquids and especially in gases reactions are often very fast. But again the theories of chemical kinetics are not very helpful in this respect. We can therefore conclude that at present it is impossible to predict exactly the velocity of a chemical reaction from a knowledge of the electronic structure of the elements and molecules and their physical properties.

11.2.2 *The Effect of Temperature on Reaction Rate*

It is a well-known fact that the velocity of a chemical reaction is usually greater the higher the temperature. There are two main theories which enable us to predict the effect of temperature on the velocity of a reaction: the simple kinetic theory of a chemical reaction, frequently referred to as the collision theory, and the theory of absolute reaction rates.

11.3 SIMPLE KINETIC THEORY OF CHEMICAL REACTIONS—COLLISION THEORY

In 1889[1] Arrhenius noticed that an equation of the same form as the Van't Hoff isochore can account in the majority of cases for the effect of temperature on the rate of a reaction:

$$\frac{d \log_e k}{dT} = \frac{E_A}{RT^2}$$

This equation may be deduced from Van't Hoff's equation and the Law of Mass Action since

$$\frac{d \log_e K_c}{dT} = \frac{\Delta H}{RT^2}$$

Thus from the Law of Mass Action we have

$$K_c = \frac{k}{k'}$$

Substituting this value into the above equation we obtain

$$\frac{d \log_e k}{dT} - \frac{d \log_e k'}{dT} = \frac{\Delta H}{RT^2}$$

Let us assume that $\Delta H = Q - Q'$, where Q is the energy change of the forward reaction and Q' the energy change for the reverse reaction; then the above equation may be split up into the following two equations:

$$\frac{d \log_e k}{dT} = \frac{Q}{RT^2} + C \quad \text{and} \quad \frac{d \log_e k'}{dT} = \frac{Q'}{RT^2} + C'$$

If we assume the constants C are equal to zero then we obtain

$$\frac{d \log_e k}{dT} = \frac{Q}{RT^2}$$

It is customary to write the Arrhenius equation in its integrated form. Thus integrating this equation we have

$$\log_e k = -\frac{Q}{RT} + \log_e A$$

or

$$k = A \cdot e^{-\frac{Q}{RT}}$$

where A = integration constant

   k = specific reaction rate or velocity constant

   Q = energy of the forward reaction

This equation is thus based on the Law of Mass Action, and it is easy to imagine the basic reason for it. Since the forces between molecules operate at very short range only, the reaction can take place only in cases where, for example, the gaseous reacting molecules are almost in contact with each other, and therefore a collision between reacting molecules must be the primary prerequisite for reaction to occur. The theory at first suffered a set-back, since in the majority of gaseous reactions studied the number of molecules which reacted was only a small fraction of all the collisions. Arrhenius overcame this difficulty by suggesting that in every system there are *normal* and *active* molecules, and that at any temperature it is only collisions between active molecules which lead to a chemical reaction. The concepts of *activated molecules* and *activation energy* can be best explained from the Boltzmann's distribution law based on a statistical approach to the problem. The exponential factor $e^{-\frac{Q}{RT}}$ may be taken to represent the fraction of all the molecules which have an energy of activation at least equal to Q.

Let us consider the physical meaning of this energy of activation. In a system consisting of atoms or molecules there is a natural tendency for them to take up positions such that the energy of the system is a minimum. However, in many cases the path leading to the position of minimum energy for the system (thermodynamically stable position) is obstructed by a certain energy barrier (Q) (see Fig. 11.1).

From Fig. 11.1 it is clear that, unless molecules or atoms of the reactants A and B colliding together possess an excess energy of at least Q, they will not be able to overcome the energy barrier in order to proceed to the thermodynamically stable energy level of the products C and D.

From Boltzmann's statistical treatment it follows that the fraction of atoms colliding which possess sufficient energy to overcome this barrier is $e^{-\frac{Q}{RT}}$. The number of fruitful collisions resulting in a chemical reaction between the molecules is proportional to the fraction of atoms, possessing this energy Q, and thus we have

$$\text{reaction rate} \propto e^{-\frac{Q}{RT}} \propto k$$

or

$$k = Ae^{-\frac{Q}{RT}}$$

where k = specific rate constant

A = proportionality constant

This equation is of a very general form, and can be successfully applied to either any physical or chemical processes.

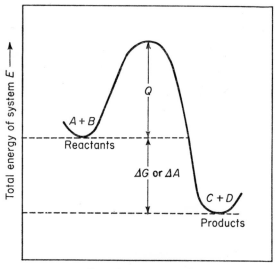

11.1. $Q = $ *energy of activation of the process.* $\Delta G = $ *free energy change for processes at constant pressure.* $\Delta A = $ *free energy change for processes at constant volume*

It follows from Fig. 11.1 that the difference in energy between products and reactants must be the energy of reaction, that is the Gibbs' free energy change for reactions carried out at constant pressure and the Helmholtz free energy for reactions proceeding at constant volume.

From Fig. 11.1 it will be seen that a prior knowledge of the value of ΔG or ΔA for a reaction is of no value for predicting the rate of the reaction.

11.3.1   *Energy of Activation and Free Energy Change of a Process*

The difference between the energy of activation and the free energy change of a reaction is illustrated in Fig. 11.2 by means of a mechanical analogy.

At A a ball is in its initial state. From the laws of mechanics it is clear that the most stable position of the ball, if allowed to proceed unhindered, would be at C. The energy which would be degraded would be the difference between the final energy and the initial energy of the ball. Since the value would be in this case negative, the system should proceed of its own accord to C. However, unless the

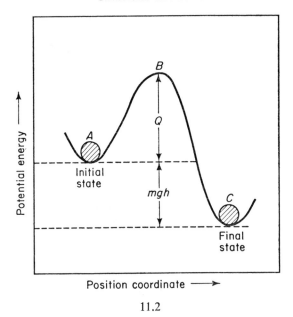

11.2

ball is given sufficient energy, such as kinetic energy, to overcome the peak B, it can never of its own accord move from A to C. Similarly in chemical reactions as molecules or atoms approach each other various energy barriers are encountered, and, unless the reacting molecules or atoms can overcome these barriers, they can never form a new chemical bond, thus the reaction will not take place.

From this simple consideration it is clear that only by coincidence may the value of ΔG be numerically the same as Q. It also follows that, providing the energy of activation is known, the effect of temperature on the rate of reaction can be easily evaluated.

The Proportionality Constant A. The constant A represents the frequency factor of encounters between the reacting molecules, irrespective of whether they possess sufficient energy to react or not. This value can be calculated theoretically for gaseous reactions.[2]

11.3.2 *Determination of the Energy of Activation*

Although some attempts have been made to evaluate the energy of activation from theoretical considerations, in the case of simple reactions it is invariably obtained as yet from experimental data. The rates of a chemical reaction are determined at different temperatures from isothermal plots of velocities of the reaction against time.

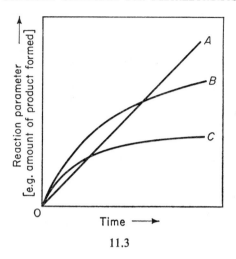

11.3

Since rate is defined as the extent of a reaction per unit time, therefore the rate can be determined from the slopes of these graphs.

The plots of the extent of a reaction with time may give curves of various shapes (some of these are shown in Fig. 11.3).

The line OA represents a linear behaviour with time, that is the velocity of the reaction is constant with time. OB represents parabolic and OC logarithmic behaviour. Because of the variety of possible curves it is sometimes difficult to evaluate with any degree of certainty the actual rates of a reaction. However, once the rate is determined at the various temperatures, then the actual calculation of the Arrhenius energy of activation Q and the reaction rate constant A is a simple matter.

In metallurgy the chemical kinetic treatment has been applied to very few processes, probably because of the practical difficulty of determining directly the rates of reactions. For this reason the progress of metallurgical chemical processes is usually followed indirectly by measuring some physical property of the system which is dependent on the extent of the chemical change and plotting the results against time. Thus changes in conductivity, resistivity, dimensions, weight and colour have often been followed, and such properties are referred to as the parameters of the reaction.

Let us consider a process whose rate constants k are known at various temperatures. Taking the logarithms to the base e of the Arrhenius equation we obtain

$$\log_e k = \log_e A - \frac{Q}{RT}$$

This equation gives a straight line when $\log_e k$ is plotted against $\frac{1}{T}$, since, providing A and Q are constant within the temperature range, the equation takes the form of $y = mx + c$, where y is $\log_e k$, x is $\frac{1}{T}$, and slope m gives us the value of $-\frac{Q}{R}$. Table 11.1 shows the values of $\log_e$ rates and $\frac{1}{T}$.

TABLE 11.1

$\log_e$ rate	y_1	y_2	y_3	y_4	y_5
$\frac{1}{T}$	x_1	x_2	x_3	x_4	x_5

The plots of $\log_e$ rate against $\frac{1}{T}$ are shown in Fig. 11.4. The slope of this graph is equal to $\frac{AB}{BC}$ and this is equal to $-\frac{Q}{R}$. Thus $Q = -(R \times \text{slope})$. The intercept OD on the y axis gives $\log_e A$ from which the value of A can be calculated.

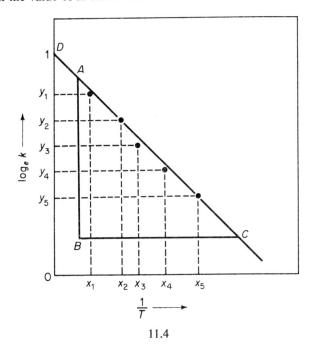

11.4

Numerical Example

From the experimental values given in Table 11.2 of the isothermal rates of dissolution of Ti in molten aluminium and the growth of titanium–aluminium intermetallic layers determine (*a*) the energy of activation of the 'dissolution' of titanium in aluminium, (*b*) the energy of activation for the formation of the intermetallic titanium–aluminium compound $TiAl_3$. From these calculated values, and a consideration of the curves showing the dimensional changes of titanium being 'dissolved' in liquid aluminium and the thickness of the intermetallic layers formed plotted against time shown in Figs. 11.5 and 11.6 respectively, comment on the possible mechanism of these processes.

TABLE 11.2

Temperature °C	Rate of Dissolution of Ti k_{Ti} (cm sec^{-1})	Rate of Growth of Interaction Layer $TiAl_3$ k_{TiAl_3} (cm sec^{-1})
700	$1 \cdot 51 \times 10^{-6}$	$1 \cdot 042 \times 10^{-5}$
750	$2 \cdot 605 \times 10^{-6}$	$1 \cdot 98 \times 10^{-5}$
800	$4 \cdot 17 \times 10^{-6}$	$2 \cdot 777 \times 10^{-5}$
850	$6 \cdot 13 \times 10^{-6}$	$3 \cdot 798 \times 10^{-5}$
900	$9 \cdot 36 \times 10^{-6}$	$6 \cdot 805 \times 10^{-5}$

The calculation of the activation energies is carried out as follows. Using the Arrhenius equation we have

$$k = A \times e^{-\frac{Q}{RT}}$$

which we can write

$$\log_e k = \log_e A - \frac{Q}{RT}$$

Let us convert for convenience $\log_e$ into $\log_{10}$ and since

$$\log_e x = 2 \cdot 303 \log_{10} x$$

then

$$\log_{10} k = \log_{10} A - \frac{Q}{RT \times 2 \cdot 303}$$

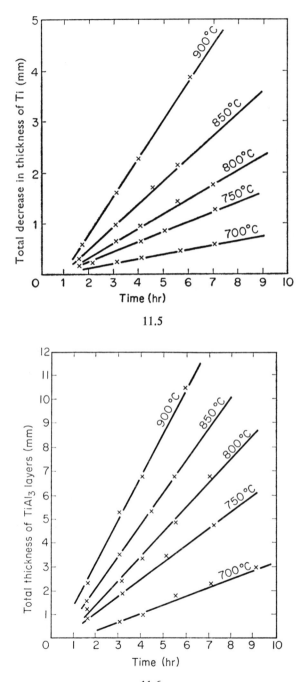

11.5

11.6

Thus the slope of this linear equation in respect of $\frac{1}{T}$ is equal to

$-\frac{Q}{2\cdot303R}$ and $Q = -2\cdot303R \times$ slope. To obtain the energy of activation Q and the equality constant A we must first calculate the values of $\log_{10} k$ and $\frac{1}{T}$ and these are shown in Table 11.3. These values are then plotted (see Fig. 11.7) to obtain the slope of the above linear equation.

TABLE 11.3

Tempera-ture °K	Rate of dissolution		Rate of growth of interaction layers		$\frac{1}{T}$
	$\log_{10} k_1$	colog k_1	$\log_{10} k_2$	colog k_2	
973	$\bar{6}\cdot1792$	$-5\cdot821$	$\bar{5}\cdot0178$	$-4\cdot9822$	$10\cdot24 \times 10^{-4}$
1,023	$\bar{6}\cdot4157$	$-5\cdot584$	$\bar{5}\cdot2967$	$-4\cdot7033$	$9\cdot776 \times 10^{-4}$
1,073	$\bar{6}\cdot6201$	$-5\cdot380$	$\bar{5}\cdot4436$	$-4\cdot5564$	$9\cdot318 \times 10^{-4}$
1,123	$\bar{6}\cdot7879$	$-5\cdot212$	$\bar{5}\cdot5795$	$-4\cdot4205$	$8\cdot906 \times 10^{-4}$
1,173	$\bar{6}\cdot9713$	$-5\cdot029$	$\bar{5}\cdot8328$	$-4\cdot1672$	$8\cdot52 \ \times 10^{-4}$

The value of the Arrhenius energy of activation Q and the constant A for the dissolution and growth processes, when calculated from the plots in Fig. 11.7, are found to be

$$Q_{\text{dissolution}} = 22 \pm 2 \text{ kcal}: A_{\text{dissolution}} = 0\cdot096 \pm 0\cdot003$$

$$Q_{\text{growth}} = 23 \pm 2 \text{ kcal}: A_{\text{growth}} = 1\cdot5 \pm 0\cdot5$$

Since the rate plots for both the dissolution of titanium and the growth of intermetallic layers are linear with time, and their energies of activation for all practical purposes are identical, it can be concluded that the dissolution of titanium in liquid aluminium depends on the rate of the chemical reaction between these two metals, and not the diffusion of either aluminium or titanium through the intermetallic layer formed on the surface of the solid titanium.

A knowledge of the values of Q and A for this intermetallic reaction enables us to calculate both the thickness of the inter-metallic layer formed in a given time and at a given temperature, and also the decrease in thickness of the titanium.

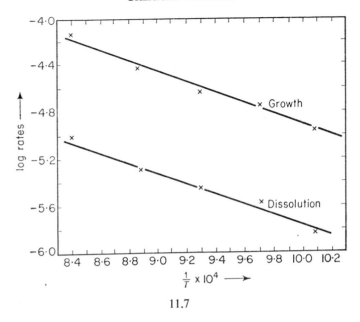

11.7

11.4 THE THEORY OF ABSOLUTE REACTION RATES

Although the simple collision theory of chemical kinetics is extremely useful for the interpretation of experimental data, it does not allow us to calculate with any certainty the rate of reaction from the number of collisions between the molecules possessing sufficient energy to react. The values calculated can differ widely from the experimental values by factors ranging anywhere between 10^{-6} and 10^4.

To overcome these difficulties various authors[3] developed what is known as the **theory of absolute reaction rates.** In this theory it is assumed that, before a reaction can take place between atoms or molecules, they have first to collide, and then form an activated complex, which in turn decomposes to give the products. Thus the reaction

$$\underbrace{A + B}_{\text{Reactants}} \rightarrow \underbrace{C + D}_{\text{Products}}$$

must now be rewritten as

$$\underbrace{A + B}_{\text{Reactants}} \xrightarrow{K^*} \underbrace{A \ldots B}_{\text{Activated Complex}} \longrightarrow \underbrace{C + D}_{\text{Products}}$$

where K^* represents the equilibrium constant between the reactants and the activated complex. Let us denote the free energy change for the equilibrium reaction between the reactants to give the activated complex as ΔG^*. Applying thermodynamics to the process we can write

$$\Delta G^* = -RT \log_e K^* \qquad \ldots(11.1)$$

Since K^* is the equilibrium constant between the reactants and the activated complex, then its value is given by

$$K^* = \frac{C_{(A \ldots B)^*}}{C_A \times C_B} \qquad \ldots(11.2)$$

where $C_{(A \ldots B)^*}$, C_A and C_B represent the appropriate concentrations.

On substitution of (11.2) into (11.1) we obtain

$$\Delta G^* = -RT \log_e \frac{C_{(A \ldots B)^*}}{C_A \times C_B} \text{ or } C_{(A \ldots B)^*} = C_A \times C_B \times e^{-\frac{\Delta G^*}{RT}} \qquad \ldots(11.3)$$

Equation (11.3) thus enables us to calculate the concentration of the activated complex at the temperature T, providing C_A, C_B and ΔG^* are known. It can be seen that the right-hand side of this equation resembles the Arrhenius equation. This reaction may be represented by the plot of energy against reaction co-ordinate (Fig. 11.8).

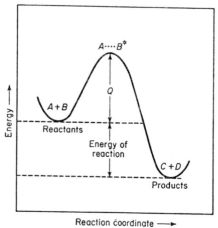

11.8

The rate of the overall reaction at any moment is assumed to be equal to the product of the concentration of the molecule of activated complex $(A \ldots B)^*$ at the top of the energy barrier ΔG^* and the frequency factor of crossing the barrier. It can be shown that this frequency factor is equal to RT/hN (here h is Planck's constant and N Avogadro's number) and the rate of the reaction v_r is given by

$$v_r = \frac{RT}{hN} C_{(A \ldots B)^*} \qquad \ldots(11.4)$$

When we substitute equation (11.3) for $C_{(A \ldots B)^*}$ into (11.4) we have

$$v_r = \frac{RT}{Nh} C_A C_B \, e^{-\frac{\Delta G^*}{RT}} \qquad \ldots(11.5)$$

From the relationship $\Delta G^* = \Delta H^* - T\Delta S^*$ we can write

$$v_r = \frac{RT}{Nh} \cdot e^{\frac{\Delta S^*}{R}} \cdot e^{-\frac{\Delta H^*}{RT}} \cdot C_A \cdot C_B \qquad \ldots(11.6)$$

Equation (11.6) is very interesting since it shows that, according to this theory, the rate of a reaction depends on a universal constant the first term of which is common to all reactions, on the values of the entropy change ΔS^* for the formation of the activated complex from the reaction and the enthalpy change ΔH^* of that reaction, and finally on the concentrations of the reactants.

It should be pointed out that, although the energy required to form the activated complex could be calculated from the knowledge of interatomic forces, in practice the calculated results very seldom agree with the experimental ones, and even then only as to the order of magnitude. This disagreement is considered to be the outcome of the complexity of the majority of reactions and our imperfect knowledge regarding the nature of interatomic forces.

11.5 EFFECT OF CONCENTRATION ON RATE OF REACTION

11.5.1 Introduction

When discussing the absolute theory of reaction rates it was shown (see equation (11.6)) that the concentrations of reactants have to be taken into account in any quantitative study of kinetics. In this section two new concepts will be introduced which will be extremely useful when considering the molecular or atomic mechanism of a chemical process. Let us then define these two concepts, which are molecularity and order of reaction, and then explain their physical meaning and the way they are determined.

Molecularity denotes the number of atoms or molecules that take part in each act leading to chemical reaction, and can be obtained from a balanced chemical equation.

Order of reaction denotes the number of reacting species (atoms or molecules) whose concentrations determine the kinetics of a process; this is determined experimentally, and is equal to the sum of the reactant concentration terms in the mathematical equation expressing the rate of reaction.

These two terms were regarded until very recently as synonymous, since this in fact appears to be the case for the majority of reactions. However, a distinction between these two sometimes has to be made; the reason for this will be clear if we consider the gaseous reactions between hydrogen and iodine and between deuterium and hydrogen.

The reaction between hydrogen and iodine is bimolecular and is found experimentally to be of the second order. Thus we have

$$\underbrace{H_2 + I_2}_{\text{2 molecules}} \rightarrow 2HI$$

On the other hand, although the balanced equation of the second reaction

$$D_2 + H_2 \rightarrow 2DH$$

looks identical with the previous one, its order of reaction is found experimentally to be 1·5.

Here, we have a bimolecular reaction having an order equal to one and a half, and to explain this the following two reaction stages have been postulated

$$H_2 \rightarrow 2H \quad \text{and} \quad D_2 \rightarrow 2D \qquad \ldots(11.7)$$

$$H + D_2 = HD + D \quad \text{and} \quad H_2 + D = HD + H \quad \ldots(11.8)$$

The overall rate of reaction is therefore determined by equations (11.8) and thus the rate v_r is given by

$$v_r = kp_{H_2} \times p_{D_2}^{\frac{1}{2}} = kp_{H_2}^{\frac{1}{2}} \times p_{D_2}$$

In this case we have $1\frac{1}{2}$ concentration terms, and thus the order of reaction will be $1\frac{1}{2}$. In general the rate of a reaction can be expressed by an equation of the form

$$v_r = k \times A^{n_A} \times B^{n_B} \times C^{n_C} \times \ldots \qquad \ldots(11.9)$$

The order of reaction is given by $n_A + n_B + n_C + \ldots$ and its value can be determined experimentally.

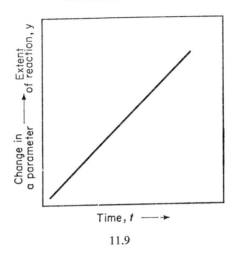

11.9

11.5.2 Zero Order Reactions

In a zero order reaction the rate of a reaction is constant with time. Thus a plot of the extent of the reaction y against time t gives a straight line (see Fig. 11.9). The slope $\dfrac{dy}{dt}$ gives the rate of reaction.

Let

$$\frac{dy}{dt} = k_0 \qquad \qquad \dots(11.10)$$

Integrating with respect to y and t we get

$$y = k_0 t + c \qquad \qquad \dots(11.11)$$

Here y is the reaction parameter which is being measured with time and which may be the concentration of the reacting substance, the decrease in dimensions of a solid metal, or the weight loss of a dissolving substance, etc. Oxidation of such metals[4] as sodium, potassium, titanium carbide, tungsten carbide, and certain solid–liquid metal reactions, such as those involving iron–zinc[5] between the temperatures 485–530°C and titanium–aluminium systems, are examples of zero order reactions.

Pseudo-Zero Order Reactions. Although the kinetic data from each of the above examples satisfies the zero order equation, it is clear that in every case the reaction must depend on the concentration terms of the reactants. In these cases, however, the reaction *appears* to be independent of the concentration of either of the reactants,

8

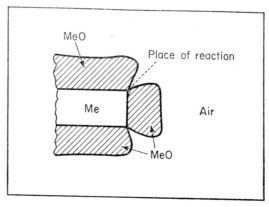

MeO

Place of reaction

Me

Air

MeO

11.10

since the concentration of, say, oxygen and of the metal at the place of reaction (interface) remains constant (see Fig. 11.10). The same is true for example in the reaction between solid titanium and liquid aluminium. Here the reaction takes place at the interface of the titanium metal, and thus its concentration is constant with time.

Since the intermetallic layer of $TiAl_3$, which is adherent to the Ti surface, is porous to molten aluminium, there is an unrestricted supply of this metal to the Ti interface, which is the place of reaction;[6] thus the concentrations of the reactants (Ti and Al) remain constant with time, and this reaction is of pseudo-zero order.

11.5.3 *First Order Reactions*

A reaction involving the decomposition of one molecule of reactant to give one or more molecules of the product usually proceeds according to the first order rate equation. For example the decomposition of nickel carbonyl at temperatures above 150°C can be represented by the equation

$$Ni(CO)_4 \rightarrow Ni + 4CO$$

In a first order reaction the rate is directly proportional to the concentration of the reacting substance, and this can be expressed mathematically as

$$-\frac{dy}{dt} = k_1 y \qquad \qquad \ldots(11.12)$$

where y is the concentration of the reacting substance and k_1 is the specific reaction constant. The minus sign indicates that the concentration of the reactant decreases with time. Let C_0 be the initial concentration and x the decrease in concentration, or the amount of reactant used up after the time t. Then the remaining concentration of the reactant at the time t will be $(C_0 - x)$. The rate of the reaction can then be obtained by substituting this value for y in equation (11.12). Thus

$$-\frac{d(C_0 - x)}{dt} = k_1(C_0 - x)$$

or

$$\frac{dx}{dt} = k_1(C_0 - x) \qquad \ldots (11.13)$$

The quantity $\frac{dx}{dt}$ is called the **reaction velocity** and the constant k_1 is known as the **specific reaction rate**, or **velocity constant**, or **velocity coefficient**.[7]

From equation (11.13) it can be seen that for a reaction proceeding at constant temperature both the reaction velocity and rate of change of reactant concentration can be calculated at any time by multiplying the instantaneous concentration of the reactant by the specific reaction rate. The specific reaction rate k_1 may be evaluated by integrating equation (11.13).

Thus the equation

$$\frac{dx}{dt} = k_1(C_0 - x)$$

becomes on rearrangement

$$\frac{dx}{(C_0 - x)} = k_1 \, dt$$

and since at time t the concentration is $(C_0 - x)$ while at $t = 0$ concentration is C_0 we can write

$$\int_{C_0}^{(C_0 - x)} \frac{dx}{(C_0 - x)} = k_1 \int_0^t dt$$

Integration gives

$$\log_e \frac{C_0}{(C_0 - x)} = k_1 t \qquad \ldots (11.14)$$

so we have

$$k_1 = \frac{2 \cdot 303}{t} \log_{10} \frac{C_0}{C_0 - x} \qquad \ldots (11.15)$$

Thus equation (11.15) enables us to calculate the specific reaction rate k_1 for the particular first order reaction we are studying.

In 1850 Wilhelmy was the first[8] to apply this mathematical treatment to experimental results obtained from the study of the inversion of sucrose. He actually denoted $(C_0 - x)$ as C_t, that is the concentration at the time t, and he expressed equation (11.14) in the form

$$C_t = C_0 \, e^{-k_1 t} \qquad \ldots (11.16)$$

Time to Complete a Definite Fraction of Reaction. Half-life Periods. The half-life period denotes the time in which the concentration of the reactant is reduced to half of its initial value. The time required for a definite fraction of a first order reaction to be completed, in this case 0·5 completion, can be conveniently calculated from equation (11.15) by substituting $\frac{1}{2}C_0$ for the value of $(C_0 - x)$; thus we have

$$k_1 = \frac{2 \cdot 303}{t_{0 \cdot 5}} \log_{10} \frac{C_0}{\frac{1}{2}C_0} = \frac{2 \cdot 303 \log_{10} 2}{t_{0 \cdot 5}} \qquad \ldots (11.17)$$

or

$$t_{0 \cdot 5} = \frac{2 \cdot 303 \log_{10} 2}{k_1} \qquad \ldots (11.17\text{A})$$

Equation (11.17A) shows that the half-life period for the disintegration of radioactive materials, which is a first order process, is independent of the initial number of atoms present, and depends only on the specific rate of disintegration k_1.

Pseudo-First Order Reactions. The meaning of pseudo-first order reactions will be illustrated using Wilhelmy's original system, in which he studied the inversion of cane sugar in aqueous solutions of acids by means of polarimetric measurements.

In this reaction each molecule of sucrose gives one molecule of glucose and one molecule of fructose according to the equation

$$\underset{\text{sucrose}}{C_{12}H_{22}O_{11}} + H_2O = \underset{\text{glucose}}{C_6H_{12}O_6} + \underset{\text{fructose}}{C_6H_{12}O_6}$$

Wilhelmy found that the reaction rate depended only on the concentration of sucrose, that is

$$\frac{dx}{dt} = k_1 C_{C_{12}H_{22}O_{11}}$$

and therefore was a first order reaction. However, according to the Law of Mass Action the forward reaction rate should be dependent on the concentrations of both sucrose and water, and the rate of inversion $\frac{dx}{dt}$ is given by

$$\frac{dx}{dt} = k_1 C_{(C_{12}H_{22}O_{11})} \times C_{H_2O}$$

Since in this reaction there is a very large excess of water molecules, the concentration of water can be considered constant throughout the inversion process, and we can write

$$\frac{dx}{dt} = k_1' C_{(C_{12}H_{22}O_{11})}$$

where now k_1' is equal to the product of the specific reaction constant k_1 and the concentration term (C_{H_2O}). The overall process can thus be interpreted in terms of a first order reaction.

Metallurgical Example of First Order Reactions. The sulphur transfer across a metal slag interface has been studied[9],[10],[11] in terms of chemical kinetics at temperatures from 1,500°C to about 1,700°C. At lower temperatures it was found that this process was a first order reaction.

11.5.4 *Second Order Reactions*

In these reactions the velocity depends on two concentration terms. If the rate of reaction between two molecules or atoms A and B depends on their concentrations, then this reaction will be one of the second order, and it will also be bimolecular, thus

$$A + B \rightarrow \text{products}$$

Let us now derive the mathematical expression for the specific reaction rate of a second order reaction. If C_a and C_b are the initial concentrations of A and B respectively, and x is the decrease in concentration of each after time t, then the rate of reaction $\frac{dx}{dt}$ is given by the following equation:

$$\frac{dx}{dt} = k_2(C_a - x) \cdot (C_b - x)$$

or

$$\frac{dx}{(C_a - x) \cdot (C_b - x)} = k_2\, dt$$

On integrating this equation within the limits $x = 0$ when $t = 0$ and $x = x$ when $t = t$ we obtain

$$\frac{dx}{(C_a - x)(C_b - x)} = k_2 \int_0^t dt$$

which gives

$$k_2 = \frac{1}{t(C_a - C_b)} \log_e \frac{C_b(C_a - x)}{C_a(C_b - x)} \qquad \ldots(11.18)$$

when k_2 is the specific reaction rate for the second order reaction.

Special Case for $C_a = C_b$. When the initial concentrations C_a and C_b are the same, it is clear that equation (11.18) cannot be used since the nominator and the denominator will become zero and

$$k_2 t = \frac{0}{0}$$

This mathematical difficulty can be overcome by using the fundamental rate equation; substituting C_a and C_b into it we obtain

$$\frac{dx}{dt} = k_2(C_a - x)(C_b - x),$$

and when $C_a = C_b$ we have

$$\frac{dx}{dt} = k_2(C_a - x)^2 \qquad \ldots(11.19)$$

On integration of equation (11.19) we have

$$k_2 = \frac{1}{t} \cdot \frac{x}{C_a(C_a - x)} \qquad \ldots(11.20)$$

From equation (11.20) an expression for the half-life period can be obtained by substituting $x = \frac{1}{2}C_a$. Thus

$$k_2 = \frac{1}{t \cdot C_a} \qquad \text{or} \qquad t_{0.5} = \frac{1}{k_2 C_a} \qquad \ldots(11.21)$$

It is interesting to note that in this case the time required to reduce the reactant concentrations by half is inversely proportional to the product of its original concentration and its specific reaction rate. It is therefore clear that under these conditions (where $C_a \neq C_b$) we cannot determine the value of k_2 from the half period alone, since we must know the initial concentration common to both reactants.

11.5.5 *Third and Higher Order Reactions*

There are very few gaseous chemical reactions of the third or higher orders, since it is thought that a simultaneous meeting of four or more molecules of the right kind before interaction could occur is very unlikely. It will be seen later that recent work suggests that in solutions and certain solid–liquid reactions between metals higher orders of reaction may be possible.

11.6 DETERMINATION OF ORDER OF REACTION

It is beyond the scope of this book to give a detailed account of the various methods for determining the order of reaction. However, it is intended to give here an outline of the principal methods which are available.

a. Integration method. In this method the experimental data are put into equations for the different orders of reaction, until an equation is found which satisfies the data. The specific rate constant k_x is then evaluated. This method is very useful in the case of simple reactions, but for more complicated ones other methods have to be used.

b. Half-life Method. In the previous section it was shown that the time taken to reduce the concentration of the reactants by half depended on the order of the particular reaction, and thus for the first order

$$t_{0.5} = \frac{1}{k_1}$$

for the second order

$$t_{0.5} = \frac{1}{k_2 C_0}$$

and for the nth order it can be shown to be

$$t_{0.5} = \frac{1}{k_n C_0^{(n-1)}} \qquad \ldots(11.22)$$

In all these equations C_0 denotes the initial concentration, which is the same for each of the reactants, and n is the order of reaction.

c. Van't Hoff's Differential Method. In homogeneous simple chemical reactions it has been found experimentally that the rate of reaction is proportional to the nth power of concentration of the reactants. Van't Hoff (1884) suggested a differential method for investigating kinetics, and proposed the following equation for an isothermal reaction:

$$-\frac{dx}{dt} = kC^n \qquad \ldots(11.23)$$

where C is the atomic or molecular concentration of the reacting atom or molecule, n is the order of reaction, and k its specific rate constant. When there are two reactants A and B, then it can be shown that equation (11.23) becomes

$$-\frac{dx}{dt} = k \cdot C_A^{n_A} \times C_B^{n_B}$$

where in this case the sum $n_A + n_B$ = order of the reaction.

d. *The Isolation Method.* This method was probably devised by W. Oswald (1902). If in a reaction of the type

$$n_A A + n_B B \rightarrow C + D$$

the conditions are adjusted in such a way that there is always a large excess of one of the reactants (for example B), then the equation as given by Van't Hoff's differential method for the initial rate of reaction will be

$$-\frac{dx}{dt} = kC_A^{n_A} \times C_B^{n_B} \ldots$$

Since in the early stages of the reaction C_B is essentially constant, the equation can be written as

$$-\frac{dx}{dt} = k'C_A^{n_A} \qquad \ldots(11.24)$$

where $k' = kC_B^{n_B}$ and is a new constant.

It is clear that from a determination of the initial rates at various concentrations of A the value of n_A can be obtained, plotting the logarithm of the initial rate against $\log C_A$. The equation for the plotted data is thus

$$\log \frac{-dx}{dt} = \log k' + n_A \log C_A \qquad \ldots(11.25)$$

The plot of log rate against $\log C_A$ gives a straight line whose slope is equal to n_A, and its intercept on the y-axis gives $\log k'$.

The following example involving the dissolution of solid titanium in molten aluminium will illustrate the application of the isolation method.

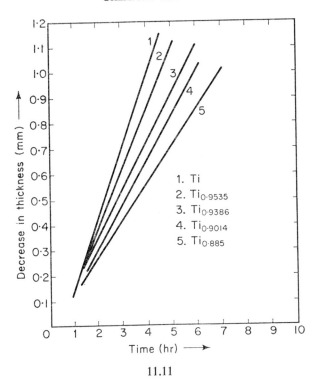

1. Ti
2. Ti$_{0.9535}$
3. Ti$_{0.9386}$
4. Ti$_{0.9014}$
5. Ti$_{0.885}$

11.11

Example

Fig. 11.11 shows the decrease in thickness of various titanium–aluminium alloys with time when in contact with molten aluminium at 800°C. Since in all cases the plots are straight lines, the rates are simply obtained from slopes of the lines (see section on zero order reactions). Data showing the rates obtained from these plots together with the respective compositions are given in Table 11.4.

TABLE 11.4

Atomic % of Ti	Log Atomic %	Rate cm sec^{-1}	Log Rate
100	2·00	4·201 × 10^{-6}	$\bar{6}$·6233
95·35	1·9793	3·527 × 10^{-6}	$\bar{6}$·5474
93·86	1·9725	2·944 × 10^{-6}	$\bar{6}$·4689
90·14	1·9549	2·50 × 10^{-6}	$\bar{6}$·3979
88·5	1·9420	2·222 × 10^{-6}	$\bar{6}$·3469

Let us now use the data in Table 11.4 to calculate what contribution titanium makes to the total order of the chemical reaction between solid titanium and molten aluminium.

In this case the chemical reaction takes place between Ti and Al atoms at their interface, and using Van't Hoff's differential method the rate $\dfrac{dc}{dt}$ is proportional to the rate of decrease in thickness and is thus given by

$$\frac{dc}{dt} = kC_{Ti}^{n_{Ti}} \times C_{Al}^{n_A} \qquad \ldots(11.26)$$

where k is the specific rate constant and n_{Ti} and n_{Al} are the contributions of Ti and Al to the overall order of reaction; C_{Ti} and C_{Al} are the atomic concentrations of $Ti_{(s)}$ and $Al_{(l)}$ respectively. In view of the fact that in this reaction the solubility of Ti in molten Al is small, it can be assumed that $C_{Al} \simeq 1$, and thus the term $C_{Al}^{n_{Al}} \simeq 1$. On substitution of this value into equation (11.26) we have

$$\frac{dc}{dt} = kC_{Ti}^{n_{Ti}}$$

where C_{Ti} is the concentration of titanium in the solid phase. Taking logarithms of this equation we obtain

$$\log \frac{dc}{dt} = \log k + n_{Ti} \log C_{Ti}$$

This is a straight line equation and therefore by plotting log rate against log atomic concentration of the isolated component, that is titanium, the value of the contribution of titanium to the total order of reaction n_{Ti} is given by the slope. Fig. 11.12 shows the plot obtained from the data given in Table 11.4; the slope of the straight line is found to be $\simeq 6$.

In this example the contribution of the titanium atoms to the total order of reaction at 800°C is found to be $n_{Ti} \simeq 6$.

This example illustrates how, by combining the Van't Hoff's differential method with the Oswald isolation method (here the C_{Al} was made the same throughout each experiment), we can determine experimentally the value for n_{Ti} which is the contribution of titanium to the total order of this intermetallic reaction.

In a homogeneous system the order of reaction can in the majority of cases be interpreted as the minimum number of atoms or molecules which take part in a complete reaction.[12] A knowledge of the total and partial orders of a given reaction often enables us to elucidate the mechanism of the reaction after suitable consideration of all possible equilibria between the reactants and products.

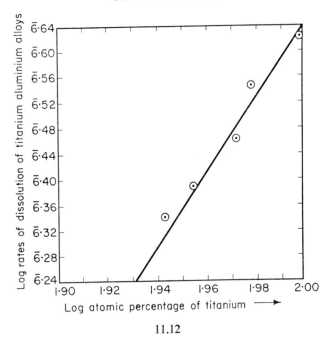

11.12

In heterogeneous systems involving the dissolution or formation of phases,[13] there are often distinct consecutive processes to be considered such as

(i) Solute molecules approach and collide with the surface.
(ii) A chemical reaction takes place.
(iii) Nucleation of a new phase.
(iv) Recession of the products of reaction from the interface into the bulk of the solutions.

The overall rate of the reaction is naturally determined by the slowest step.

A high order of reaction may indicate nucleation to be the rate determining step.

Christiansen and Nielsen[14] postulated from their results on the precipitation of $BaSO_4$ that formation of clusters of four barium ions and four sulphate ions is the rate determining step.

Berelius[15] showed that in the Pb–Sn system the number of atoms forming an aggregate at 360°C is 90 and at 400°C it is 140. In all these cases the new phase formation can only proceed if the phase formed is stable and does not redissolve in the solvent (whether liquid or solid).

11.7   CONSECUTIVE AND SIMULTANEOUS REACTIONS

Reactions can generally be classified according to the chemical and physical properties of the reactants. In the preceding sections reactions were considered from the point of view of chemical kinetics, and thus led us to consider various orders of reactions.

From a physical point of view reactions may be homogeneous, that is they take place in a single phase such as a solution, or heterogeneous as in gas–solid, liquid–solid, and gas–liquid reactions.

Chemical reactions may also be classified according to the number of steps by which they proceed. We have already considered opposing reactions which explained the concept of equilibrium constants (p. 105). In this case we discussed the equilibrium set up by

$$A + B \underset{v_2}{\overset{v_1}{\rightleftharpoons}} C + D$$

where v_1 and v_2 were the velocities of the forward and reverse reactions respectively. Another type of reaction is recognised as the result of the products being unstable, and thus a series of *consecutive steps* may occur. This type of reaction can be represented by

$$A \overset{k_1}{\longrightarrow} B \overset{k_1'}{\longrightarrow} C \overset{k_1''}{\longrightarrow} D$$

where k_1, k_1' and k_1'' are the specific rate constants of the consecutive reactions. If one of these steps is very much slower than the other, then it is this one which is the **rate determining (regulating) step** for the overall reaction $A \rightarrow D$. In chemical kinetics we frequently require to elucidate such a step, since then we can perhaps devise a method of speeding up the change in order to make the process more economic.

In some processes reactants may react in two or more simultaneous ways, thus giving two or more products. This type of reaction is known as a **simultaneous** or **parallel reaction.** It can be represented as

$$A \rightarrow \begin{cases} \rightarrow k_1 \rightarrow B \\ \rightarrow k_1' \rightarrow C \\ \rightarrow k_1'' \rightarrow D \end{cases}$$

where A is the reactant and B, C and D are the products, and k_1 and k_1' and k_1'' are the specific rate constants. Obviously the relative amounts of B, C and D produced with time will depend on the values of their specific rate constants .It is interesting to note that, since the energies of activation of the three parallel reactions are most probably different, then by raising the temperature of the reaction, we may bring about a considerable change in the relative amounts of B, C and D which are produced. Again, if the three activation energies differ very greatly, a lower temperature of reaction may practically eliminate the formation of, say, C and D, so as to give almost pure B as the product.

11.8 CATALYSIS IN CHEMICAL REACTIONS

11.8.1 *Introduction*

In the preceding sections three of the four factors which affect the velocity of chemical reactions were considered. In this section we shall consider the fourth factor which may alter the reaction rate, namely the presence of catalysts in reacting systems.

It has long been known that the presence of even traces of foreign substances may have a pronounced effect on both the initiation and the velocity of a reaction. Thus oxygen and hydrogen may be mixed and kept 'indefinitely' at room temperature without interacting, but the introduction of platinum powder into the system results in combination between the two gases on the surface of the metal with the formation of water. It is also known that concentration as low as 10^{-6} g mole litre^{-1} of molybdic acid doubles the velocity of the reaction between hydrogen peroxide and hydrogen iodide.

These examples are but two of the numerous examples of catalytic action. The first example illustrates a heterogeneous type of catalysis, while the other is an example of homogeneous catalysis.

A catalyst can therefore be defined as a substance which affects the velocity of a reaction but is itself not represented as a reagent in a chemical equation. If the presence of such a substance results in an increased reaction rate, then the substance is often called a **positive catalyst** or just simply a **catalyst**. However, if the substance causes a decrease in the reaction rate, then it is known as a **negative catalyst** or **inhibitor.**

It is interesting to note that some reactions which normally proceed very quickly will not take place at all if the reactants are perfectly dry, or when a catalyst is absent.

11.8.2 *Properties of Catalysts*

Although catalytic reactions may be either heterogeneous or homogeneous, they have the following three characteristics in common:

(i) The catalyst remains unchanged chemically at the end of the reaction.

(ii) A very small amount of a catalyst may maintain an increased reaction velocity for long periods of time.

(iii) The catalyst does not influence the position of equilibrium in reversible reactions.

Let us now consider these three common characteristics of catalysts in turn.

(i) *Chemical Stability of the Catalyst.* This common characteristic refers to the fact that the chemical nature of the catalyst, as well as the total amount, remains constant with time. Although in practice the chemical nature remains constant, its physical nature undergoes a change. For example, when lumps of manganese dioxide are used as a catalyst in the decomposition of potassium chlorate, they are found at the end of the decomposition to consist of a fine powder. This change in the physical nature of the catalyst is also illustrated by the reaction between hydrogen and oxygen. Here, if initially shiny metallic platinum is used as a catalyst, it is found after a certain time to be coated with fine particles of platinum.

These two examples indicate that the surface of solid catalysts must take some part in speeding up these chemical reactions.

(ii) *A Very Small Amount of a Catalyst may Maintain a Higher Reaction Rate for Long Periods of Time.* Although in practice some of the catalysts are extremely efficient for certain specific reactions (see previous examples), it is found that, in the majority of cases of homogeneous catalysis, increase in the reaction rate is proportional to the catalyst concentration. In heterogeneous catalytic reactions involving reactant gases and solid surfaces the total surface area of the solid may also influence the rate of reaction.

(iii) *Catalysts do not Influence the Position of Equilibrium in Reversible Reactions.* It is an experimental fact that the presence of a catalyst in a system does not affect the position of equilibrium. This fact is also consistent with thermodynamic considerations. It is clear that, since during a catalytic reaction the chemical nature of the catalyst remains constant, the catalyst does not supply any chemical energy to the system. Thus the free energy change for the chemical reaction is unaltered by the addition of the catalyst. It follows from Van't Hoff's Isotherm that the equilibrium constant for this reaction must be the same with or without a catalyst.

Any theories regarding the catalytic effect of substances will thus have to account for these three characteristic factors.

11.8.3   *Theories of Catalysis*

The name catalysis was first used by Berzelius in 1835. There is at present no universal explanation of catalysis; it is probable that the role of the catalyst differs according to the reaction in which it is employed. However, it is convenient to discuss catalysis according to the two classes: homogeneous and heterogeneous.

Homogeneous Catalysis. In a homogeneous catalytic reaction the catalyst is uniformly distributed throughout the system. Usually we distinguish between gaseous and liquid systems.

The function of the catalyst is to decrease the activation energy of the given reaction, and thus to increase its rate, because more molecules will then have the required energy for reaction to occur. This is thought to be achieved by forming a compound between the reactants and the catalyst, which then decomposes to regenerate the catalyst and form the reaction products.

Thus in a reaction between reactants A and B to give a product AB without a catalyst, we find $A + B \rightarrow AB$. In the presence of a catalyst C the reaction may be represented as proceeding in the following two steps:

$$A + C \rightarrow AC$$

$$AC + B \rightarrow AB + C$$

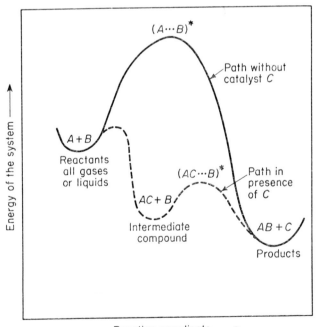

Reaction coordinate ⟶

11.13

From Fig. 11.13 it is clear that the rate of compound formation along the reaction path in the presence of a catalyst will be much higher than that without a catalyst.

If the intermediate compound AC is too unstable, C cannot act as a catalyst, while if it is too stable the reaction ceases. The intermediate compound AC must therefore be of the right degree of stability for the catalyst to be effective.

It must be emphasised that the catalyst will accelerate the forward reaction to the same extent as the reverse reaction, so that their ratio

$$\frac{k_1}{k_2} = k$$

is unaffected.

The following two cases provide examples of homogeneous catalytic reactions:

(i) *Gaseous—the action of nitric oxide in increasing the rate of reaction between sulphur dioxide and oxygen to give sulphur trioxide.* This reaction without a catalyst can be represented by the equation

$$2SO_2 + O_2 \rightarrow 2SO_3$$

It proceeds extremely slowly. The catalytic action of nitric oxide on the reaction may be represented by the following equations

$$2NO + O_2 \rightleftarrows 2NO_2$$

$$2SO_2 + 2NO_2 \rightleftarrows 2SO_3 + 2NO$$

$$2NO + O_2 \rightleftarrows 2NO_2, \text{ etc.}$$

In this case the AC intermediate compound is the $2NO_2$, and the catalyst nitric oxide is regenerated continuously.

(ii) *Liquid.* The action of acids and bases which catalyse such reactions as the hydrolysis of cane sugar to glucose (see page 214).

Heterogeneous Catalysis. In this type of catalysis the catalyst is not uniformly distributed throughout the system, but forms a separate phase. These catalysts have been conveniently classified according to their functions by Bond.[16] Numerous examples of this type of catalysis are to be found in the use of solid catalysts for many gaseous reactions. The well-known Haber Process is an example of such a reaction. Here ammonia is synthesised from a mixture of nitrogen and hydrogen, which is passed over a heated catalyst of either platinum or iron containing a promoter (see page 228).

The Adsorption Theory of Heterogeneous Catalysis. This theory considers that the gaseous reactants are first adsorbed on the surface

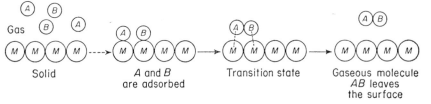

Gas

Solid

A and B
are adsorbed

Transition state

Gaseous molecule
AB leaves
the surface

11.14

of the catalyst, and then, after passing through a transition state, they form a compound with simultaneous desorption from the surface. Fig. 11.14 shows diagrammatically these three steps for a reaction $A + B \rightarrow AB$. When one considers the surface of any metal it is clear that there is a net resultant force on each atom in the surface acting inwards towards the bulk of the metal. This is the reason for the existence of surface tension in liquids and solids. Since each atom in the bulk of the solid metal forms more bonds than those in the surface, it follows that the latter must have one or more unused valencies available to form chemical bonds in an outward direction from the metal surface (free valencies). One can visualise the adsorption of gas molecules as an interaction between these free valencies of the surface atoms of the metal and the gaseous molecules. Furthermore, it can be argued that, since the gaseous molecules are now more restricted (cannot move as freely), the entropy change on adsorption must be negative. Since

$$\Delta G = \Delta H - T\Delta S$$

and since the value of ΔG must be negative, it follows that the condition for adsorption to take place is that the process must be exothermic.

Again, similarly to the intermediate compound theory, the efficiency of the catalyst will depend on the stability of the intermediate step. If the binding forces between the adsorbed reactants and the catalyst surface (see Fig. 11.14) are too strong, the formation of the transition state and the removal of the product will be difficult and the catalyst may be poisoned, that is to say made ineffective; on the other hand, if the reactants are adsorbed too weakly, they may not remain long enough on the surface to react.

It is beyond the scope of this book to consider theoretically the types of adsorption and their influence on catalytic action. It is possible however to calculate with reasonable accuracy the rates of adsorption for many systems.[16] In many heterogeneous processes it is found that the activation energy for the catalysed process is between

20 to 40 kcal less than that of the corresponding homogeneous process. Some comparative values[17] of the given activation energies are shown in Table 11.5.

TABLE 11.5

Decomposing compound	Catalysing surface	$Q_{heterog.}$ kcal	$Q_{homog.}$ kcal
Hydrogen iodide	Gold	25·0	44·0
Hydrogen iodide	Platinum	14·0	44·0
Nitrous oxide	Gold	29·0	58·5

From Glasstone's *Textbook of Physical Chemistry*, copyright 1946, D. Van Nostrand Company, Inc., Princeton, N.J.

Negative Catalysts. It is sometimes beneficial to retard chemical reactions by the presence of other substances. A substance which causes the retardation of a reaction is called a **negative catalyst.** Negative catalysts can act in two different ways:

(i) they can change the normal mechanism of a reaction in the way that lead tetraethyl is used in petrol to prevent a premature reaction between petrol vapour and oxygen in a cylinder of an engine on compression, or

(ii) they remove positive catalysts by combining with them, as when a small amount of urea renders nitrocellulose stable (and thus safe) by removing nitrogen oxides, which are positive catalysts for the decomposition of nitrocellulose.

Promoters. The activity of a catalyst may sometimes be increased by adding some other substance or substances to it, which are not necessarily themselves catalysts. In the Haber process it was found that a mixture of iron, alumina and potassium oxide had much greater catalytic effect than iron alone.

REFERENCES

1 ARRHENIUS, S. A., *Z. Phys. Chem.*, 1889, **4**, 226.
2 DANIELS, F., *Outline of Physical Chemistry*, p. 377, Chapman & Hall Ltd., London, John Wiley & Sons, Inc., New York, 1948.
3 MOELWYN-HUGHES, E. A., *The Kinetics of Reactions in Solution*, second edition, Clarendon Press, Oxford, 1947.
GLASSTONE, S., *Textbook of Physical Chemistry*, second edition, p. 1098, Macmillan & Co. Ltd., London, 1946.
4 KIEFFER, R. and F. KOLBL, *Z. Anorg. Chem.*, 1950, **262**, 229–247.
5 SCHEIL, E. and H. WURST, *Zeit. Metal.*, 1937, **7**, 224–229.
6 MACKOWIAK, J. and L. L. SHREIR, *J. Less Com. Met.*, 1959, **1**, 456–465.

7 See reference 3 above, p. 1046.
8 MOORE, W. J., *Physical Chemistry*, second edition, p. 428, Longmans, Green & Co. Ltd., London, 1956.
9 GOLDMAN, DERGE, and PHILBROOK, *J. Met.*, 1954, **6,** 534.
10 TRAVIN and SHVARTSMAN, Sessicya Akad. Nauk., S.S.S.R. Mirnomu, Izpol, Zovaniyu Atomni Energia, zasedaniyon *Otd. Tekh. Nauk.*, 1955, p. 48.
11 SKALA and TRAVIN, *Hutn. Listy.*, 1957, **12,** 1000.
12 See reference 3 above.
13 GARNER, W. E. (Ed.) *Chemistry of the Solid State*, contribution by Dunning, Butterworth & Co. (Publishers) Ltd., London, 1955.
14 CHRISTIANSEN and NIELSEN, *Acta Chem. Scand.*, 1951, **5,** 673.
15 BERELIUS, *Arkiv. Mat. Fysik.* (A), 1, 1945, i.
16 BOND, G. C., *Catalysis by Metals*, p. 2, Academic Press Inc., London, 1962.
17 See reference 3 above, p. 1146.

CHAPTER XII

Electrochemistry—Conduction by Electrolytes

12.1 INTRODUCTION

Electrochemistry is concerned in general with the study of the quantitative relationship between the electrical and chemical aspects of matter. Thus the ultimate aim of this study is to predict quantitatively either the chemical effects produced in an electrolyte* by the passage of electricity, or the amount of electricity that can be produced by a chemical reaction. Our present knowledge of both of these aspects has proved extremely useful in such diverse branches of metallurgy as extraction and refining of metals, understanding of the mechanism of corrosion and protection of metals, metallurgical analysis, and production of electric power by means of chemical cells.

In general the study of electrochemical phenomena has proved useful in the better understanding of the constitution of matter. The knowledge gained has been frequently applied both in the theoretical treatment of existing processes and in the development of new ones.

Its origin can be attributed to Swammerdam,[1] who in 1678 demonstrated the contraction of a frog's muscle when in contact with a silver wire soldered to a copper base. Nearly a hundred and ten years later this phenomenon was rediscovered by Galvani, who produced the same effect by contracting the nerves with couples of dissimilar metals. Volta[2] explained this effect by attributing the contraction to the discharge of electricity through the nerve. He subsequently developed many different electric cells by separating two dissimilar metals, such as zinc–silver, tin–copper, and zinc–copper couples with materials impregnated with salt solutions or acids.[2]

These cells, by providing a continuous supply of electric current,

* Compounds which in solution or the fused state conduct an electric current with simultaneous decomposition.

enabled him to make a systematic study of the behaviour of different electrical conductors.

Nowadays all conductors of electricity are classified as either: (i) **metallic** or **electronic,** (ii) **electrolytic** or **ionic,** or (iii) **mixed conductors.**

In the first type electrons alone are responsible for the transfer of electricity and the conductor remains for all practical purposes chemically unchanged.

In the second type the passage of electricity through the conductor is brought about by the movement of positive and negative ions, and is therefore accompanied by the transfer of matter. The electrolytic conductors can be further subdivided into pure substances, such as fused salts, and solutions, such as aqueous solutions of salts, acids and bases.

Certain oxides and sulphides can be classified as mixed conductors, since here the conduction of electricity occurs by both the electronic and the ionic type of conduction. In silver sulphide 80% of the conduction is electrolytic and the rest electronic.

In electrochemistry we are concerned only with the electrolytic type of conduction.

12.2 ELECTROLYSIS AND FARADAY'S LAWS

The discovery of electric cells by Volta was the starting point of the systematic study of electrolysis. Nicholson and Carlisle[3] showed that water was decomposed by current into oxygen and hydrogen gas, oxygen being evolved at the positive pole and hydrogen at the negative pole. Solutions of various salts were decomposed in this way, and in 1807 Davy succeeded in obtaining metallic potassium and sodium from their fused hydroxides respectively.[4]

From 1813 Faraday carried out an extensive systematic study of the qualitative and quantitative aspects of electrolysis, and between 1833 and 1834 published[5] a series of papers which formed the basis of well-known laws of electrolysis. These laws may be summarised as follows:

(i) Chemical decomposition during electrolysis occurs only at the electrodes.

(ii) The amount of chemical decomposition (measured by weight or volume) during electrolysis is directly proportional to the strength of the current and the time for which it flows, that is to the quantity of electricity which passes through the solution. The electrochemical equivalent of a substance is that weight in grammes which is liberated at an electrode by the passage of one coulomb of electricity through a solution of an electrolyte.

(iii) If the same quantity of electricity is passed through a number of different electrolytes, the weights of the substances liberated are in proportion to their chemical equivalents.

From these laws it follows that the same amount of electricity is required to liberate one gramme equivalent of substance from any electrolyte. This quantity of electricity, which is called a **Faraday** and denoted by F, is equal to 96,494 coulombs. Faraday also suggested that the two poles should be called electrodes, the negative electrode being called the cathode and the positive one the anode. Metals in solution which were deposited at the cathode during electrolysis he termed **cations,** while substances such as chlorine and iodine were termed **anions** in solutions, since they were evolved at the anode.

Thus Faraday assumed the flow of electricity to be due to the movement of charged particles which we call ions, cations moving towards the cathode and anions towards the anode. On reaching the electrodes these ions are usually deposited in the form of neutral atoms or molecules.

Faraday's laws imply that each ion is associated with a definite quantity of electricity, and, since the number of ions in one mole of any univalent substance is equal to the Avogadro's number $N = 6\cdot023 \times 10^{23}$, therefore it is possible to calculate the charge which is associated with one ion.

Thus

$$\frac{F}{N} = \frac{96,494}{6\cdot023 \times 10^{23}} = 1\cdot602 \times 10^{-19} \text{ coulombs (amp-secs)}$$

This quantity of electricity will deposit 107·88 g of silver or $\dfrac{63\cdot57}{2}$ g of copper or 1·0081 g of hydrogen.

The electrochemical equivalent of any substance can thus be calculated by dividing its gramme ion weight by the Faraday number multiplied by the number of charges which the ion possesses. Thus the electrochemical equivalent of silver is given by

$$\frac{107\cdot88}{96,494} = 0\cdot001118 \text{ g coulombs}^{-1}$$

and that of Cu^{++} by

$$\frac{63\cdot57}{2 \times 96,494} = 0\cdot000326 \text{ g coulombs}^{-1}$$

Table 12.1 gives the electrochemical equivalents of some elements.

TABLE 12.1

Element	Electrochemical Equivalent mg coulomb^{-1}	Valency
Silver	1·1180	1
Aluminium	0·0932	3
Gold	0·6812	3
Bismuth	0·722	3
Cadmium	0·5824	2
Chromium	0·1797	3
Copper (divalent)	0·3294	2
Copper (monovalent)	0·6588	1
Hydrogen	0·01045	1
Oxygen	0·0829	2
Chlorine	0·3674	1

12.3 MECHANISM OF ELECTROLYTIC CONDUCTION

The mechanism of electrolytic conduction was at first a matter of much speculation. Although it was believed that it took place by the transfer of positively and negatively charged ions, it was not clear how charged ions could exist in solutions. Thus Grotthus in 1805 proposed the so-called chain theory, while Clausius in 1857 put forward his ionic theory, which postulated an equilibrium between charged ions and the undissociated electrolyte. During electrolysis each ion moved towards the electrode possessing an opposite electric charge, and, once the ions came into contact with an electrode, they became discharged. In 1887 Arrhenius[6] proposed the theory of electrolytic dissociation, which was to form the basis of our modern treatment of electrolytes. Arrhenius proposed that, when an acid, base, or salt is dissolved in water, then a considerable amount of it is dissociated into positive and negative ions: thus

$$AB \rightleftarrows A^+ + B^-$$

These ions are free in the solution, and during electrolysis they move towards oppositely charged electrodes. Arrhenius considered that an equilibrium existed between the ions and the undissociated molecules of the solute, the proportion of dissociated molecules α depending on the concentration of the solution. Arrhenius proposed that the **degree of dissociation** α, that is the fraction of the total electrolyte split up into ions, approaches unity at infinite dilution.

This theory of electrolytic dissociation became very popular, since it was able to explain such abnormal behaviour of electrolytic solutions as

(i) lowering of vapour pressure,
(ii) depression of freezing point,
(iii) elevation of boiling point,
(iv) osmotic pressure.

For example, the depression of freezing point was often found to be two to three times lower than that observed for non-electrolytic solutions at the same molar concentration. Van't Hoff[7] on the other hand had shown that different solutions of the same molar concentration generally gave the same freezing point depression, electrolytic solutions being the only exception to this rule. Van't Hoff used the factor i, which is the ratio of the observed depression of freezing point to that calculated from its molar concentration, to express the abnormal behaviour of electrolyte solutions where

$$i = \frac{\text{observed depression of freezing point}}{\text{calculated depression of freezing point}}$$

Arrhenius obtained a series of values of the Van't Hoff's factor for a range of electrolytes comprised of acids, bases, and salts. He used two independent methods to determine i, by measuring the depression of the freezing point, and by comparing the conductivity values at a given concentration and at infinite dilution. Table 12.2 shows some of the results obtained.

By comparing the values of i (Table 12.2) obtained directly from freezing points measurements with those obtained from conductivity measurements, Arrhenius showed the relationship between i, the degree of dissociation α, and the number of ions ν produced by the dissociation of one molecule of the solute. Let us suppose that there are n molecules of the solute in a given volume of a solution. Then the number of undissociated molecules is $n(1 - \alpha)$ and of ions $n\nu\alpha$. The total number of 'free particles' is therefore

$$n(1 - \alpha) + n\nu\alpha = n(1 - \alpha + \nu\alpha) \tag{12.1}$$

Since

$$i = \frac{\text{observed depression of freezing point}}{\text{calculated depression of freezing point}}$$

$$= \frac{\text{total number of particles}}{\text{total number of molecules}}$$

thus

$$i = \frac{n(1 - \alpha + \nu\alpha)}{n} = 1 - \alpha + \nu\alpha \qquad \ldots(12.2)$$

or

$$\alpha = \frac{i - 1}{\nu - 1} \qquad \ldots(12.3)$$

The value of i from the conductivity measurements was obtained from equation (12.2) by substituting the value of $\dfrac{\Lambda_c}{\Lambda_\infty}$ for α, where Λ_c is the equivalent conductance at concentration c and Λ_∞ is its value at infinite dilution. The new equation then becomes

$$i = 1 + (\nu - 1)\frac{\Lambda_c}{\Lambda_\infty} \qquad \ldots(12.4)$$

TABLE 12.2

Arrhenius Values of Van't Hoff's Factor i in 0·1 % solutions[8]

Solutions	i from depression of freezing point	i from conductivity
Non-electrolytes	1·00	1·00
Strong acids and bases		
HCl	1·98	1·90
HNO_3	1·94	1·92
H_2SO_4	2·06	2·19
KOH	1·91	1·93
$Ba(OH)_2$	2·69	2·67
Weak electrolytes		
NH_3	1·03	1·01
CH_3COOH	1·03	1·01
HCN	1·02	1·00
Salts		
KCl	1·82	1·86
NH_4Cl	1·88	1·84
K_2CO_3	2·26	2·38
CH_3COOK	1·86	1·83
$CuSO_4$	0·97	1·35
$FeSO_4$	1·00	1·35
$MgSO_4$	1·04	1·40

From Table 12.2 it can be seen that the value i is equal to about 1·00 for non-electrolytes and weak electrolytes, whereas for electrolytes its value is greater than unity. The degree of dissociation α for the strong electrolytes is apparently less than unity in each case. According to modern theories, however, strong acids and bases and their salts are considered to be completely dissociated, but in more concentrated solutions the interionic attraction between the positive and negative ions is the cause of abnormal behaviour in solution, the net effect of which is to lower the value of α. The poor agreement between two values of i obtained for electrolytes containing Mg, Cu and Fe ions was considered to be due to complex ion formation.

12.3.1 *Measurement of Electrolytic Conductance*

Kohlrausch[9] in his extensive studies showed that ionic conductors resembled metallic conductors in that they obeyed Ohm's law. In both cases the heat generated by the conduction process depends on the resistance of the conducting medium. However, ionic conductance increases with temperature, whereas metallic conductance decreases with temperature. Thus at constant temperature we have

$$I = \frac{E}{R}$$

where I is the current flowing due to a constant emf E, and R is the resistance of the electrolyte between the electrodes. The resistance R depends on the dimensions of the electrolyte contained between the electrodes (Fig. 12.1). Thus

$$R = \frac{\rho l}{A} \qquad \ldots (12.5)$$

Here ρ is the specific resistance or resistivity of the electrolyte, l is the length, and A is the cross-sectional area of the parallel electrodes. Since the reciprocal of resistance $\frac{1}{R}$ is a measure of conducting power of an electrical conductor, it is called the conductance and is expressed in mhos, that is the reciprocal of the resistance in ohms.

Specific Conductance (κ). **The specific conductance of an electrolyte is the conductance of an electrolyte at a given temperature and concentration when measured between two parallel electrodes one centimetre apart and each being one square centimetre in area.**
Thus the specific conductance

$$\kappa = \frac{1}{\rho} \text{ ohms}^{-1} \text{ cm}^{-1}$$

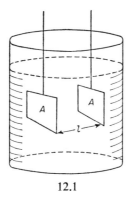

12.1

Since from (12.5)

$$R = \frac{\rho \times l}{A} \quad \text{and} \quad C = \frac{1}{R}$$

where C is conductance, then

$$C = \frac{A}{\rho \times l} \, \text{ohms}^{-1} \qquad \qquad \ldots(12.6)$$

Equivalent Conductance (Λ). The specific conductance of any electrolyte is found to vary with concentration (see Table 12.3). Kohlrausch, in his theoretical interpretation of the results obtained from his conductivity measurements, found it necessary to reduce conductance values to a common basis. He defined a new function Λ as **the conductance of a volume of solution containing one gramme equivalent of an electrolyte between parallel electrodes 1 cm apart.** In this way it is easy to correlate the equivalent conductance with specific conductance, since if the volume of an electrolyte containing 1 g equivalent is v cc, then the area of each electrode enclosing this volume of electrolyte is v sq cm. From equation (12.6) we have

$$C = \frac{1}{R} = \frac{\kappa A}{l}$$

and if v cc of solution contains one g equivalent of electrolyte we have

$$\Lambda = \kappa v \qquad \qquad \ldots(12.7)$$

The volume v can be expressed in terms of the concentration C of the electrolyte. Thus if C is in g equivalent per litre then the volume is given by

$$v = \frac{1,000}{C} \qquad \qquad \ldots(12.8)$$

On substituting (12.8) into (12.7) we obtain

$$\Lambda = \frac{1,000\kappa}{C} \qquad \ldots(12.9)$$

or equivalent conductance = specific conductance × volume in cc containing one g equivalent.

Molar Conductance (μ). This is the conductance of a volume of solution containing 1 g mole of an electrolyte when placed between parallel electrodes 1 cm apart.

Thus

$$\mu = \kappa \times \text{volume}$$

in cc containing 1 g mole. For univalent electrolytes

$$\mu = \Lambda$$

For divalent electrolytes

$$\mu = 2\Lambda$$

Earlier studies of the conductivity of electrolytes, especially those of Kohlrausch, had shown that reproducible results could only be obtained when measurements were carried out in such a way that no gases were liberated at the electrodes and no electrolysis took place. Kohlrausch overcame these difficulties by using an alternating current A/C having a frequency of about 1,000 cycles/sec. In this way any polarisation produced by one pulse was removed by the next (see sub-section 13.3.8, p. 284). A Wheatstone bridge (Fig. 12.2) can be used to measure the resistance of the electrolyte solution, which is placed in a suitable conductivity cell (see Fig. 12.3). The bridge consists of a potentiometric slide-wire AC with a sliding contact B, dividing it into the two arms AB and BC through the galvanometer G. The other two arms of the bridge are formed by the conductivity cell D and the variable resistance E in parallel with a variable condenser F.

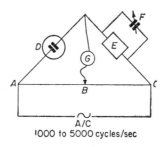

A/C
1000 to 5000 cycles/sec

12.2

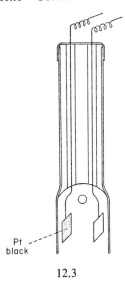

Pt
black

12.3

The value of E is so chosen that the bridge balances with B as near to the midpoint of the slide-wire as possible. The purpose of the variable condenser is to compensate for the capacitance of the conductivity cell. Since the value of the resistance E is known, and the ratio at the balance point AB to BC can be measured, then the value of the resistance R_D due to the electrolyte in the cell D can be calculated from the relationship

$$\frac{R_D}{R_E} = \frac{AB}{BC}$$

$\therefore$

$$R_D = \frac{AB \times R_E}{BC} \qquad \ldots(12.10)$$

Various types of conductivity cells are available commercially; these are usually constructed from insoluble glass, fused silica, or plastic materials. The electrodes are made of sheet platinum covered with platinum black to decrease polarisation. Fig. 12.3 shows a typical dipping electrode.

The Cell Constant. It is extremely difficult to prepare a cell with electrodes exactly 1 cm apart and of 1 sq cm in area. It is easier first to determine the cell constant either by direct measurement of the area and spacing of the electrodes (only reliable in very special cases), or by calibration using a standard solution of known conductivity (for example KCl solution). On rearranging equation (12.6) the specific conductance or conductivity is given by

$$\kappa = \frac{l}{A} \cdot C = \frac{l}{A} \cdot \frac{1}{R} \qquad \ldots(12.11)$$

Since the value of κ for a standard solution of KCl at a given temperature is known and the resistance R is measured, then the value of $\frac{l}{A}$, which is the cell constant, can be calculated. Once a cell is calibrated it may be used for the measurement of the specific conductance of any electrolyte using equation (12.11).

12.3.2 The Effect of Concentration and Temperature on Equivalent Conductance

Both concentration and temperature have a marked effect on the values of equivalent conductances. Fig. 12.3 shows some values for potassium chloride.

TABLE 12.3

Temperature °C	Normality	cc containing 1 g equivalent v	Specific conductance κ	Equivalent conductance $= \kappa v$
10	1	1,000	0·08319	83·19
	0·1	10,000	0·00933	93·30
	0·01	100,000	0·001020	102·0
15	1	1,000	0·09252	92·52
	0·1	10,000	0·01048	104·8
	0·01	100,000	0·001147	114·7
	1	1,000	0·10207	102·07
	0·1	10,000	0·01167	116·7
	0·01	100,000	0·001278	127·8
25	1	1,000	0·11180	111·8
	0·1	10,000	0·01288	128·8
	0·01	100,000	0·001413	141·3
	0·001	10^6	0·0001469	146·9
	0·0001	10^7	0·00001489	148·9

It is clear from this table that the temperature has a marked effect on the conductivity of electrolytes. The effect of solution concentration is not very marked in this case because potassium chloride is a strong electrolyte. However, from the results at 25°C it can be seen that the equivalent conductivity increases with dilution and ultimately tends to a limiting value. Table 12.4 gives the equivalent conductance of some electrolytes.

TABLE 12.4

Equivalent Conductances at 18°C in ohm^{-1} cm^2

Concentration g equiv. per litre	HCl	NaCl	$\frac{1}{2}$CuSO$_4$	CH$_3$CO
0·001	377	106	98·4	41
0·002	375·5	105·3	91·8	30·2
0·01	369·3	101·7	71·6	14·3
0·05	357·6	95·5	51·1	6·48
0·1	350·1	91·8	43·8	4·60
0·2	341·5	87·5	37·6	3·24
0·5	326·6	80·8	30·7	2·01
1·0	300·5	74·2	25·7	1·32

It is clear from this table that the equivalent conductance increases in every case with dilution. This means that the conductive power of one gramme equivalent of any electrolyte increases with dilution. With electrolytes such as hydrochloric acid and sodium chloride the increase is not very large, but in the case of acetic acid the conductive power obviously increases very rapidly with dilution. Fig. 12.4 shows

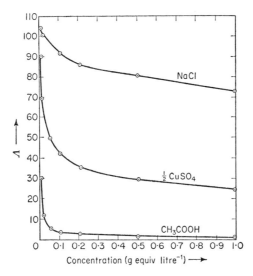

12.4

a plot of equivalent conductance against concentration in g equivalent per litre. The sodium chloride gives a typical curve of a strong electrolyte. For this type of curve it is possible to extrapolate the curve and read off the equivalent conductance at an infinite dilution, Λ_∞. This value is a measure of the conducting power of one g equivalent of the given electrolyte when it is completely dissociated and the resulting ions are too far apart to exert any influence on each other. In practice Λ_∞ is usually extrapolated by plotting Λ_c against $\sqrt{C}$, since at very low concentrations these plots give straight lines.

From Fig. 12.4 it can be seen that it is quite impossible to extrapolate the curve to obtain Λ_∞ for acetic acid, because of the very sharp rise in Λ at dilute solutions. Electrolytes, such as organic acids and ammonium hydroxide, which give this type of curve are called weak electrolytes, and their equivalent conductance at infinite dilution must be determined by an indirect method.

The curve for copper sulphate is an example of the behaviour of an intermediate electrolyte.

12.3.3   The Independent Migration of Ions

Kohlrausch established that each ion in an electrolyte contributes a definite amount to the total conductance of the electrolyte, irrespective of the nature of any other ions present. This becomes apparent when one examines Table 12.5.

TABLE 12.5

Equivalent Conductance at Infinite Dilution at 18°C

Electrolyte		Electrolyte		Difference
KCl	130·1	NaCl	109	21·1
KNO$_3$	126·3	NaNO$_3$	105·2	21·1
KOH	236·6	NaOH	215·5	21·1

In this case the difference in equivalent conductance between two strong electrolytes containing either potassium or sodium in presence of the same anion is constant and amounts to 21·1 ohm^{-1} cm^2. The values of some equivalent ionic conductances are given in Table 12.6.

Table 12.6 shows that the hydrogen and hydroxyl ions have much greater ionic conductances than any of the other ions. According to the **Law of Independent Migration of ions** the equivalent conductance of an electrolyte at infinite dilution Λ_∞ is given by the relationship

$$\Lambda_\infty = \lambda_+ + \lambda_-$$

TABLE 12.6

The Equivalent Ionic Conductances at 18° and 25°C

Cation	18°C	25°C	Anion	18°C	25°C
H$^+$	314	350	OH$^-$	172	198
Na$^+$	43·5	50·9	Cl$^-$	65·5	75·5
K$^+$	64·6	74·5	NO$_3^-$	61·7	70·6
NH$_4^+$	64·5	74·5	$\frac{1}{2}$SO$_4^=$	68	79
Ag$^=$	54·3	63·5	CH$_3$COO$^-$	35	41
$\frac{1}{2}$Ba^{++}	55	65			
$\frac{1}{2}$Ca^{++}	51	60			

We may recall that it was impossible to obtain the value of Λ_∞ for weak acids by extrapolation (see page 241), but from a knowledge of the corresponding ionic conductances it is now possible to calculate the equivalent conductance of any electrolyte at infinite dilution. For example the value of Λ_∞ for acetic acid at 18°C is given by

$$(\Lambda_\infty)_{CH_3COOH} = \lambda_{CH_3COO^-} + \lambda_{H^+}$$

$$(\Lambda_\infty)_{CH_3COOH} = 35 + 314 = 349 \text{ ohms}^{-1} \text{ cm}^2$$

12.3.4 *Some Applications of Conductivity Measurements*

The measurement of the conductivity of electrolyte solution finds application in the following cases:

(i) determination of solubilities of sparingly soluble substances,

(ii) conductimetric titrations,

(iii) determination of degree of dissociation (α).

Determination of Solubilities of Sparingly Soluble Substances. The solubility of a sparingly soluble substance can be conveniently determined from specific conductance measurements. By definition $\Lambda_c = \kappa \cdot v$, where v is the volume in cc which contains 1 g equivalent of the sparingly soluble substance. Since the solution is very dilute, Λ_c can be assumed to be equal to Λ_∞, which in turn can be calculated from the ionic conductivities; so that

$$\Lambda_c = \lambda_+ + \lambda_- = \kappa \cdot \frac{1,000}{S} \qquad \ldots (12.12)$$

where S is the solubility of the substance in g equivalents per litre and κ is the specific conductance of the saturated solution.

Example

The specific conductance of a saturated solution of silver chloride in water is $2 \cdot 97 \times 10^{-6}$ ohm^{-1} cm^{-1} at $18°C$. If the specific conductance of water is $1 \cdot 67 \times 10^{-6}$ ohm^{-1} cm^{-1} at $18°C$, calculate

(*a*) the solubility of silver chloride in g moles per litre,

(*b*) the solubility in g weight of the salt in 100 cc of saturated solution.

(*a*) Using the values from Table 12.6,

$$\lambda_{Ag^+} = 54 \cdot 3 \quad \text{and} \quad \lambda_{Cl^-} = 65 \cdot 5$$

Thus

$$\Lambda_\infty = 54 \cdot 3 + 65 \cdot 5 = (2 \cdot 97 - 1 \cdot 67) \times 10^{-6} \times \frac{1,000}{S_{AgCl}}$$

Therefore

$$S_{AgCl} = \frac{1 \cdot 30 \times 10^{-3}}{119 \cdot 8} \text{ g equivalents per litre}$$

$\therefore \qquad S_{AgCl} = 1 \cdot 08 \times 10^{-5}$ g equivalents per litre

(*b*) The weight of silver chloride in 100 cc can be obtained by multiplying the above result by the equivalent weight of silver chloride and then dividing by ten.

Thus weight

$$AgCl/100 \text{ cc} = \frac{1 \cdot 30 \times 10^{-3} \times 143 \cdot 5}{119 \cdot 8 \times 10} \text{ g}$$

$$AgCl/100 \text{ cc} = 1 \cdot 55 \times 10^{-4} \text{ g}$$

Answer: The solubility of silver chloride in water at $18°C$ was found to be $1 \cdot 08 \times 10^{-5}$ g equivalent per litre or $1 \cdot 55 \times 10^{-4}$ g per 100 cc. This method is very useful for many salts, but in certain solutions the calculations are not reliable because of uncertainties as to the nature of the ions formed.

Conductimetric Titrations. The principle of conductimetric acid–alkali titrations is based on the high ionic conductances of hydrogen and hydroxyl ions. Let us consider, for example, the titration of sodium hydroxide (strong base) with hydrochloric acid (strong acid). When the acid is added to the alkali the conductance of the solution decreases. This is because the highly conductive hydroxyl ions are

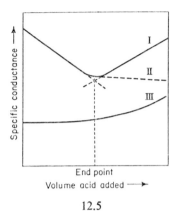

End point

Volume acid added ⟶

12.5

replaced in the solution by chloride ions according to the following equation:

$$HCl + Na^+ + OH^- = Na^+ + Cl^- + H_2O \quad ...(12.13)$$
$$(50\cdot9) \quad (198) \quad (50\cdot9) \quad (75\cdot5)$$

The figures in parentheses are the equivalent ionic conductances at 25°C.

This fall in conductance will continue until the sodium hydroxide is neutralised, when any further addition of hydrochloric acid will cause the conductance to increase because of the excess of highly mobile hydrogen ions. Fig. 12.5 shows typical titration curves for strong base–strong acid (curve I), strong base–weak acid (curve II), and weak base–weak acid (curve III). From Fig. 12.5 it can be seen that the curve for the strong alkali–strong acid titration gives a rather sharp end point (point of intersection), and therefore this method is suitable for solutions which are very dilute or contain coloured ions. It can also be used for solutions which are polluted and thus unsuitable for the use of internal or external indicators. The other two curves do not give a very clear end point. However, it is still a comparatively easy matter to titrate strong base or acid with a weak acid or base. This method is not so reliable for titrations which only involve weak acids and bases, but even then it may have to be used because it is the only practicable method.

Determination of Degree of Dissociation (α). At infinite dilution all the ions that are obtained from an electrolyte are conducting the current. Since a number of solutions, each containing one g equivalent of a different electrolyte, contain the same number of ionic charges, therefore the quantity of electricity Q passing through an electrolyte is given by Q = number of ions × charge × velocity; or, since the product of number of ions times their charge is the same at infinite dilution for all electrolytes, we have therefore

$$\Lambda_\infty = k(u_+ + u_-) = ku_+ + ku_- \qquad \ldots(12.14)$$

where u_+ and u_- are the velocities of the cation and anion respectively, and the constant k is the same for all electrolytes. Thus ku_+ and ku_- are the contributions made by the cation and anion respectively to the total conductance of the electrolyte in solution. Thus we can write

$$\lambda_+ = ku_+ \qquad \text{and} \qquad \lambda_- = ku_-$$

Arrhenius postulated that at higher concentrations only a fraction of each g equivalent dissociates into ions. Assuming that the velocity of the ions are the same at a concentration c and at infinite dilution and the degree of dissociation is α, then the conductance is given by

$$\Lambda_c = \alpha k(u_+ + u_-) \qquad \ldots(12.15)$$

Dividing (12.15) by (12.14) we have

$$\frac{\Lambda_c}{\Lambda_\infty} = \frac{\alpha k(u_+ + u_-)}{k(u_+ + u_-)} = \alpha \qquad \ldots(12.16)$$

and thus the degree of dissociation of an electrolyte may be calculated from the knowledge of Λ_c and Λ_∞.

Obviously equation (12.16) applies only to cases where the velocities of the ions do not vary with the concentration. This is true in solutions of weak acids, bases, and their salts. The ratio $\frac{\Lambda_c}{\Lambda_\infty}$ for strong electrolytes does not give the correct value of α, since in these solutions there is a strong interattractive force between ions, which influences the ionic velocities, and the higher the concentration of these electrolytes the lower their ionic velocities. Thus the value obtained from equation (12.16) is frequently called the **conductance ratio.**

12.3.5   *Transport Numbers*

When a current of electricity is passed through a solution of an electrolyte, it is found that the resultant changes in concentration at the two electrodes are usually not the same. It follows therefore that, since equivalent amounts of positive and negative ions are discharged at the two electrodes, the supply from the bulk of the solution to the vicinity of the electrodes must be different. Thus it can be concluded that the velocity of the positive and negative ions under the same potential drop (voltage) must be different. It also follows from this argument that the amount of electricity carried through the electrolyte by the positive ions must be different from that carried in the opposite direction by the negative ions, and these two amounts of electricity must be in the same ratio as the corresponding ion velocities. Thus the total amount of electricity transferred across the cell is equal to $k(u_+ + u_-)$, where k is a proportionality constant depending on the concentration and temperature of the electrolyte, and $u_+ + u_-$ are the ionic velocities. If we denote the fraction of the total current carried by the cation as t_+, that is the transport number of the cation, then

$$t_+ = \frac{k'u_+}{k'(u_+ + u_-)} = \frac{u_+}{u_+ + u_-} \qquad \ldots (12.17)$$

and

$$t_- = \frac{u_-}{u_+ + u_-} \qquad \ldots (12.18)$$

These equations apply to electrolytes composed of two ions each possessing the same number of charges. As a result of the difference in the ion velocities u_+ and u_- different concentration changes will take place near the anode and cathode. Hittorf (1853) utilised these changes for the determination of transport numbers.

Hittorf's Method for the Determination of Transport Numbers. Consider an electrolytic cell (Fig. 12.6) consisting of three interconnected compartments, each containing silver nitrate of the same concentration. The cathode and anode compartments are fitted with silver electrodes, and the cell is connected in circuit with a direct current supply of a suitable voltage. The amount of electricity that passes

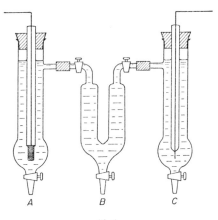

12.6

through the circuit is determined by means of a coulometer. When the electrodes A and C are included in the electric circuit, we have the following reactions taking place:

anodic reaction

$$Ag \rightarrow Ag^+ + e$$

cathodic reaction

$$Ag^+ + e \rightarrow Ag$$

Let us now consider the anode and cathode compartments separately. The amount of silver in the anode compartment at any time will depend on the relative rates at which silver ions are supplied from the dissolution of the anode and the rate of silver ions leaving the anode compartment due to the voltage drop across the electrolyte.

Let the original amount of silver in the anode compartment be m_1 g equivalents, and its final amount m_2 g equivalents. The total amount of electricity which was transferred through the cell is obtained by means of the coulometer. From Faraday's laws of electrolysis this value enables us to calculate the amount of silver that has dissolved into the anode compartment, which we can express as m_3 g equivalents.

From these three values, m_1, m_2 and m_3, it is possible to calculate the transport number of the silver ion t_{Ag^+}, since by definition

$$t_{Ag^+} = \frac{\text{amount of current carried by } Ag^+}{\text{total current passed through the cell}}$$

$$t_{Ag^+} = \frac{\text{total amount of Ag which has left the anode compartment}}{\text{total amount of Ag dissolved into the anode compartment}}$$

Substituting the appropriate values for silver we have

$$t_{Ag^+} = \frac{m_3 - (m_2 - m_1)}{m_3}$$

The values m_1 and m_2 are obtained by titration of the solutions in the anode compartment.

It should be noted that the sum of the two transport numbers comes to unity, since from equations (12.17) and (12.18) we have

$$t_+ + t_- = \frac{u_+}{u_+ + u_-} + \frac{u_-}{u_+ + u_-} = 1 \qquad \ldots(12.19)$$

Thus, once one of the transport numbers is determined for an electrolyte, the other can easily be obtained from equation (12.19). Here

$$t_{NO_3^-} = 1 - \left[\frac{m_3 - (m_2 - m_1)}{m_3} \right]$$

Effect of Concentration and Temperature on the Value of Transport Number. Tables 12.7 and 12.8 show the effect of concentration and temperature respectively on transport numbers of some aqueous electrolytes.

TABLE 12.7

Transport Numbers of Cations at 18°C

Concentration M	NaCl	KCl	AgNO₃	HCl	LiCl
0·01	0·397	0·496	0·471	0·833	0·329
0·05	0·393	0·496	0·471	0·834	0·321
0·10	0·390	0·495	0·471	0·835	—
1·0	0·365	0·490	—	0·844	0·317

TABLE 12.8

Effect of Temperature on Transport Number of Cations in 0·01M solutions

Temperature °C	NaCl	KCl	HCl
0	0·387	0·493	0·846
10	—	0·495	0·840
18	0·397	0·496	0·833
30	0·404	0·498	0·822

From Table 12.7 it can be seen that the transport numbers vary slightly with concentration. It might be expected that the smaller the ionic diameter, or the larger the ionic charge, the greater should be the mobility of the ions, and therefore the larger the transport number. This is the case with the hydrogen ion but Li^+, Ca^{++}, Al^{+++} and many other ions show anomalies. It can be shown that this is due to the fact that their ions are hydrated in solution, and therefore their effective ionic radii are much larger than one would expect.

REFERENCES

1 ADAM, N. K., *Physical Chemistry*, 1958, p. 356, Clarendon Press, Oxford, 1958.
2 VOLTA, A. G. A. A., *Phil. Trans.*, 1783, 10 and 1800, 405.
3 NICHOLSON and CARLISLE, *Nicholson's J.*, 1800, **4**, 179.
4 DAVY, H., *Phil. Trans.*, 1808, **1**, 333.
5 FARADAY, M., *Experimental Researches in Electricity*, 1833–4, iv, v, vii, viii.
6 ARRHENIUS, S. A., *Z. Physikal. Chem.*, 1887, **1**, 631.
7 VAN'T HOFF, *Z. Physikal. Chem.*, 1887, **1**, 557.
8 ARRHENIUS, S. A., *Z. Physikal. Chem.*, 1888, **2**, 494.
9 KOHLRAUSCH, F. W. G., *Ann. Physik.*, 1879, **6**, 1, 145; 1885, **26**, 161.

CHAPTER XIII

Equilibria in Electrolytes

13.1 INTRODUCTION

Electrolytes are usually classified as aqueous or non-aqueous (for example fused salts). Although a knowledge of fused electrolytes is important for metallurgists, we shall confine our discussion in this chapter only to aqueous electrolytes.

In the preceding chapter we have already learnt that when electrovalent compounds are dissolved in water the resulting solutions conduct electricity, and the conductive power of solutions of equivalent concentrations varies for different substances. Solutes which are completely dissociated are called **strong electrolytes,** while those which dissociate to an extremely small degree are called **weak electrolytes.**

13.2 ACIDS, BASES, AND SALTS

Since we are only concerned at the moment with aqueous electrolytes, we can define acids simply as substances which when dissolved in water yield hydrogen ions, and bases as substances which yield hydroxyl ions.* When these two electrolytes are mixed together they form a salt and water, and when hydrochloric acid is neutralised with sodium hydroxide we obtain sodium chloride and water according to the equation

$$HCl + NaOH \rightarrow NaCl + H_2O$$
$$acid + base \rightarrow salt + water$$

13.2.1 Strength of Acids and Bases

Acids and bases are called 'strong' or 'weak' according to the extent to which they dissociate when dissolved in water. Thus strong acids and bases are considered to be nearly completely dissociated

---

* According to Lowry-Brönsted's theory an acid is any substance whose molecules may liberate a proton, and a base is any molecule which accepts a proton.

(see page 232), whereas weak ones are dissociated only to a very small extent.

Strong Acids. In dilute solutions hydrogen chloride is completely dissociated into hydrogen ions (H^+) and chloride ions (Cl^-). Thus a 0·001 N solution of hydrochloric acid contains 0·001 g of hydrogen ions per litre and 0·0355 g of chloride ions per litre.

Weak Acids. The strength of a weak acid may be expressed numerically by means of

(i) the degree of dissociation of the acid α at a given concentration,

(ii) its dissociation constant K_a, or

(iii) the pH at a given concentration (see sub-section 13.2.2).

(i) *Degree of Dissociation* α has already been explained on page 233 and can be easily calculated from equation (12.16). For example, the degree of dissociation of a normal solution of acetic acid at 18°C is calculated below using data shown in Table 12.4 as follows:

$$\alpha_{CH_3OOH} = \frac{\Lambda_c}{\Lambda_\infty} = \frac{1\cdot32}{349} = 3\cdot783 \times 10^{-3}$$

Since α denotes the fraction of the total number of g moles of the electrolyte which splits up into ions, then the hydrogen ion concentration in a weak electrolyte solution is given by the product of the electrolyte concentration and its degree of dissociation which in this case becomes

$$C_{CH_3COOH} \times \alpha_{CH_3COOH} = 1 \times 3\cdot783 \times 10^{-3} \text{ g } H^+ \text{ per litre}$$

(ii) *The Dissociation constant K_a* for a weak acid at a given temperature is obtained from the application of the Law of Mass Action to electrolytes. Thus when a weak monobasic acid HA is dissolved in water, then the equilibrium set up can be represented as follows:*

$$HA \rightleftarrows H^+ + A^-$$
$$\frac{1-\alpha}{v} \quad \frac{\alpha}{v} \quad \frac{\alpha}{v}$$

where the concentration of the undissociated acid molecules and of the ions are shown in terms of the degree of dissociation α, and v the

---

* For an aqueous solution of an acid HA it would be more correct to represent this equation as $HA + H_2O \rightleftarrows H_3O^+ + A^-$, where H_3O^+ is the hydroxonium ion. It can be shown that both these equations give finally the same value of K_a for dilute solutions of weak acids.

volume of the solution in litres containing 1 g mole of the acid. According to the Mass Action Law the equilibrium constant K_a is given by

$$K_a = \frac{\text{Product of concentration of the resultants}}{\text{Product of concentration of reactants}} = \frac{\dfrac{\alpha}{v} \times \dfrac{\alpha}{v}}{\dfrac{1 - \alpha}{v}}$$

and thus we obtain

$$K_a = \frac{\alpha^2}{(1 - \alpha)v} \qquad \ldots(13.1)$$

Example 1

Calculate the dissociation constant for a normal solution of acetic acid at 18°C.

On substituting into equation (13.1) the previously calculated value for α we have

$$K_a = \frac{\alpha^2}{(1 - \alpha)v} = \frac{(3 \cdot 783 \times 10^{-3})^2}{(1 - 0 \cdot 0003783) \times 1} = 1 \cdot 431 \times 10^{-5}$$

Example 2

The dissociation constant of a weak monobasic acid is $1 \cdot 44 \times 10^{-6}$. What is the hydrogen ion concentration in 0·01 N solution of this acid at 18°C?

Using equation (13.1) we have

$$K_a = 1 \cdot 44 \times 10^{-6} = \frac{[H^+][A^-]}{[HA]} = \frac{[H^+]^2}{0 \cdot 01}$$

since

$$[H^+] = [A^-]$$

Solving the above equation we obtain

$$[H^+] = \sqrt{\frac{K_a}{100}} = \sqrt{\frac{1 \cdot 44 \times 10^{-6}}{100}} = 1 \cdot 2 \times 10^{-4} \text{ g ion per litre}$$

at 18°C.

Answer: The hydrogen ion concentration in a 0·01 N solution of this acid is $1 \cdot 2 \times 10^{-4}$ g ion litre^{-1} at 18°C.

13.2.2 *Dissociation Constant of Water, Ionic Product of Water and pH*

Conductivity measurements in pure water show that it is slightly ionised. Its specific conductance is found to be $5 \cdot 6 \times 10^{-8}$ ohm^{-1}

cm^{-1} at 25°C. From this value it is now possible to calculate the degree of dissociation of water, since

$$\Lambda_\infty = \kappa \times v$$

where v is the volume in cc containing one g equivalent of water.

Using equation (12.16) we have

$$\alpha = \frac{\Lambda_e}{\Lambda_\infty} = \frac{5\cdot6 \times 10^{-8} \times 18}{(\lambda_{H^+} + \lambda_{OH^-})} = \frac{5\cdot6 \times 18 \times 10^{-8}}{(350 + 198)}$$

$$= \frac{5\cdot6 \times 18 \times 10^{-8}}{548}$$

If we substitute this value for α into equation (13.1) remembering that the volume of one g mole of water is 0·018 litres, we obtain

$$K_{H_2O} = \frac{\left(\dfrac{5\cdot6 \times 18 \times 10^{-8}}{548}\right)^2}{0\cdot018} = 1\cdot879 \times 10^{-16}$$

But since

$$K_{H_2O} = \frac{[H^+][OH^-]}{[H_2O]} = 1\cdot879 \times 10^{-16}$$

and the concentration of water in a litre is its weight divided by its equivalent weight, that is $\dfrac{1,000}{18}$, thus

$$K_{H_2O} = \frac{[H^+][OH^-]}{\dfrac{1,000}{18}} = 1\cdot879 \times 10^{-16}$$

or

$$[H^+][OH^-] = \frac{1\cdot879 \times 10^{-16} \times 1,000}{18} = 1\cdot043 \times 10^{-14}$$

The product of the hydrogen and hydroxyl ion concentrations, expressed in grammes per litre, is called the **ionic product of water** and is denoted by the symbol K_w.

Thus we have

$$K_w = [H^+][OH^-] = 1\cdot043 \times 10^{-14} \text{ at } 25°C$$

The above calculation shows that the ionic product of water is numerically equal to approximately 10^{-14} at 25°C. Since K_w is constant at constant temperature it follows that, if the ionic concentration of, say, H^+ increases, that of OH^- must decrease and vice versa. It also follows that in pure water or in a neutral solution the hydrogen ion concentration must be equal to that of hydroxyl ions, and at 25°C we have

$$[H^+] = [OH^-] \simeq 1 \times 10^{-7} \text{ g ion per litre}$$

This fact of the interdependence of the hydrogen and hydroxyl ion concentration in aqueous solutions is the basis of the so-called **pH scale**. By definition **the pH of a solution is the minus logarithm to the base ten of its hydrogen ion concentration.** Mathematically it can be expressed by

$$pH = -\log_{10} [H^+] \qquad \ldots(13.2)$$

This logarithmic scale has been found to be extremely convenient, since it enables us to express a very wide range of hydrogen concentration values in terms of simple numbers. Table 13.1 shows some pH

TABLE 13.1

Normality	$[H^+]$ g ion litre^{-1}	$[OH^-]$ g ion litre^{-1}	pH	Reaction of the solution
1·0 N acid	1	10^{-14}	0	
0·1 N acid	10^{-1}	10^{-13}	1	
0·0001 N acid	10^{-4}	10^{-10}	4	acidic
0·000001 N acid	10^{-6}	10^{-8}	6	
Pure water	10^{-7}	10^{-7}	7	neutral
0·000001 N base	10^{-8}	10^{-6}	8	
0·0001 N base	10^{-10}	10^{-4}	10	
0·1 N base	10^{-13}	10^{-1}	13	basic
1·0 N base	10^{-14}	1	14	

values for acids and bases at different concentrations assuming that they are completely dissociated.

Example 1

Calculate the pH for a 0·01 N solution of HCl assuming that (*a*) the acid is completely dissociated, (*b*) the degree of dissociation is 0·9.

(*a*) 0·01 N solution of HCl contains 0·01 g ion of H$^+$ per litre. On substitution of this concentration value for H$^+$ into equation (13.2) we have

$$pH = -\log_{10} 0·01 = -(\bar{2}·0000)$$

or

$$pH = 2·00$$

(b) The hydrogen ion concentration in this case will be less than before, and is given by $[H^+] = 0.01 \times 0.9 = 0.009$ g ion per litre.

In this case we have

$$pH = -\log_{10} 0.009 = -(\bar{3}.9542) = 3 - 0.9542$$

or

$$pH = 2.0458 \simeq 2.05$$

Example 2

The pH of a monobasic 0.1 N acid solution is found to be 3.15; calculate (a) the hydrogen ion concentration per litre, (b) the degree of dissociation of this acid, and (c) the dissociation constant of this acid.

(a) $$pH = 3.15 = -\log_{10}[H^+]$$

Rearranging this equation we have

$$\log_{10}[H^+] = -3.15 = \bar{4}.8500$$

From the antilogarithm we obtain

$$[H^+] = 7.079 \times 10^{-4} \text{ g ion per litre}$$

(b) A completely dissociated 0.1 N monobasic acid would yield 10^{-1} g ion of H^+ per litre. Since the actual hydrogen ion concentration is found to be much less, therefore the acid is only partially dissociated. The degree of dissociation α is thus given by the ratio of the actual hydrogen ion concentration to the theoretical one obtained on complete dissociation. Thus in this example we have

$$\alpha = \frac{7.079 \times 10^{-4}}{1 \times 10^{-1}} = 7.079 \times 10^{-3}$$

(c) Using equation (13.1) we can write

$$K_{HA} = \frac{\alpha^2}{(1-\alpha)v} = \frac{(7.079 \times 10^{-3})^2}{(1 - 7.079 \times 10^{-3}) \times 10} = \frac{(7.079)^2 \times 10^{-6}}{0.9929 \times 10}$$

$$K_{HA} = 5.047 \times 10^{-6}$$

13.2.3 Solubility Product K_s

The **solubility product** (sometimes called **ion product constant**) of a sparingly soluble salt is the product of the concentrations of the ions in its saturated solution.

The concentrations are expressed as g moles per litre of solution. The concept of solubility product is applied to electrolytes which are saturated solutions of sparingly soluble compounds, and which are therefore in equilibrium with some undissolved solid. The dissolved compound is then regarded as completely ionised, since its concentration is very small. Thus for a compound AB ionised into A^+ and B^- the equilibrium between the solid and the ions can be represented by

$$AB_s \rightleftarrows A^+ + B^-$$

$$AgCl_s \rightleftarrows Ag^+ + Cl^-$$

According to the Mass Action Law we have

$$K = \frac{[A^+][B^-]}{[AB]_s}$$

For a pure solid compound AB, the concentration term $[AB]_s$ is independent of the amount of the solid present in the solution and is therefore a constant. Thus the above equation can be written as

$$K_s = [A^+][B^-] \qquad \qquad ...(13.3)$$

where K_s is a new constant and is numerically equal to

$$K[AB]_s$$

Example

The solubility product K_s of silver bromide is $7 \cdot 7 \times 10^{-13}$ at 25°C. Calculate the solubility of silver bromide in grammes per litre.

The balanced equation for the equilibrium between solid AgBr and its saturated solution is given by

$$AgBr_s \rightleftarrows Ag^+ + Br^-$$

Substituting the given value of $7 \cdot 7 \times 10^{-13}$ into equation (13.3) we have

$$K_{s_{AgBr}} = [Ag^+][Br^-] = 7 \cdot 7 \times 10^{-13}$$

Since in this electrolyte the ionic concentrations of silver and bromide are equal, therefore the product

$$[Ag^+][Br^-] = [Ag^+]^2 \quad \text{and} \quad [Ag^+]^2 = 7 \cdot 7 \times 10^{-13}$$

or

$$[Ag^+] = \sqrt{7 \cdot 7 \times 10^{-13}} = 8 \cdot 775 \times 10^{-7}$$

The ionic concentration of $Ag^+ = 8 \cdot 775 \times 10^{-7}$ g ion per litre. Since the weight of the dissolved silver bromide is equal to the product of its molar concentration and its molecular weight, therefore its weight in this case is

$$8 \cdot 775 \times 10^{-7} \times 187 \cdot 8 = 1 \cdot 648 \times 10^{-4} \text{ g per litre}$$

13.2.4 *Common Ion Effect*

If two solutions each containing one of the ions of a sparingly soluble salt are mixed no precipitation takes place, unless the product of the two ion concentrations for the salt is greater than its solubility product. If, however, to a saturated solution of a sparingly soluble compound an acid or base is added which contains one ion in common with the compound, then precipitation will take place. Let us consider, for example, the mixing of a saturated solution of silver chloride with an equal volume of 0·01 N HCl solution. During the mixing process (i) the volume of the saturated silver chloride solution will be doubled, and (ii) the concentration of chloride ions will increase.

The solubility product of silver chloride is equal to $1·56 \times 10^{-10}$ at 25°C and using equation (13.3) we have

$$[Ag^+] = \sqrt{1·56 \times 10^{-10}} = 1·249 \times 10^{-5} \text{ g ion per litre}$$

Since the volume of the solution is doubled, concentration $[Ag^+]$ is halved and becomes $6·245 \times 10^{-6}$ g ion per litre. The original concentration of the Cl^- ions was $1·249 \times 10^{-5}$, and its final concentration will be that due to the ions obtained from the ionisation of AgCl and those from the hydrochloric acid solution. Thus

$$[Cl^-] = 6·245 \times 10^{-6} + 5 \times 10^{-3} = 5·006 \times 10^{-3} \text{ g ion per litre}$$

Since the temperature of the solution remained constant, the $K_{s_{AgCl}}$ is constant, and from equation (13.3) we have

$$[Ag^+][Cl^-] = (6·245 \times 10^{-6})(5·00 \times 10^{-3}) = 3·12 \times 10^{-8}$$

This value of the ionic product is thus 200 times higher than the solubility product of the saturated solution. As a result of this AgCl will precipitate until the ionic product in the solution becomes equal to the saturated one. Let the amount which will precipitate be X. Then equation (13.3) becomes

$$[6·245 \times 10^{-6} - X][5·006 \times 10^{-3} - X] = 1·56 \times 10^{-10}$$

$$\therefore \quad 3·12 \times 10^{-8} - 5·015 \times 10^{-3}X + X^2 = 1·56 \times 10^{-10}$$

$$\therefore \quad X^2 - 5·015 \times 10^{-3}X + 3·05 \times 10^{-8} = 0$$

$$\therefore \quad X = 2 \times 10^{-6} \text{ g ion per litre}$$

This value of X shows that the concentration of Ag^+ remaining in the final solution is extremely small.

The principle of the common ion effect is frequently used in analytical chemistry.

13.2.5   *Hydrolysis of Salts*

The hydrolysis of a salt in an aqueous solution may be regarded as the reverse of neutralisation. During hydrolysis water takes part in the reaction acting either as an acid or a base. In general acids and bases, depending on their strength, form four types of salts:

(i)   salt formed from strong acid and strong base [e.g. $NaCl$; Na_2SO_4],

(ii) salt formed from strong acid and weak base [e.g. NH_4Cl; $(NH_4)_2SO_4$],

(iii) salt formed from weak acid and strong base [e.g. CH_3COONa; Na_2CO_3],

(iv) salt formed from weak acid and weak base [e.g. NH_4COOCH_3; $(NH_4)_2S$].

Although hydrolysis will occur when types (ii) and (iii) are dissolved in water, let us also consider the effect of dissolution of each of the above four types of salts in water.

Strong Acid–Strong Base Salt. When sodium chloride is dissolved in water it dissociates according to the following equation:

$$NaCl \rightarrow Na^+ + Cl^-$$

We have also $\qquad\qquad\quad +\qquad\ +$

$$H_2O \rightleftarrows OH^- + H^+$$

All these ions are in constant motion in solution, and, when sodium and hydroxyl ions meet to form $NaOH$, this being a strong base instantaneously dissociates. Similarly, when H^+ and Cl^- ions meet, any HCl formed immediately dissociates. Therefore the net result is that solutions of these salts remain practically neutral.

Strong Acid–Weak Base Salt. Let us consider the ionic equilibria in an aqueous solution of ammonium chloride. Here we have again

$$NH_4Cl \rightarrow NH_4^+ + Cl^-$$
$$+\qquad\quad +$$
$$H_2O \rightleftarrows OH^- + H^+$$
$$\updownarrow$$
$$NH_4OH$$

When ammonium ions meet hydroxyl ions, then some undissociated ammonium hydroxide is formed, and, as it is a weak base, only a small fraction will dissociate. Eventually an equilibrium is reached between the NH_4OH and NH_4^+ and OH^- ions. The net result of this equilibrium is a considerable removal of OH^- from the solution.

When chloride and hydrogen ions meet they do not form any undissociated hydrogen chloride, since HCl completely dissociates, and thus no hydrogen ions are removed from solution.

This solution therefore will have an excess of hydrogen ions and the electrolyte will exhibit an acidic reaction (i.e. pH < 7).

Weak Acid–Weak Base Salt. In this case the resulting solution will usually have a neutral character (i.e. pH $\simeq$ 7), but it can be weakly alkaline or acidic depending on the relative strengths of acid and base.

13.2.6. *Buffer Solutions*

When a few drops of strong acid or alkali are added to pure water, or to very weak solutions of strong acids or bases, their pH is greatly changed. On the other hand, when a few drops of acid or alkali are added to solutions containing a mixture of a weak acid and its salt, the pH remains virtually unchanged. Solutions which possess this resistance to changes in pH when bases or acids are added are called **buffer solutions**. The action of a buffer solution can be accounted for by means of dissociation constants and the common ion effect. Let us consider, for example, the effect of adding either hydrogen ions or hydroxyl ions to a solution consisting of acetic acid and sodium acetate. Thus

$$CH_3COOH \rightleftharpoons CH_3COO^- + H^+$$

$$CH_3COONa \rightleftharpoons CH_3COO^- + Na^+$$

If an acid is added to this solution, its hydrogen ions combine with the acetate ions from the salt to give undissociated acetic acid, and are therefore effectively removed from the solution leaving the pH undisturbed, as long as acetate ions are available for this reaction:

$$H^+ + CH_3COO^- \rightarrow CH_3COOH$$

If on the other hand a base is added to this solution, the alkali is neutralised by the acetic acid to give water and the acetate salt. For example, when sodium hydroxide is being added we have

$$CH_3COO^- + NaOH \rightarrow CH_3COONa + H_2O$$

The net result of this is that once again the pH of this solution remains unchanged.

There are many well-known buffer solutions and some of these are given in Table 13.2.

TABLE 13.2

Buffer Solutions	pH Range
Phthalic acid and potassium hydrogen phthalate	2·2–3·8
Acetic acid and sodium acetate	3·7–5·6
Boric acid and sodium borate	7·0–9·1

13.3 ELECTROCHEMICAL CELLS

13.3.1 *General*

Electrochemical cells enable us to obtain electrical energy directly from chemical reactions. There are two main types of electrochemical cells (i) **galvanic** and (ii) **concentration cells.** Both these types consist of two electrodes dipping into suitable electrolytes, which must be in electrical contact with each other either directly or through a suitable salt bridge to allow ionic conductance. In galvanic cells the two electrodes are made of different metals (**dissimilar metals**), whereas in concentration cells they are of the same metal. An electric current is obtained when these two electrodes are connected with metallic conductors. Let us consider separately the origin of the electromotive force (e.m.f.) in galvanic and concentration cells.

13.3.2 *Galvanic Cells*

When a metal is dipped in a solution containing its own ions a dynamic equilibrium is set up between the ions in the solution in the vicinity of the electrode and the surface of the metal. This equilibrium may be achieved in two ways, either by metallic ions passing from the metallic surface into the solution, or by the deposition of ions from the solution on to the metallic surface.

In the former case (see Fig. 13.1) we have

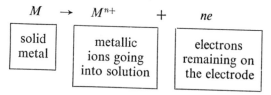

$$M \quad \rightarrow \quad M^{n+} \quad + \quad ne$$

solid metal	metallic ions going into solution	electrons remaining on the electrode

where n is the number of electrons involved in the process, and as a result of this the metal acquires a negative potential with respect to its own ions in the solution in the immediate vicinity of its surface.

Whether an electrode will be ionised or ions deposited from the solution will depend on the activity of the metallic ions in the electrolyte and its temperature.

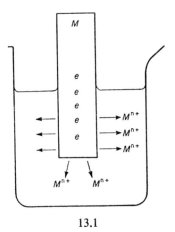

13.1

Different metals exhibit different tendencies to ionise, and there-fore, when they are immersed in solutions containing their own salts of equivalent strength and at the same temperature, they acquire different potentials. Metals which ionise more readily will be more negatively charged with respect to the solution than those which have less tendency to do so. It is clear therefore that when two dissimilar metals are dipped in solutions containing their ions and are connected by means of a salt bridge, then electrons will flow through an external conductor from the electrode which is more negatively charged to that which has a less negative potential to produce an electric current.

The potential difference between various combinations of metals is thus responsible for the electromotive force in galvanic cells.

To illustrate a galvanic cell, let us consider a cell formed by immersing a zinc rod in a molar solution of zinc sulphate and a copper rod in a molar solution of copper sulphate (see Fig. 13.2). The copper sulphate and zinc sulphate solutions are separated from one another by a porous pot, which prevents them from mixing, but allows ionic contact between them. When the zinc rod is first dipped into the zinc sulphate solution, there is a spontaneous dissolution of zinc, and an equilibrium potential is set up between the solid zinc and the zinc ions in the solution. When the copper rod is immersed in the copper sulphate solution, some of the copper ions are spon-taneously deposited on it, and again an equilibrium potential established. These electrode potentials prevent any further deposition or dissolution of Cu and Zn. If, however, the circuit is externally closed by connecting the two electrodes with a metallic conductor, then electrons will flow from the zinc electrode (higher electron density) to the copper electrode (lower electron density). As a result of this flow of electrons in the external circuit the equilibrium in each of the two compartments will be disturbed, and therefore zinc will pass zinc ions into its solution to make up for the loss of electrons as given by

$$Zn \rightarrow Zn^{++} + 2e$$

and copper will discharge its ions from the copper sulphate solutions to remove the excess of electrons gained from the zinc electrode via the metallic conductor, as given by

$$Cu^{++} + 2e \rightarrow Cu$$

The zinc will continue to dissolve and copper ions will be deposited until either the zinc is used up, or the concentration of the copper ions in the solution becomes so low that the copper electrode potential becomes equal to that of the zinc electrode.

Since any galvanic cell consists of two compartments each of them is called a **half cell**. The half cell with the more negative potential is called the **anode** (see Table 13.5, p. 291) and the other the **cathode.** At the anode an oxidation reaction takes place, and on the cathode we have a reduction reaction. Thus we have:

Anode: the zinc anode dissolves giving zinc ions to the solution and retaining the electrons on the solid anode:

$$Zn \rightarrow Zn^{++} + 2e \text{ (zinc loses electrons; } \mathbf{oxidation})$$

Cathode: the copper ions from the solution are reduced on the cathode:

$$Cu^{++} + 2e \rightarrow Cu \text{ (copper ions gain electrons; } \mathbf{reduction})$$

The overall chemical reaction taking place in this galvanic cell is clearly the sum of the anodic and cathodic reactions, and it is thus:

$$Zn + Cu^{++} \rightarrow Zn^{++} + Cu$$

and the e.m.f. of this cell is the algebraic sum of the two electrode potentials

$$E = E_{Zn/Zn^{++}} + E_{Cu^{++}/Cu}$$

where $E_{Zn/Zn^{++}}$ and $E_{Cu^{++}/Cu}$ are the zinc and copper electrode potentials respectively.

This cell can be conveniently represented in the following manner

$$Zn|ZnSO_4(aq) \vdots CuSO_4(aq)|Cu$$

(While the cell is working, the current in the cell is carried by the zinc, copper and sulphate ions. For accurate work the liquid junction

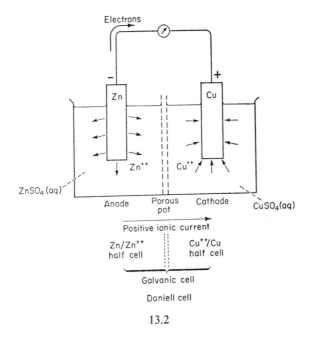

13.2

potential between the two half cells has to be taken into account or eliminated by a suitable salt bridge.)

Phase boundaries are shown by vertical lines, thus $Zn|ZnSO_4$ denotes solid zinc dipped into zinc sulphate solution. The dotted line shows the boundary between the two electrolytes. It is customary to write the half cell with the negative pole (anode) on the left-hand side.

The Daniell cell is an example of a reversible cell, and thus its e.m.f. can be measured by a potentiometer and a sensitive galvanometer (see Fig. 13.3). The cell is connected to the potentiometer in such a way that the e.m.f. of the battery opposes that of the Daniell cell. The sliding contact B is moved until the galvanometer shows no deflection. At this point the e.m.f. of the cell is just balanced by the opposing potential drop between A and B. At this point virtually no current is being taken from the cell, and this is the highest electromotive force that the cell is capable of producing. If the sliding contact is moved by the smallest possible distance towards C, that is the opposing e.m.f. is made just greater than the e.m.f. in the Daniell cell, the anodic and cathodic reactions in the cell will be reversed. When, however, the contact is slightly displaced towards A,

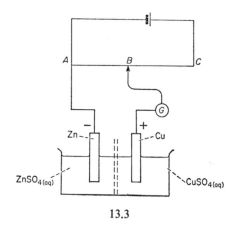

13.3

the normal cell reaction takes place, and a small current will flow through the cell. In general reversible cells are characterised by the reversibility of their electrodes, and in this case the normal cell reaction can be reversed by passing a current through the cell in the opposite direction.

13.3.3 *Chemical and Electrical Energy*

If a cell works reversibly at a constant temperature and pressure, then a measure of the maximum useful work that can be derived from the current produced by this cell is the decrease in Gibbs' free energy of the system. From electrical theory it follows that work done in moving an electrical charge from one potential to another is equal to the product of the charge and the potential difference. In an electrochemical cell working reversibly the potential difference is its reversible electromotive force E, and the charge associated with the transfer of 1 g atom of a metal of valence n is equal to nF coulombs, where F is one faraday (96,494 coulombs). Thus the energy available during a reaction

$$M_1 + M_2^{n+} \rightarrow M_1^{n+} + M_2$$

is given by

$$-\Delta G = nFE \qquad \ldots(13.4)$$

where M_1 and M_2 represent two different metals and n is the number of electrons involved in the reaction. This equation is extremely useful, since it correlates the Gibbs' free energy change of a chemical reaction with the reversible electromotive force that can be obtained from a galvanic cell utilising this cell reaction.

Example

The reversible e.m.f. of a copper–zinc galvanic cell when measured was found to be 1·10 V. Calculate the Gibbs' free energy change in this cell when 1 g ion of copper ions is reduced to metallic copper and 1 g atom of metallic zinc is oxidised to its ions.

The overall cell reaction is given by

$$Zn + Cu^{++} \rightarrow Zn^{++} + Cu$$

and since copper and zinc are divalent n is two.

Using equation (13.4) we have

$$\Delta G = -nFE$$

On substitution of the known values for E, F and n we have

$$\Delta G = -2 \times 96{,}494 \times 1{\cdot}10 \text{ J g mole}^{-1}$$

and since

$$4{,}184 \text{ joules} = 1 \text{ calorie}$$

therefore

$$\Delta G = -\frac{2 \times 96{,}494 \times 1{\cdot}10}{4{\cdot}184} = -50{,}740 \text{ cal g mole}^{-1}$$

Answer: The Gibbs' free energy change for this cell reaction is found to be $-50{,}740$ cal g mole^{-1}.

13.3.4 *Thermodynamics of Electrochemical Cells*

In the previous chapters on thermodynamics expressions were deduced which enabled us to calculate the free energy change of a reaction at different concentrations, temperatures, and pressures. In this section it is intended to derive an expression from which it will be possible to calculate the effect of electrolyte concentration and temperature on the reversible electromotive force.

Let us consider a cell working under reversible conditions in which one metal electrode M_1 is dipped into a solution containing its own ions of activity a_1, and the other metal electrode M_2 is dipped into a solution of activity a_2. If the overall cell reaction under reversible conditions is

$$M_1 + M_2^{n+} \rightarrow M_1^{n+} + M_2$$

then the free energy change which accompanies this reaction can be calculated from Van't Hoff's Isotherm,

$$\Delta G = -RT \log_e K + RT \log_e \frac{a_1 \times a_{M_2}}{a_2 \times a_{M_1}}$$

where K is the equilibrium constant for this reaction at temperature T. Since activities of pure solid metals are equal to unity

$$a_{M_2} = a_{M_1} = 1 \quad \text{and} \quad \Delta G = -nFE$$

then on substitution of these values the above expression becomes

$$\Delta G = -RT \log_e K + RT \log_e \frac{a_1}{a_2} = -nFE$$

On rearranging this expression and dividing by $-nF$ we have

$$E = \frac{RT}{nF} \log_e K - \frac{RT}{nF} \log_e \frac{a_1}{a_2}$$

It is customary, however, to rearrange the second term to change its negative sign into a positive one; thus

$$E = \frac{RT}{nF} \log_e K + \frac{RT}{nF} \log_e \frac{a_2}{a_1} \qquad \ldots(13.5)$$

The right-hand side of this expression consists of two terms, the first of which contains all constants at a constant temperature. The second term depends on the ratio of the activities of reactants and products, that is the activity of the metal ions in the cathodic half cell divided by that for the ions in the anodic one.

Standard or Normal Reversible Electromotive Force of a Cell. It is clear from equation (13.5) that, when the metal ions in both half cells are at unit activity, then the second term becomes zero, and we have

$$E = \frac{RT}{nF} \log_e K = E^0$$

Since the value of this electromotive force of the cell is constant at a constant temperature, it is known as the **standard** or **normal electromotive force** of the cell, and is denoted by E^0. It is clear that

$$\Delta G^0 = -nFE^0$$

and substituting E^0 into equation (13.5) we have

$$E = E^0 + \frac{RT}{nF} \log_e \frac{a_2}{a_1}$$

and since the overall cell reaction is

$$\underbrace{M_1 + M_2^{n+}}_{\text{reactants}} \rightarrow \underbrace{M_1^{n+} + M_2}_{\text{resultants}}$$

$$\therefore \quad E = E^0 + \frac{RT}{nF} \log_e \frac{\text{product of activities of reactants}}{\text{product of activities of resultants}}$$

$$\ldots (13.6)$$

Reversible Electrode Potential. Combining equations (13.5) and (13.6) the electromotive force of a cell represented by:

$$
\begin{array}{ccc}
\hline
\multicolumn{3}{c}{\text{---}E\text{---}} \\
M_1 \mid M_1^{n+} & \vdots & M_2^{n+} \mid M_2 \\
\text{solid} \;\; a_1 & & a_2 \;\; \text{solid} \\
\underbrace{\phantom{M_1 \mid M_1^{n+}}}_{E_1} & & \underbrace{\phantom{M_2^{n+} \mid M_2}}_{E_2}
\end{array}
$$

$$E = [E_2^0 + (-E_1^0)] + \frac{RT}{nF} \log_e \frac{a_2}{a_1} = E_2 + E_1$$

On rearranging this equation we obtain

$$E_2 + E_1 = [E_2^0 + (-E_1^0)] + \frac{RT}{nF} \log_e \frac{a_2}{a_1} \qquad \ldots (13.7)$$

or

$$E_2 = E_2^0 + \frac{RT}{nF} \log_e a_2 \qquad \ldots (13.8)$$

$$E_1 = -\left(E_1^0 + \frac{RT}{nF} \log_e a_1\right) \qquad \ldots (13.9)$$

Standard Electrode Potential. It is clear from the above equations that, when the activities of the metallic ions are equal to unity, then the electrode potentials will be constant at a constant temperature, and they are therefore called **standard electrode potentials.**

It is impossible to determine directly the absolute single electrode potentials, but changes in their values can be measured. Nernst, therefore, decided to take as an arbitrary zero the reversible potential of a hydrogen electrode where hydrogen at one atmosphere pressure is in equilibrium with hydrogen ions at unit activity. Such a hydrogen electrode can in practice be constructed by passing hydrogen gas at one atmosphere pressure into a solution containing hydrogen ions at unit activity into which a platinum electrode is dipped (see Fig. 13.4).

Sign Convention of Electrode Potentials. The sign convention of electrode potentials used in this book is based on the reduction reaction taking place in the given half cell, and is therefore referred

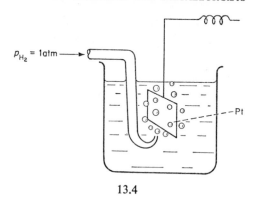

$p_{H_2} = 1 \text{atm}$

Pt

13.4

to as the reduction potential (or European) sign convention.* In this convention the electrode reaction is written for a metallic ion M^{n+} being reduced to a metal M as

$$M^{n+} + ne \rightarrow M$$

and its standard electrode potential E^0 is given a positive sign if its ions, under standard conditions, have a greater tendency to gain electrons than the hydrogen ions in a standard hydrogen half cell. To illustrate this sign convention let us consider a cell made up of (i) hydrogen and copper reversible standard electrodes and (ii) hydrogen and zinc reversible standard electrodes both at 25°C.

(i) Since we do not know which of these half cells will gain or lose electrons more readily than the hydrogen half cell, we write the hydrogen half cell on the left-hand side, thus:

electrons⟶

$E \nearrow$

$$^{\ominus}\text{Pt, H}_2 \,(1 \text{ atm}) \mid a_{H^+} = 1 \vdots a_{CuSO_4} = 1 \mid \text{Cu} \,^{\oplus}$$

positive ionic current

In this cell it is found experimentally that the copper electrode is the positive pole, and the reversible standard electromotive force E is equal to 0·34 volts at 25°C. Thus

$$E = E^0_{H_2/H^+} + E^0_{Cu^{++}/Cu} = 0·34$$

* The American sign convention is based on the oxidation reactions in the half cells and thus gives the same numerical values but with an opposite sign (see also equation (13.9)).

Since $E^0_{H_2/H^+}$ is arbitrarily fixed to equal zero, thus

$$E^0_{Cu^{++}/Cu} = + 0.34 \text{ volts}$$

This cell reaction is then given by

Cathode:	$Cu^{++} + 2e \rightarrow Cu$	(reduction)
Anode:	$H_2 \rightarrow 2H^+ + 2e$	(oxidation)

It is clear, therefore, that copper ions have a greater tendency to gain electrons than the hydrogen ions, and its sign according to this convention is positive.

(ii) Writing the cell in this case exactly the same as before we have

$$E = 0.76 \text{ volts}$$

$$\text{Pt, } H_2 \text{ (1 atm) } | \ a_{H^+} = 1 \ \vdots \ a_{ZnSO_4} = 1 \ | \text{ Zn}$$

positive ionic current

In this cell the zinc electrode is found to be negative, showing that it has less tendency to gain electrons than the hydrogen electrode, and thus the zinc reversible reduction potential is given a negative sign. Since $E^0_{H_2/H^+}$ is zero, therefore $E^0_{Zn^{++}/Zn}$ equals -0.76 V at 25°C.

A list of standard electrode potentials in order of magnitude for various elements is called the **Electrochemical Series.** In this series (see Table 13.3) all the electrodes which have a tendency to lose electrons more readily than the hydrogen electrode possess a negative sign, while those which more readily gain electrons are given a positive sign. Their potentials are said to be measured on the **hydrogen scale.**

Let us illustrate the use of Table 13.3 for the calculation of the standard electromotive force of cells constructed from any two electrodes included in the Table.

Example

Calculate the e.m.f. of a cell at 25°C made of (*a*) standard zinc and copper electrodes, and (*b*) zinc and copper electrodes, dipped into zinc sulphate solution of activity 0·1, and copper sulphate solution of activity 0·01, respectively. Use the standard reduction potential values given in Table 13.3, and assume that any liquid junction potential is negligible.

TABLE 13.3

Standard (Reduction) Potentials of Metals at 25°C

Electrode	E^0 Volts	Reaction	
Li$^+$/Li	−3.00	Li$^+$ + e → Li	
Rb$^+$/Rb	−2·92	Rb$^+$ + e → Rb	
K$^+$/K	−2·92	K$^+$ + e → K	
Sr$^+$/Sr	−2·92	Sr^{++} + 2e → Sr	
Ca^{++}/Ca	−2·87	Ca^{++} + 2e → Ca	
Na$^+$/Na	−2·71	Na$^+$ + e → Na	
Mg^{++}/Mg	−2·39	Mg^{++} + 2e → Mg	
Al^{+++}/Al	−1·67	Al^{+++} + 3e → Al	base metals
Zn^{++}/Zn	−0·76	Zn^{++} + 2e → Zn	
Cr^{+++}/Cr	−0·60	Cr^{+++} + 3e → Cr	
Fe^{++}/Fe	−0·44	Fe^{++} + 2e → Fe	
Ni^{++}/Ni	−0·24	Ni^{++} + 2e → Ni	
Sn^{++}/Sn	−0·14	Sn^{++} + 2e → Sn	
Pb^{++}/Pb	−0·12	Pb^{++} + 2e → Pb	
H$^+$/H$_2$	0·00	H$^+$ + e → $\frac{1}{2}$H$_2$	
Cu^{++}/Cu	+0·34	Cu^{++} + 2e → Cu	
Ag$^+$/Ag	+0·80	Ag$^+$ + e → Ag	noble metals
Au^{++}/Au	+1·35	Au^{++} + 2e → Au	

(a) Since the electrode potential of zinc is found to be lower than that of copper, it will form the anode of this cell.

Thus the cell can be represented as

$$\overline{\;E\;}$$

Zn | ZnSO$_4$($a_{Zn^{++}}$ = 1) ⦙ CuSO$_4$($a_{Cu^{++}}$ = 1) | Cu

positive ionic current

$\longrightarrow$

The e.m.f. of the cell is given by the sum of the electrode potentials, thus, since the flow of positive ionic current through the cell is from left to right, we have

$$E^0 = E^0_{Cu^{++}/Cu} + E^0_{Zn/Zn^{++}}$$

and the cell reaction will be

Cathode:
$$Cu^{++} + 2e \rightarrow Cu; \qquad E^0_{Cu^{++}/Cu} = +0.34$$

Anode:
$$Zn \rightarrow Zn^{++} + 2e; \qquad E^0_{Zn/Zn^{++}} = -(-0.76)*$$

Thus
$$E^0 = +0.34 + [-(-0.76)] = 1.10 \text{ V}$$

Answer: The reversible electromotive force of the cell under standard conditions will be 1·10 V.

(*b*) In this case the cell is given by
$$Zn \mid ZnSO_4(a_{Zn^{++}} = 0.1) \mid CuSO_4(a_{Cu^{++}} = 0.01) \mid Cu$$

and the overall reaction will be:

$$\underbrace{Zn + Cu^{++}}_{\text{reactants}} \rightarrow \underbrace{Cu + Zn^{++}}_{\text{resultants}}$$

Using equation (13.6) we have
$$E = E^0 + \frac{RT}{nF} \log_e \frac{a_{\text{reactants}}}{a_{\text{products}}} = E^0 + \frac{RT}{nF} \log_e \frac{a_{Zn} \cdot a_{Cu^{++}}}{a_{Cu} \cdot a_{Zn^{++}}}$$

On substitution of the value for E^0 (calculated above), and the given values of $a_{Cu^{++}}$ and $a_{Zn^{++}}$, and remembering that activities of the solid metals are taken as unity we have

$$E = 1.10 + \frac{8.314 \times 298 \times 2.303}{2 \times 96,494} \log_{10} \frac{0.01}{0.1}$$

$$E = 1.10 + \frac{0.0591}{2} \log_{10} 0.1 = 1.10 - 0.0295$$

$$E = 1.0705 \text{ volts}$$

Answer: The reversible electromotive force of this cell under these conditions will be 1·0705 V.

Application of Gibbs-Helmholtz Equation to Galvanic Cells. The Gibbs-Helmholtz equation for a given cell reaction can be expressed in terms of the enthalpy change ΔH, the electromotive force of the cell E, and its temperature coefficient $\frac{dE}{dT}$ by combining equations (4.13) and (13.4).

* The potential which applies here is that of the oxidation reaction, that is, the reduction potential with opposite sign.

Thus we have

$$\Delta G = \Delta H + T \cdot \left(\frac{\partial \Delta G}{\partial T} \right)_p$$

and

$$\Delta G = -nFE$$

Differentiation of the latter with respect to temperature at constant pressure gives

$$\left(\frac{\partial \Delta G}{\partial T} \right)_p = -nF \left(\frac{\partial E}{\partial T} \right)_p \qquad \ldots (13.10)$$

Substitution for $\left(\frac{\partial \Delta G}{\partial T} \right)_p$ into equation (6.13) gives

$$\Delta G = \Delta H - nFT \left(\frac{\partial E}{\partial T} \right)_p$$

or

$$-nFE = \Delta H - nFT \left(\frac{\partial E}{\partial T} \right)_p$$

$$\therefore \qquad \Delta H = -nF \left[E - T \left(\frac{\partial E}{\partial T} \right)_p \right] \text{ J g mole}^{-1}$$

or

$$\Delta H = \frac{-nF}{4 \cdot 184} \left[E - T \left(\frac{\partial E}{\partial T} \right)_p \right] \text{ cal g mole}^{-1} \quad \ldots (13.11)$$

Equation (13.11) enables us to determine indirectly the heat of the cell reaction. This indirect method is frequently more accurate than calorimetric methods.

Using equation (13.10) we have

$$\left(\frac{\partial G}{\partial T} \right)_p = -\Delta S = -\frac{q_{rev}}{T} = -nF \left(\frac{\partial E}{\partial T} \right)_p$$

$$\therefore \qquad \frac{q_{rev}}{T} = nF \left(\frac{\partial E}{\partial T} \right)_p \qquad \ldots (13.12)$$

where q_{rev} is the heat absorbed by the cell when the cell works reversibly. From this expression it follows that if

$$\left(\frac{\partial E}{\partial T} \right)_p = \ominus \text{ ve}$$

then heat is evolved (exothermic reaction); if

$$\left(\frac{\partial E}{\partial T}\right)_p = 0$$

then heat is neither evolved nor absorbed), and if

$$\left(\frac{\partial E}{\partial T}\right)_p = \oplus\text{ve}$$

then heat is absorbed (endothermic reaction).

Example
The electromotive force of a cell is found to be 1·1 volt at 300°K, its temperature coefficient of electromotive force equals 4×10^{-5}V deg^{-1}, and the number of charges per ion is one. Calculate the heat of reaction at 300°K.

$$\Delta H = -\frac{nF}{4\cdot184}\left[E - T\left(\frac{\partial E}{\partial T}\right)_p\right] \text{cal}$$

$$\Delta H = -\frac{1 \times 96{,}494}{4\cdot184}[1\cdot1 - 300 \times 4 \times 10^{-5}]$$

$$\Delta H = -\frac{96{,}494}{4\cdot184}[1\cdot1 - 1\cdot2 \times 10^{-2}]$$

$$\Delta H = -\frac{96{,}494}{4\cdot184}[1\cdot088] = -22{,}000 \text{ cal g mole}^{-1}$$

Thus for a general reaction

$$A^+ + B = C^+ + D; \quad \Delta H = -22{,}000 \text{ cal g mole}^{-1}$$

13.3.5   Concentration Cells

If two electrodes of metal M are dipped into two solutions, their ions having activities a_1 and a_2 respectively, and are combined to form a cell whose junction potential is negligible, then the electromotive force of this cell may be calculated using equation (13.6). The cell can be represented as

$$M \mid M^{n+}(a_{Mn^+} = a_1) \parallel M^{n+}(a_{Mn^+} = a_2) \mid M$$

The tendency of a metal to ionise and pass into solution is greater the lower its activity in the solution, and thus more metallic ions have to leave its surface in order to reach equilibrium. Thus if $a_2 > a_1$, then the electrode in contact with the solution of an activity a_1 will be more negative than that in a_2 and will become the anode in the cell. The electrode reactions will then be:

Cathode: $M^{n+} + ne \rightarrow M$ (reduction)

Anode: $M \rightarrow M^{n+} + ne$ (oxidation)

From equation (13.9) the reduction electrode potentials are given by

$$E_2 = E^0_{M^{n+}/M} + \frac{RT}{nF} \log_e a_2$$

$$E_1 = E^0_{M^{n+}/M} + \frac{RT}{nF} \log_e a_1$$

Since the electromotive force of a cell E is given by the algebraic sum of the cathodic and anodic potentials, we have

$$E = E_2 + (-E_1)^*$$

$$E = \left[E^0_{M^{n+}/M} + \frac{RT}{nF} \log_e a_2 \right] + \left\{ - \left[E^0_{M^{n+}/M} + \frac{RT}{nF} \log_e a_1 \right] \right\}$$

$$E = \frac{RT}{nF} \log_e \frac{a_2}{a_1} \qquad \qquad \dots (13.13)$$

Example

Calculate the e.m.f. of a copper concentration cell in which the activities of copper ions in the two half cells are 0·5 and 0·005 respectively (*a*) at 25°C, and (*b*) at 50°C.

(*a*) On substitution of the given activities into equation (13.13) and remembering that $n = 2$ for copper, we have

$$E = \frac{RT}{nF} \log_e \frac{0 \cdot 5}{0 \cdot 005} = \frac{8 \cdot 314 \times 298 \times 2 \cdot 303}{2 \times 96,494} \log_{10} 100$$

$$\therefore \quad E = 0 \cdot 0591 \text{ V at } 25°C$$

(*b*) Using equation (13.13) as in the previous calculation the electromotive force E is given by:

$$E = \frac{8 \cdot 314 \times 323 \times 2 \cdot 303}{96,494} = 0 \cdot 0645 \text{ V at } 50°C$$

---

* Since $a_2 > a_1$ the electrode in contact with the solution of activity a_1 will be the anode. Thus the minus sign is required to change the value of the reduction potential of the electrode to the *oxidation potential* of an anode.

13.3.5   Oxidation-Reduction Potentials

When an inert electrode (e.g. Pt, Au, Rh) is dipped into a solution containing ions of an element which exist in two forms of oxidation, it acquires a certain potential, which is known as the **oxidation-reduction potential** or simply the **redox potential.** For example the redox potential of a platinum electrode placed in a solution containing ferric and ferrous ions will refer to the electrode reaction

$$Fe^{+++} \quad + e \rightarrow \quad Fe^{++}$$

$$\underbrace{\text{reactant}}_{\text{oxidised form}} \qquad \underbrace{\text{resultant}}_{\text{reduced form}}$$

Using equation (13.6) we have

$$E = E^0 + \frac{RT}{nF} \log_e \frac{\text{product of activity terms of reactants}}{\text{product of activity terms of resultants}}$$

Thus

$$E = E^0 + 0.0591 \log_{10} \frac{a_{Fe^{+++}}}{a_{Fe^{++}}} \qquad \ldots(13.14)$$

where E^0 is the standard electrode potential of the ferric–ferrous system, measured on the hydrogen scale, when the activities of the ferric and ferrous ions are equal. The value of E^0 for this system is $+0.77$ V at 25°C. On examining equation (13.14) it is clear that the redox potential of this system depends on the ratio of the number of ferric to ferrous ions. The positive sign of its standard redox potential signifies that the above electrode reaction has a greater affinity for electrons than the reaction $H^+ + e \rightarrow \frac{1}{2}H_2$ for the hydrogen electrode; thus a solution of a ferric salt may be reduced to ferrous by passing hydrogen into it under atmospheric pressure.

There are many possible redox systems. Values of standard redox potentials for some common elements are given in Table 13.4.

TABLE 13.4

Standard Redox Potentials at 25°C

Ions in equilibrium	E^0 in Volts
Ce^{++++}/Ce^{+++}	$+1.61$
$2Hg^{++}/2Hg$	$+0.915$
Fe^{+++}/Fe^{++}	$+0.77$
Cu^{++}/Cu	$+0.156$
Sn^{++++}/Sn^{++}	$+0.15$
Cr^{+++}/Cr^{++}	-0.41

The oxidising power of these systems is higher the more positive the standard redox potential. Thus ceric ions may be used for the oxidation of any ions of lower redox potential.

Example:

Calculate the equilibrium constant for the oxidation of ferrous ions by ceric ions,

$$Ce^{++++} + Fe^{++} \rightarrow Ce^{+++} + Fe^{+++}$$

The E^0 of this reaction can be calculated as for galvanic cells; thus

$$E^0 = E^0_{Ce} + (-E^0_{Fe}) = 1\cdot61 + (-0\cdot77)$$

$$E^0 = 0\cdot84 \text{ V at } 25°C$$

The equilibrium constant K for this reaction can be calculated using equation (13.6):

$$E^0 = \frac{RT}{nF} \log_e K$$

$$\log_{10} K = \frac{0\cdot84}{0\cdot0591} = 14\cdot2$$

so that

$$K = 10^{14\cdot2}$$

This means that ceric ions for all practical purposes completely oxidise ferrous ions in solution.

13.3.6 *Reference Electrodes*

The potential of a single electrode cannot be measured directly. It is possible, however, to measure the difference between two electrodes by combining them into a cell. In sub-section 13.3.4 it was shown how, by combining either the copper or the zinc electrode with a normal hydrogen electrode, their potentials could be measured. In practice the **hydrogen reference electrode** is very seldom used, since a number of very convenient reproducible reversible electrodes can be obtained commercially. In this section it is intended to describe three such electrodes, the **Calomel,** the **Glass,** and the **Antimony Electrode,** and then to discuss some of their uses.

Calomel Electrode. The normal calomel electrode consists of mercury in contact with a normal solution of potassium chloride which is saturated with mercurous chloride. A platinum wire sealed into a glass tube is in contact with the mercury. For ordinary work an electrode having a saturated solution of potassium chloride is

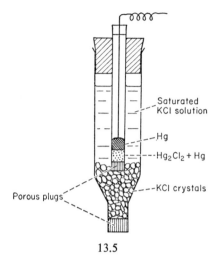

Saturated KCl solution

Hg

Hg$_2$Cl$_2$ + Hg

KCl crystals

Porous plugs

13.5

preferred, since it is more easily prepared. Fig. 13.5 shows a typical calomel electrode. The following equilibria are set up between mercury and the solution:

$$Hg_2Cl_2 \rightarrow Hg_2^{++} + 2Cl^-$$

$$Hg_2^{++} + 2e \rightarrow 2Hg$$

The overall equilibrium is given by

$$Hg_2Cl_2 + 2e \rightleftarrows 2Hg + 2Cl^-$$

Using equation (13.6) we can write its potential as follows:

$$E_{(calomel)} = E_{(calomel)}^0 + \frac{RT}{nF} \log_e \frac{a_{Hg_2Cl_2}}{a_{Hg}^2 \times a_{Cl^-}^2}$$

Since mercurous chloride is a pure solid, and mercury a pure metal, then their activities are both unity; that is,

$$a_{Hg_2Cl_2} = a_{Hg} = 1$$

Thus $E_{(calomel)}$ becomes

$$E_{(calomel)} = E_{(calomel)}^0 - 0.0591 \log_{10} a_{Cl^-} \text{ at } 25°C$$

Since the value of the normal potential $E_{(calomel)}^0$ is 0.2801 V, we can write

$$E_{(calomel)} = 0.2801 - 0.0591 \log_{10} a_{Cl^-} \qquad \ldots(13.15)$$

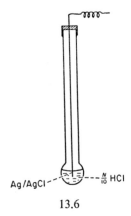

Ag/AgCl -- $\frac{N}{10}$ HCl

13.6

The potential of this electrode with a saturated solution of potassium chloride is +0·242 V at 25°C, and that for 0·1 N KCl is +0·3335 V, when compared with the standard hydrogen electrode.

The Glass Electrode. The glass electrode is widely used in pH measurements. It consists of a silver–silver chloride electrode dipped into a hydrochloric acid solution contained in a glass tube, at whose lower end is a thin glass bulb which is permeable to hydrogen ions (see Fig. 13.6). When the glass electrode is dipped into a solution containing hydrogen ions of a different activity from that in the bulb, there is a movement of H^+ ions towards the solution of lower activity, and a potential difference is set up across the glass boundary between the two solutions. The potential of a glass electrode E_G at constant temperature and hydrogen pressure, in contact with a solution containing hydrogen ions of activity a_{H^+}, is given by:

$$E_G = \text{constant} + \frac{RT}{nF} \log_e (a_{H^+})^2$$

where the constant incorporates the term $- \dfrac{RT}{nF} \log_e \dfrac{1}{0·1}$. At 25°C the above expression becomes

$$E_G = \text{constant} + 0·0591 \log_{10} a_{H^+} \qquad \ldots(13.16)$$

Since

$$pH = -\log_{10} a_{H^+}$$

then

$$E_G = \text{constant} - 0·0591 \, pH \qquad \ldots(13.17)$$

Equation (13.17) shows that the glass electrode potential is a linear function of pH.

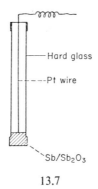

13.7

The Antimony Electrode. A simple form of the antimony–antimonious oxide electrode is shown in Fig. 13.7. This consists of a plug of antimony cast into the end of a glass tube in air, so that some antimonious oxide is formed on its surface. A platinum wire connects the electrode with the external measuring circuit. If this electrode is dipped into an aqueous solution the equilibrium set up is

$$Sb_2O_3 + 3H_2O + 6e \rightleftarrows 2Sb + 6OH^-$$

and its potential depends on the activity of the hydroxyl ions in the solution; but since the product of hydroxyl and hydrogen ion activities in a solution at a given temperature is constant, the potential of this electrode will therefore also depend on the activity of the hydrogen ions. Let us consider the dependence of its potential on the ion activities a_{OH^-} and a_{H^+}. Using the Nernst equation for this electrode potential we have

$$E_{Sb_2O_3/Sb} = E^0_{Sb_2O_3/Sb}$$
$$+ \frac{RT}{nF} \log_e \frac{\text{product of activity terms of reactants}}{\text{products of activity terms of resultants}}$$

Thus

$$E_{Sb_2O_3/Sb} = E^0_{Sb_2O_3/Sb} + \frac{RT}{nF} \log_e \frac{a_{Sb_2O_3}(a_{H_2O})^3}{(a_{Sb})^2 \times (a_{OH^-})^6}$$

Taking the solid antimony, its solid oxide, and water to be at unit activity at 25°C we have

$$E_{Sb_2O_3/Sb} = E^0_{Sb_2O_3/Sb} + \frac{0.0591}{6} \log_{10} \frac{1}{(a_{OH^-})^6}$$

$$E_{Sb_2O_3/Sb} = E^0_{Sb_2O_3/Sb} - 0.0591 \log_{10} a_{OH^-}$$

Since

$$a_{OH^-} = \frac{K_w}{a_{H^+}} = \frac{10^{-14}}{a_{H^+}} \text{ at } 25°C$$

then

$$E_{Sb_2O_3/Sb} = E^0_{Sb_2O_3/Sb} - 0·0591 \log_{10} \frac{10^{-14}}{a_{H^+}}$$

$$E_{Sb_2O_3/Sb} = E^0_{Sb_2O_3/Sb} + 0·8274 + 0·0591 \log_{10} a_{H^+}$$

Putting

$$pH = -\log_{10} a_{H^+} \quad \text{and} \quad E^0_{Sb} = E^0_{Sb_2O_3/Sb} + 0·8274$$

we have

$$E_{Sb_2O_3/Sb} = E^0_{Sb} - 0·0591 \text{ pH}$$

$$E_{Sb_2O_3/Sb} = 0·1445 - 0·0591 \text{ pH} \qquad \ldots(13.18)$$

Equation (13.18) shows that *the potential of the antimony electrode is a linear function of the pH of the solution.*

13.3.7 Standard Cells

Standard cells provide an e.m.f. of a known value against which the e.m.f. of other cells may be accurately determined. They are thus used for the calibration of potentiometers. A good standard cell must be convenient to use, easily reproducible, and must have a small temperature coefficient of electromotive force. Various cells have from time to time been developed as standards of e.m.f., but the most convenient and generally employed is the Weston cell (see Fig. 13.8). This cell is made up of electrodes consisting of mercury and cadmium amalgam (12·5% cadmium). The electrolyte is a saturated solution of hydrated cadmium sulphate $3CdSO_4 \cdot 8H_2O$. When the cell supplies current, cadmium ions are released from the cadmium

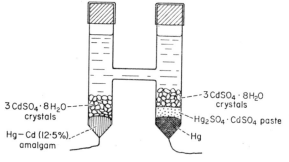

$3CdSO_4 \cdot 8H_2O$ crystals

Hg–Cd (12·5%) amalgam

$3CdSO_4 \cdot 8H_2O$ crystals

$Hg_2SO_4 \cdot CdSO_4$ paste

Hg

13.8

amalgam into the solution, and mercuric ions are discharged on the mercury electrode. The cell may be written

$$Cd(12.5\% \text{ amalgam}) \mid CdSO_4 \cdot 8H_2O_{(e)} \text{ } \vdots \text{ } CdSO_{4(sat)} \text{ } \vdots \text{ } Hg_2SO_{4(s)} \mid Hg$$

and the anodic and cathodic reactions are thus given by

Anode: $\qquad\qquad Cd \rightarrow Cd^{++} + 2e$

Cathode: $\qquad Hg^{++} + 2e \rightarrow Hg$

Since the electrolyte consists of a saturated solution of $3CdSO_4 \cdot 8H_2O$, the activity of the cadmium ions remains constant while the cell is working, providing no excessive current is drawn from the cell. The e.m.f. of this cell is thus very stable and has a constant value of 1.0183 V at $20°C$.

13.3.8 *Potentiometric Titrations*

The end-points of neutralisation, oxidation-reduction, and precipitation titrations may conveniently be determined by means of potentiometric titrations. In each case two reference electrodes are immersed in the solution to be titrated and connected externally to a potentiometer, or to a sensitive valve voltmeter when the glass electrode is being used.*

Neutralisation Titrations. The apparatus is set up as shown in Fig. 13.9, antimony and calomel electrodes are dipped into the acid

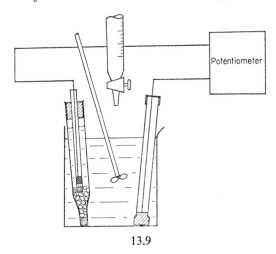

13.9

* The glass electrode has a very high electrical resistance, and therefore the current in the circuit is so small that it cannot be detected by an ordinary potentiometer circuit.

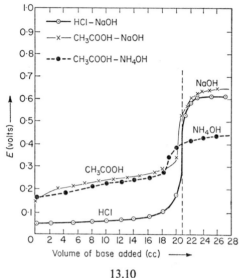

13.10

solution to be titrated, and are connected to the potentiometer, which has previously been calibrated using the Weston standard cell. A stirrer is used during titration, and there is a steady change in the potential of the solution as the titration proceeds. The equivalence point of the neutralisation is shown by the sudden change in potential measured; thus, if a plot of e.m.f. against titration volume is made during the titration, the volume at the end-point may easily be read off. Fig. 13.10 shows e.m.f. against volume titration curves for 0·1 N HCl with 0·1 N NaOH, 0·1 N CH₃COOH with 0·1 N NaOH and 0·1 N CH₃COOH with 0·1 N NH₄OH. From these curves it can be seen that for titrations of strong acid–strong base and weak acid–strong base the sharp change in e.m.f. enables the end-point to be accurately determined. In the case of the weak acid–weak base titration the end-point is not so well defined; nevertheless it can be still used to give an approximate end-point.

It should be noted that the two electrodes used were so chosen that the electrochemical cell consisted of one calomel reference electrode having a potential independent of the activity of hydrogen ions or any other ions present in the solution, and another electrode whose potential was a linear function of the activity of the hydrogen ions.

Oxidation-Reduction Titrations. The apparatus is set up as shown in Fig. 13.9. In this titration, however, the antimony electrode is

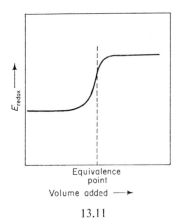

Equivalence
point

Volume added ⟶

13.11

replaced by an inert electrode (e.g. Pt). The potential between the
saturated calomel and redox electrodes is read off after each addition
of the titrant. The equivalence point of the titration is again indicated
by the sudden change in potential (see Fig. 13.11). To illustrate
this type of titration let us consider the oxidation of ferrous ions with
ceric ions. It has been shown that the reaction

$$Ce^{++++} + Fe^{++} \rightarrow Ce^{+++} + Fe^{+++}$$

goes virtually to completion. The only effect of the addition of ceric
solution up to the equivalence point will be to oxidise the ferrous
ions. Thus the redox potential will depend on the ratio $\dfrac{a_{Fe^{+++}}}{a_{Fe^{++}}}$.

Once the equivalence point is exceeded any subsequent addition
of ceric solution will increase the ratio $\dfrac{a_{Ce^{++++}}}{a_{Ce^{+++}}}$, which in turn will
increase the redox potential,* since the ratio $\dfrac{a_{Fe^{+++}}}{a_{Fe^{++}}}$ will remain
virtually constant.

13.3.9 *Irreversible Electrode Potentials*

So far all the electrode potentials and electromotive forces of cells
have referred to values obtained under reversible conditions.
Although such values are extremely useful in determining ΔG, ΔS,

---

* For calculation of this potential see Vogel, A. I., *Textbook of Quantitative
Inorganic Analysis*, p. 110, Longmans, Green & Co. Ltd., London, 1944.

ΔH, pH, end-points of titrations, and activities they are not usually the same as those values found under working conditions of a cell, as will be explained later.

Polarisation and Overvoltage. When an electrochemical cell is working under irreversible conditions, that is current is drawn from it, its e.m.f. usually falls below the equilibrium value. The greater the current drawn from the cell the greater is the departure in the e.m.f. Thus the extent of irreversibility of a cell can be measured by the departure of its potential from the equilibrium value under the same conditions. Since the e.m.f. value of a cell is given by the algebraic sum of the cathodic and anodic potentials, it follows that their potentials most probably also depart under irreversible conditions. These effects are known as **cathodic polarisation** and **anodic polarisation** respectively. In general we can say that polarisation describes the departure of an electrode potential from its reversible potential under given conditions of temperature and pressure, as well as composition of the electrode and electrolyte.

Polarisation can arise from four factors:

   (i) concentration polarisation,
   (ii) activation overpotential,
   (iii) resistance polarisation, and
   (iv) presence of polarising and depolarising agents.

(i) *Concentration Polarisation.* This source of departure from the reversible electrode potential is caused by the concentration gradient which develops under irreversible conditions between the electrolyte immediately in contact with the electrode and the bulk of the electrolyte. Let us illustrate this effect in the case of a Daniell cell from which current is being drawn. Cupric ions are discharged on the cathode (see Fig. 13.12) and, the greater the current, the higher the rate of

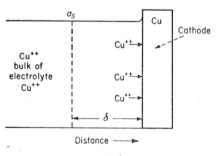

13.12

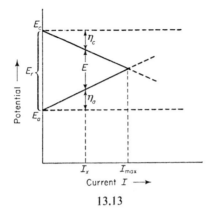

13.13

copper deposition. As the cupric ions are discharged, they may be replenished by ionic migration, ionic diffusion, or agitation (either stirring or convection). If the ions are adequately replenished, there is no concentration gradient, and thus there is no concentration polarisation. However, in electrochemical cells the ionic migration and convection is usually unable to replenish the discharged ions, and thus a diffusion gradient is set up. To obtain a quantitative expression for this effect let us assume the activity of cupric ions at the cathode is a_c and those at the distance δ from the cathode is a_s. From the Nernst equation the concentration polarisation potential η_{conc} is given by

$$\eta_{conc} = \frac{RT}{nF} \log_e \frac{a_c}{a_s} \qquad \ldots (13.20)$$

Since $a_s > a_c$, therefore the ratio $\frac{a_c}{a_s}$ is less than one, and the η_{conc} value will have a *negative sign*.

Using the same argument for the anodic reaction it is clear that the ionic activity at the anode a_a is greater than that in the solution a_s. The anodic concentration polarisation η_{conc} is thus given by

$$\eta_{conc} = \frac{RT}{nF} \log_e \frac{a_a}{a_s} \qquad \ldots (13.21)$$

Since $a_a > a_s$, the anodic concentration polarisation has a positive value. Thus the net effect of the cathodic and anodic polarisations is a decrease in the potential of the cathode and an increase in the potential of the anode (see Fig. 13.13).

(ii) *Activation Overpotential.** When a metal is dipped into a solution containing its own ions a dynamic equilibrium is set up between the metal M passing into the solution (oxidation), and metal ions M^{n+} being discharged on the metal (reduction).

Thus at equilibrium we can write

$$M^{n+} + ne \underset{v_a}{\overset{v_c}{\rightleftharpoons}} M$$

where v_c and v_a denote the velocity of the reduction and oxidation processes respectively (see Fig. 13.14). The bottom half of Fig. 13.14 shows a hypothetical free energy plot against distance, and ΔG_a^* and ΔG_c^* are the activation free energies of the anodic and cathodic reactions of this electrode.

The upper half in Fig. 13.14 shows the corresponding electrode in the solution of its ions in the cell. It is obvious that when $v_a = v_c$ there is no net transfer of either the metal into the solution or metal ions into metal, and thus a dynamic equilibrium is set up. ΔG_a^* can be regarded as the energy barrier that the metallic atoms must surmount before they can pass into solution. Similarly ΔG_c^* is the energy barrier for the ions to discharge on the metal.

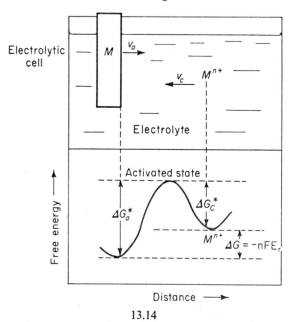

13.14

* For a more extensive treatment of this subject see Potter, E. C., *Electrochemistry*, pp. 124–143, Cleaver-Hume Press Ltd., London, 1956.

Using the Arrhenius type equation (see p. 198) the velocities v_a and v_c are given by

$$v_a = k_a e^{\frac{-\Delta G_a^*}{RT}}$$

and

$$v_c = k_c e^{\frac{-\Delta G_c^*}{RT}}$$

where k_a and k_c are the appropriate velocity constants. Since at equilibrium $v_a = v_c$ thus we have

$$k_a e^{\frac{-\Delta G_a^*}{RT}} = k_c e^{\frac{-\Delta G_c^*}{RT}} \quad \text{or} \quad \frac{k_c}{k_a} = e^{\left(\frac{-\Delta G_a^*}{RT} + \frac{\Delta G_c^*}{RT}\right)}$$

and

$$\frac{k_c}{k_a} = e^{-\left(\frac{\Delta G_a^*}{RT} - \frac{\Delta G_c^*}{RT}\right)} = e^{\frac{-\Delta G}{RT}}$$

Taking $\log_e$ of both sides and rearranging the expression we have

$$\Delta G = -RT \log_e \frac{k_c}{k_a} = -RT \log_e K$$

where K is now the equilibrium constant of the electrode process. This equation is identical with that previously obtained from Van't Hoff's Isotherm (see p. 112) for the standard free energy of a process.

In an irreversible process this kinetic equilibrium at the electrode can be disturbed in various ways, either by the free energy of the metal being lowered or raised by connecting it to a system of a different potential energy (see Fig. 13.15), or by altering the electrolyte by adding polarising or depolarising agents. Fig. 13.15 shows the same system as Fig. 13.14, except that now the metallic electrode is connected to an electrode having a lower potential, and thus its free energy is also lowered. From Fig. 13.15 it is clear that the value of the new free energy of activation ΔG_a^* for the metal M to pass into solution has become higher, whereas that for the metal ions to be discharged is lower. As a result of this the number of ions discharged is much greater than that of metallic ions passing into the solution. The dynamic equilibrium is thus disturbed and the overall effect is the discharge of ions on the electrode (deposition of M). Using the same argument it follows that an increase in the potential of the metal causes more ions to pass into solution than those discharged, and the overall effect is the anodic dissolution of the metal.

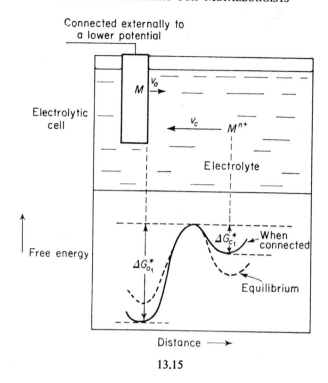

13.15

If the cathodic activation free energy ΔG_c^* is not very high, then a small polarisation voltage, that is to say activation overpotential, is sufficient to bring about a measurable cathodic current (e.g. Cu, Ag, Zn, etc.). If on the other hand the cathodic activation free energy is high, then a much higher activation overpotential is required to disturb the equilibrium and cause a measurable cathodic current (e.g. Fe, Ni, etc.).

The activation overpotential depends on such factors as current density, temperature, the material of the electrode, and presence of impurities in the metal and the electrolyte.

The effect of the material of an inert electrode on the overvoltage during hydrogen and oxygen evolution will be outlined in the section on electrolysis. Expressions can be derived correlating the exchange equilibrium current, i.e. the activation overpotential η, with the temperature and the actual electric current passing through the cell.

(iii) *Resistance Polarisation*. This polarisation is caused by two main factors namely (*a*) the potential drop (Ohmic potential) between the

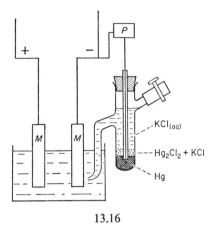

13.16

tip of the reference electrode (see Fig. 13.16) and the electrode
surface, and (b) the resistance caused by any products accompanying
either the discharge or dissolution of the ions. The second factor
may produce a very high polarisation value where the product
forms an adherent and continuous surface layer, as for example
an oxide film possessing a very high electrical resistance. The same
effect is obtained when gaseous products are occluded on the
electrode.

(iv) *Presence of Polarising and Depolarising Agents.* There are
various compounds which, when added to an electrolyte, have the
effect of either increasing its polarisation and thus decreasing the
total maximum current in the circuit, or decreasing the polarisation
and thus facilitating the flow of current. These compounds are of
much interest in electrodeposition and in corrosion (inhibitors).

Impurities on the surface of the metal itself may also have a
pronounced effect on polarisation. For example, any traces of
platinum embedded in a lead cathode act as sources of discharge
for hydrogen ions, and this electrode, which normally is unsuitable
because it has a very high hydrogen overvoltage, can by this means
be used in practice.

13.4 ELECTROLYSIS

13.4.1 *Introduction*

**Electrolysis can be defined as a process in which a chemical reaction
is brought about on electrodes in contact with an electrolyte by means
of an external electromotive force.** From this definition it follows

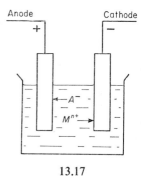

13.17

that electrolysis can be regarded as the converse of electrochemical action, in which a spontaneous chemical reaction is harnessed to give electricity. In the former case electric power brought from the outside of the cell is utilised to bring about a chemical reaction whose products are thermodynamically less stable than the reactants.

13.4.2   Mechanism of Electrolysis

The mechanism of electrolysis has already been outlined in Chapter XII. An electrolytic cell consists essentially of two or more electrodes dipped into an electrolyte. The electrodes are connected to an external source of electric power (see Fig. 13.17), so that the anode becomes positively charged and the cathode negatively charged when the current is switched on. During electrolysis the positive and negative ions in the solution are attracted towards the electrodes with the opposite sign. Thus the cations M^{n+} move towards the cathode, and anions A^- towards the anode (see Fig. 13.17). Although the terms "electrochemical" and "electrolytic" cells are often used indiscriminately in the literature, in this book a cell in which the process is spontaneous is called an "electrochemical cell" and "electrolytic cells" are those which require an external source of electric power to bring about a chemical reaction. The main difference between these two types of cells are summarised in Table 13.5.

13.4.3   Cathodic and Anodic Reactions

The cathodes and anodes in electrolytic cells can be made of various materials such as solid metals (both pure and alloys), liquid metals (e.g. mercury), oxides (e.g. lead peroxide), and graphite. Since electrolytic processes are used in many fields of metallurgy such as extraction, refining, electrochemical analysis, protection of metals, electrolytic cleaning, etc., all these types of electrodes are likely to be encountered.

TABLE 13.5

Type of Cell	Cathode		Anode		Means of Producing Reaction
	Sign	Reaction	Sign	Reaction	
Electro-chemical	Positive	Reduction e.g. $M^+ + e \rightarrow M$	Negative	Oxidation e.g. $M \rightarrow M^+ + e$	Spontaneous
Electrolytic	Negative	Reduction	Positive	Oxidation	by impressed electric current

In this section, however, we shall only be concerned with general types of cathodic and anodic reactions and the voltage requirement in cells with aqueous and fused electrolytes.

There are many possible cathodic reactions, but nearly all of them can be classified under one of the following headings:

(i) metal discharge $M^{n+} + ne \rightarrow M$, e.g.

$$Cu^{++} + 2e \rightarrow Cu$$

(ii) gas evolution, e.g.

$$2H^+ + 2e \rightarrow H_2$$

(iii) gas absorption, e.g.

$$O_2 + 2H_2O + 4e \rightarrow 4OH^-$$

(iv) reduction of an ion from a higher to a lower valency $M^{n+} + xe \rightarrow M^{(n-x)+}$, e.g.

$$Fe^{+++} + e \rightarrow Fe^{++}$$

The types of anodic reactions which can occur are the same as the previous ones, except that they proceed in the opposite direction, and thus we have:

(i) dissolution of a metal (oxidation), $M \rightarrow M^{n+} + ne$, e.g.

$$Cu \rightarrow Cu^{++} + 2e$$

(ii) gas evolution, e.g.

$$4OH^- \rightarrow 2H_2O + O_2 + 4e$$

(iii) absorption of a gas, e.g.

$$H_2 \rightarrow 2H^+ + 2e$$

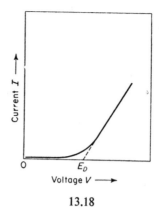

13.18

(iv) oxidation of an ion from a lower to a higher valency, e.g.

$$Fe^{++} \rightarrow Fe^{+++} + e$$

This list of the possible cathodic and anodic reactions shows that during any theoretical consideration of electrolysis many possible reactions have to be postulated. Let us consider therefore the main factors which can regulate the different reactions.

13.4.4 Decomposition Potential

When the voltage across the electrodes in an electrolytic cell is gradually increased, and the corresponding current flowing through the cell is measured, then a plot of the measured current I against the applied voltage V gives the type of curve shown in Fig. 13.18. The current–voltage curve shows that at low voltages practically no current flows through the cell, and it is only when the applied voltage reaches a certain value that the current begins to increase rapidly; in this region even a small increase in voltage causes a marked increase in current. The voltage at which appreciable current begins to flow corresponds to that at which, for example, copper starts plating out from a copper sulphate solution, or bubbles of hydrogen begin to form at a cathode. **The voltage at which this rapid increase in the current begins to take place is called the decomposition potential.** Some values of the decomposition potential for a number of salts in normal solution at 25°C is shown in Table 13.6.

The decomposition potentials vary,* not only for solutions of different electrolytes, but also for solutions of the same electrolytes

---

* The conditions of temperature, concentration, and nature of the electrodes must always be stated when giving the value of the decomposition potential.

TABLE 13.6

Electrolyte	E_D Volts	Electrolyte	E_D Volts
$AgNO_3$	1·03	H_2SO_4	1·67
$Cd(NO_3)_2$	2·35	NaOH	1·69
$CuSO_4$	1·63	NH_4OH	1·74
$Pb(NO_3)_2$	1·80		

due to changes in concentration, material of the electrodes, size of cell, temperature, and the presence of complexing, polarising, and depolarising agents.

Let us now consider the theoretical reasons for the existence of decomposition potentials and their variation with the size of cell and electrolyte conditions. Fig. 13.19 shows a cell in which the reversible anodic potential for the anodic reaction is E_a, and the cathodic potential E_c. If the resistance of the electrolyte contained between the two electrodes is R, then it is clear that the theoretical decomposition potential must be just greater than the algebraic sum of potentials of the cathode E_c, the anode E_a (with an opposite sign), and the value of the product of current I flowing through the cell and the resistance R. Thus we have

$$E_D > [E_c + (-E_a)] + IR$$

This will only apply where there are no other potential drops in the circuit such as contact potentials or activation overpotentials. For an electrolytic process to proceed at a given current I the required voltage will have to be greater than E_D, since during electrolysis

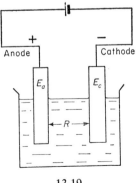

13.19

anodic (η_a) and cathodic (η_c) polarisation will be set up. The total voltage E_{tot} required to maintain the process will thus be given by

$$E_{tot} = (E_c - E_a) + IR + \eta_a + \eta_c + E_R$$

where E_R is the resistance of contacts and connecting wires in the circuit, thus

$$E_{tot} = E_r + IR + E_\eta + E_R \qquad \ldots (13.24)$$

where E_r represents the reversible e.m.f. of the electrolytic cell reaction, and E_η the polarisation overvoltage at the steady current I associated with the deposition of a metal and/or liberation of a gas.

E_r in equation (13.24) depends on the nature of the cathodic and anodic reactions, the activities and pressures of the reactants and products, and the temperature of the electrolyte. The other three terms will be functions of the current flowing in the circuit and the temperature. The term E_η will depend also on the presence of polarising and depolarising agents.

Example

Calculate the voltage requirement for the electrolytic refining of copper in a cell made up of copper electrodes, where the anode is the copper to be refined and the electrolyte solution is one molar copper sulphate (see Fig. 13.20). The current I in the cell is 50 amps, the resistance of the electrolyte R equals 0·005 ohms, and the contact resistances and polarisation are negligible.

Using equation (13.24) we have

$$E_{tot} = [E_{Cu^{++}/Cu} + E_{Cu/Cu^{++}}] + E_\eta + E_R + IR$$

Here

$$[E_{Cu^{++}/Cu} + E_{Cu/Cu^{++}}] = 0 \quad \text{and} \quad E_\eta = \eta_a + \eta_c$$

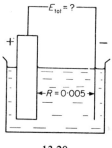

13.20

Since the rate of copper deposition on the cathode will be equal to the rate of copper dissolving from the anode, η_a may be considered to be equal to η_c with an opposite sign; thus on putting these relationships into the previous equation we have

$$E_{tot} = 0 + 0 + 0 + 50 \times 0.005$$

$$E_{tot} = 0.25 \text{ V}$$

From this calculation it follows that 0.25 V will be sufficient to carry out the electrolytic refining of copper in this cell.

Electrolysis of Mixtures of Electrolytes. So far we have considered aqueous solutions containing only one electrolyte. Let us now consider a solution containing a mixture of electrolytes as for example copper, nickel, and iron chlorides (see Fig. 13.21). In this case two anodic reactions are possible:

$$2Cl^- \rightarrow Cl_2 + 2e$$

or

$$4OH^- \rightarrow O_2 + 2H_2O + 4e$$

The standard electrode potential of $E^0_{Cl_2/Cl^-}$ is $+1.359$ V, and that of $E^0_{O_2/4OH^-}$ is $+0.40$ V at 25°C. Assuming that this electrolyte is neutral, then $a_{OH^-} = 10^{-7}$ and the oxygen electrode potential can be calculated at 25°C using the Nernst equation as follows:

$$E_{O_2/OH^-} = 0.40 + \frac{0.059}{4} \log_{10} \left(\frac{1}{10^{-7}} \right)^4$$

$$E_{O_2/OH^-} = 0.40 + [0.059 \times (+7)] = +0.81$$

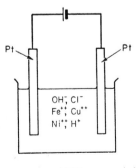

OH⁻; Cl⁻
Fe⁺⁺; Cu⁺⁺
Ni⁺⁺; H⁺

13.21

Since the oxygen overvoltage (polarisation) on a platinum electrode is equal to 0·45 V, then the minimum potential required for the evolution of oxygen is $+0·81 + 0·45 = 1·26$ V. Since the voltage required to carry out this reaction is lower than that for a normal chlorine electrode, it follows that oxygen will be evolved on the anode in preference to chlorine.

There are four possible reactions at the cathode, namely, the reduction of each of the metallic ions to the metals and the reduction of hydrogen ions to hydrogen. The standard electrode potentials of the appropriate reduction reactions are given by

$$E^0_{Cu^{++}/Cu} = +0·34; \quad E^0_{H^+/H_2} = 0; \quad E^0_{Ni^{++}/Ni} = -0·25$$

and

$$E_{Fe^{++}/Fe} = -0·44$$

Since the electrolyte solution is assumed to have pH of 7, then

$$E_{H^+/H_2} = 0 + \frac{0·0591}{2} \log_{10} (a_{H^+})^2 = 0 + 0·0591 \log_{10} 10^{-7}$$

$$E_{H^+/H_2} = -0·413 \text{ V}$$

Since from the above E values it is clear that copper has the highest affinity for electrons (having the highest value), it will be preferentially deposited. Thus the cell reaction will be

Cathode: $Cu^{++} + 2e \rightarrow Cu$

Anode: $4OH^- \rightarrow 2H_2O + O_2 \uparrow + 4e$

The voltage requirement for this cell will be

$$E_{tot} = 1·26 - (+0·34) = +0·92 \text{ V}$$

From this example it can be seen that, providing the conditions are known at which the cell is working, and the polarisation terms can be evaluated, it is possible to predict the products of electrolysis.

13.4.5 Hydrogen and Oxygen Overvoltage

During the evolution of gases on the cathode or anode a marked overpotential is usually observed. When dealing with the electrolysis of aqueous electrolytes the evolution of hydrogen and oxygen has always to be considered as a likely process, and therefore the knowledge of their overpotentials is of considerable practical importance. Overpotentials are a function of the current for conditions of constant temperature, concentration, electrode material, and the presence of polarising and depolarising agents. Tafel proposed the following linear equation for the relationship between overpotential and current density:

$$\eta = a + b \log_{10} I \qquad \ldots(13.25)$$

where a and b are called the **Tafel line parameters** or just simply **Tafel constants**, and I is the current density flowing through the cell. Table 13.7 shows some of these constants for the hydrogen overpotential* in aqueous solution at $20°C$.

TABLE 13.7

Cathode	Electrolyte	Tafel line parameter in volts per amp per geometrical cm^2	
		a	b
Iron	$1·9 \text{ N } H_2SO_4$	0·65	0·115
Tin	$1·85 \text{ N } H_2SO_4$	0·9	0·135
Lead	$0·1 \text{ N } H_2SO_4$	1·41	0·118

From data in Potter, *Electrochemistry* Cleaver-Hume Press Ltd., 1956.

The existence of the overvoltage is of great practical significance in electrodeposition, since because of the high hydrogen overvoltage it is possible, for example, to plate such metals as Pb, Sn, Fe and Zn from their aqueous electrolytes in preference to hydrogen. This takes place even though their reversible reduction potentials are well below that of the hydrogen ion.

Metals which have a higher electronegative potential than zinc cannot be easily deposited from aqueous electrolytes, since they decompose water. These metals can, however, be produced by electrolysis of their fused salts.

13.4.6 *Electrolysis of Fused Salts*

In electrovalent compounds the bonding between atoms or groups of atoms is due to the electrostatic attraction between positive and negative ions. Therefore, when they are in the molten state, their melts consist of positive and negative ions which are free in an electric field and are thus good conductors of electricity. The same fundamental principles, such as the Ohm's Law and Faraday's Laws of Electrolysis, apply to their electrolysis as for aqueous solutions.

In metallurgy the electrolysis of fused salts finds its main application in the extraction and refining of very *active metals* such as

* For some practical applications of this equation see Potter, E. C., *Electrochemistry*, pp. 137–138, Cleaver-Hume Press Ltd., London, 1956.

aluminium, magnesium, potassium, sodium and calcium, which cannot be deposited from aqueous solutions. The electrolyte in these processes is usually a mixture of fused salts, or sometimes salts and the appropriate oxide. The composition of these electrolytes must be carefully chosen to give a suitable melting point, viscosity, conductivity, and purity of the melt. Since the processes are carried out at high temperatures, the choice of materials for construction of the cell and electrodes is limited by corrosion problems. For the metals Al, Mg, K and Na the operating temperature is above their melting points, so that the cathode deposit is a molten pool of liquid metal, which must be protected from oxidation by a suitably constructed electrolytic cell.

Decomposition Potential. As with aqueous electrolytes there is a minimum voltage which is required to maintain the electrolysis of fused salts. The theoretical decomposition voltage for the electrolytic production of Al, for example, can be calculated from a knowledge of the anodic and cathodic reactions in the electrolytic cell and the respective free energies of the electrode processes. Thus in this case the electrolyte consists of molten cryolite (Na_3AlF_6) with about 20% of dissolved alumina (Al_2O_3) at 900°C. Graphite is used to form both the cathode and anode in this process. As long as there is sufficient alumina in the solution there is no liberation of fluorine. The electrode reactions are then

At the Cathode:

$$\tfrac{2}{3}Al_2O_3 \rightarrow \tfrac{4}{3}Al + O_2; \quad \Delta G^0_{1,000°C} = 200 \text{ kcal}$$

At the Anode:

$$C + O_2 \rightarrow CO_2; \quad \Delta G^0_{1,000°C} = -95 \text{ kcal}$$

Overall Cell Reaction:

$$\tfrac{2}{3}Al_2O_3 + C \rightarrow \tfrac{4}{3}Al + CO_2; \quad \Delta G^0_{900°C} = 105 \text{ kcal}$$

The standard potential required for this reaction can be calculated from the free energy change as follows:

$$-\Delta G^0 = 105 \text{ kcal} = nFE^0$$

$$\therefore \qquad E^0 = \frac{105,000}{4 \cdot 183 \times 23,060} = 1 \cdot 13 \text{ V}$$

In practice the decomposition potential for this overall cell reaction is found to be about 1·5 volts, probably because of the polarisation and contact resistances. It is worth noting that the carbon anode is being "consumed" during the electrolysis.

The current efficiency in the case of fused salts is usually much smaller than in electrolytic cells containing aqueous electrolytes, since only a part of the power is used for the cathodic reductions to the metal. For example in the electrolytic extraction of aluminium the total current is used up as follows:

34% for conversion to metal

33% for heating of the electrolyte

and 33% for contact resistances

Sometimes difficulty is experienced during the operating of fused electrolyte cells because of short-circuits caused by a floating molten metal or *fog formation* in the cell, which may arise from the supersaturation of the electrolyte with the metal and temperature gradients set up in the bath.

CHAPTER XIV

Methods for Determining the Thermodynamic Functions

In this chapter it is intended to summarise the methods which are available for the determination of the thermodynamic functions, ΔH, ΔS and ΔG. Readers wishing to find values of these functions, or to review the possible experimental methods for their determination, are referred to the bibliography included in the second part of this chapter.

Summary of the methods for determining the Standard Enthalpy Change ΔH^0.

1. *Calorimetric methods*—these can be classified according to K. K. Kelley as:

   (i) the method of mixtures,
   (ii) methods depending on heating or cooling rates,
   (iii) methods of obtaining true heat capacities directly.

2. *Calculation methods:*

   (i) from enthalpy data using Hess's Law (see p. 42),
   (ii) from specific heat data and enthalpy known at one temperature using Kirchhoff's Law (see p. 49),
   (iii) from spectroscopic data.

3. Determination of *equilibrium constants* at different temperatures to find ΔH from Van't Hoff's Isochore (see p. 115).

4. From the Gibbs-Helmholtz Equation (see p. 90).

5. By *electrochemical methods* using Gibbs-Helmholtz Equation (see p. 272).

Summary of methods for determining the Standard Entropy Change ΔS^0.

1. *Calorimetric methods*—are the same as those described for ΔH^0 determination. Equation (3.26) is used to evaluate ΔS^0.

2. *Calculation methods:*

(i) calculations based on the third law of thermodynamics and a knowledge of specific heats (see pp. 69–71),

(ii) from quantum mechanics (see U.S. Bureau of Mines, Bulletin No. 592, U.S. Govt. Printing Office, New York, 1961),

(iii) from spectroscopic data (see as ii),

(iv) from molecular constants data.

3. From the thermodynamic relationship:

$$\left(\frac{\partial \Delta G}{\partial T}\right)_p = -\Delta S$$

4. From electrochemical measurements on a suitable cell using the following relationship:

$$\Delta S_T^0 = nF \left(\frac{dE_r^0}{dT}\right)_p$$

Summary of methods for determining the Standard Free Energy Change ΔG^0.

1. From a knowledge of ΔH^0 and ΔS^0 values and substitution into the equation $\Delta G^0 = \Delta H^0 - T\Delta S^0$.

2. From electrochemical methods in which the reversible standard electromotive force of a suitable cell is determined, so that

$$\Delta G^0 = -nFE_r^0$$

3. From a determination of the equilibrium constant K of a reaction and its substitution into the Van't Hoff Isotherm (see p. 112).

4. By calculation using the extended Hess's Law (see p. 167).

5. From the activities of components in an alloy using the equation (see p. 189),

$$\Delta G = RT(N_A \log_e a_A + N_B \log_e a_B)$$

Bibliography of Thermodynamic Values and Methods for their Determination

A selected list of publications containing experimental methods and tables of thermodynamic functions which are of special interest to metallurgists is given below.

1 KELLEY, K. K., *Contributions to Data on Theoretical Metallurgy: XIII, High Temperature Heat Content, Heat Capacity, and Entropy Data for the Elements and Inorganic Compounds*, U.S. Bureau of Mines, Bulletin 584, U.S. Government Printing Office, Washington, 1960.
The reader will find tables of thermodynamic data to September 1958. An explanation of experimental methods is included at the beginning of this Bulletin. 800 references to the original sources of the quoted data are also given.
XIV. Entropies of the Elements and Inorganic Compounds, U.S. Bureau of Mines, Bulletin 592, U.S. Government Printing Office, Washington, 1961.
Entropy values of nearly 1,300 elements and substances are given to September 1959. Explanation of methods of measuring and calculating these values is also given; 1,095 references are quoted.

2 KUBASCHEWSKI, O. and E. L. EVANS, *Metallurgical Thermochemistry*, second edition, Pergamon Press Ltd., London, 1958.
This book contains a detailed account of experimental methods of determining and of estimating unknown data. Tables of ΔH^0, ΔG^0, ΔS^0 as well as structures, vapour pressures, and thermodynamic values for some binary metallic systems are presented together with 765 references.

3 BOCKRIS, J. O., J. L. WHITE, and J. D. MACKENZIE, (Eds.), *Physicochemical Measurements at High Temperatures*, Butterworth & Co. (Publishers) Ltd., London, 1959.
A detailed account is given of experimental methods of determining thermodynamic data, density, surface tension, and other physical properties of liquid metals. Appendices contain very useful thermodynamic tables and examples of thermodynamic calculations. Over a thousand references are quoted.

4 D.S.I.R., *The Physical Chemistry of Metallic Solutions and Intermetallic Compounds:* Proceedings of N.P.L., Symposium No. 9, H.M.S.O., London, 1958.
Many experimental techniques and results are presented together with the ensuing discussions of the papers.

5 HULTGREN, R., R. L. ORR, P. D. ANDERSON, and K. K. KELLEY, *Selected Values of Thermodynamic Properties of Metals and Alloys*, John Wiley & Sons Ltd., London and New York, 1963.
An account is given of methods for evaluation of thermodynamic data and values are also quoted for elements and binary alloys. A useful alphabetical list of 32 general references to the world literature is also included.

6 *Thermodynamics in Physical Metallurgy*, Seminar, 31st National Metal Congress, American Society for Metals, Cleveland, 1949.
This publication contains many papers and discussions dealing with experimental techniques and calculations of thermodynamic data.

7 LEWIS, G. N. and M. RANDALL, revised by K. S. PITZER and L. BREWER, *Thermodynamics*, second edition, McGraw-Hill Publishing Co. Ltd., London, 1961.

In this textbook there are many thermodynamic calculations. There is a bibliography of free energy compilations (13 books) as well as many tables of thermodynamic data.

8 LUMSDEN, J., *Thermodynamics of Alloys*, Institute of Metals Monograph and Report Series No. 11, Institute of Metals, London, 1952.
This book contains many tables and references to thermodynamic data of alloys.

9 ST. PIERRE, C. R. (Ed.), *Physical Chemistry of Process Metallurgy*, Parts I & II, (Amer. Met. Soc. Conf.), Interscience Publishers Inc., New York, 1961.
These two volumes contain many papers dealing with experimental techniques and evaluation of thermodynamic data, as well as interesting discussions regarding these papers.

10 LATIMER, W. M., *The Oxidation States of the Elements and Their Potentials in Aqueous Solutions*, second edition, Prentice-Hall Inc., New York, 1952.
Thermodynamic data for electrochemical calculations is critically presented. Numerous references are given to the original sources of quoted data.

11 SHREIR, L. L. (Ed.), *Corrosion*, Vols. I & II, George Newnes Ltd., London, 1963.
This book contains numerous tables of electrochemical thermodynamic data.

In addition to the above bibliography, there are sources of thermodynamic data referred to in the abstracts included in metallurgical and chemical journals.

INDEX

GEORGE ALLEN & UNWIN LTD
London: 40 Museum Street, W.C.1

Auckland: P.O. Box 36013, Northcote Central, Auckland, N.4
Bombay: 15 Graham Road, Ballard Estate, Bombay 1
Barbados: P.O. Box 222 Bridgetown
Buenos Aires: Escritorio 454–459, Florida 165
Calcutta: 17 Chittaranjan Avenue, Calcutta 13
Cape Town: 68 Shortmarket Street
Hong Kong: 105 Wing On Mansion, 26 Hancow Road, Kowloon
Ibadan: P.O. Box 62
Karachi: Karachi Chambers, McLeod Road
Madras: Mohan Mansions, 38c Mount Road, Madras 6
Mexico: Villalongin 32–10, Piso, Mexico 5, D.F.
Nairobi: P.O. Box 4536
New Delhi: 13–14 Asaf Ali Road, New Delhi 1
Ontario: 81 Curlew Drive, Don Mills
Rio de Janeiro: Caixa Postal 2537–Zc–00
São Paulo: Caixa Postal 8675
Singapore: 36c Prinsep Street, Singapore 7
Sydney, N.S.W.: Bradbury House, 55 York Street
Tokyo: P.O. Box 26, Kamata

No. 1. MECHANICAL PROPERTIES OF METALS

J. G. TWEEDDALE, Imperial College of Science and Technology

The book presents a comprehensive survey of the assessment of the mechanical properties of engineering materials.

'. . . will serve as a standard work of reference . . .' *Draughtsman.*

'Examination candidates will recognize that their syllabuses have been sensibly appraised and honestly covered.' *Times Educational Supplement.*

No. 3. THE METALLURGY OF WELDING, BRAZING AND SOLDERING

J. F. LANCASTER, Kellogg International Corporation

'. . . can be thoroughly recommended for use by students . . . Practising engineers and metallurgists, even when directly concerned with welding, will find it valuable to have in their bookshelves.' *Nature.*

'some 290 pages cover the essentials of welding metallurgy and technology with scarcely any superfluous words and exactly in the spirit of the present Institution of Metallurgists series . . . This book is extremely well written and cannot be faulted on technical grounds . . . is very good value for money . . . should be in constant demand for a very long time to come.' *Engineering.*

No. 4. BASIC ELECTROTECHNOLOGY

N. JONES, University of Aston in Birmingham

The book is suitable for courses leading to the awards of University Degree, Diploma of Technology and A.I.M. where a knowledge of electrotechnology is required in support of the main discipline. Part I covers general theory, and Part II the construction and operation of machinery, measuring instruments and electronic apparatus, including semiconductor devices; there is a chapter on control systems.

GEORGE ALLEN & UNWIN LTD.